A SLICE OF BREAD & JAM

BY
TOMMY RATTIGAN

To/ Frank,
Best wishes

A SLICE OF BREAD & JAM

BY
TOMMY RATTIGAN

First published in Great Britain in 2015
10 9 8 7 6 5 4 3 2 1

A catalogue record for this book is available from the British Library
ISBN 978-0-9932423-0-4

Printed in Great Britain by
Orbital Print, Sittingborne, Kent
ORBITAL PRINT

To Jill for putting up with me!

Acknowledgements.

The Manchester Evening News
Burst Universe Design & Publishing
Rose Mcgiven
& Friends on hulme, c.on.m
St Wilfrid's RC Primary school Hulme past and present
Ex Hulme. Moss Side. Manchester Memories.
Friends of Platts Fields Park. Gorton M18 Places of places!
Firmstart. Hulme Manchester
Image Credit:Shirley Baker/Mary Evans Picture Library
Jackie Levescontie and family.
'Mam told me off!'

Michael Gavin-Rattigan
Was here!

-1963-

Standing just a short distance away from me, with her head leaning slightly to one side and grabbing my attention, Myra Hindley had thrown a coy look and the briefest of smiles in my direction. A short distance behind her, Ian Brady stood staring off to his right with a hand dug deep in to his overcoat pocket while he had dragged on his cigarette. I'd first noticed the two figures walking past the park near Ducie Street, as the pair of them had stopped and I'd seen the flare of a light as Brady had lit a cigarette, before they'd headed through the park and past me the play area, where I'd been happily swinging on the swing as I'd waited for my two brothers, Martin and Nabby, to show up.

The pair of them had stopped some fifteen or twenty yards away from me and seemed to have had a brief conversation with one another before Myra Hindley had suddenly turned and had headed back to the swings, while Brady had stayed put, looking about him and dragging on his fag. When she was about five or six feet away she'd stopped as I had let the swing slow under its own momentum. And from the distance she'd stood from me, I was able to smell a mixture of heavy perfume and hairspray which had immediately reminded me of my two eldest sisters, Mary and Rose, who would smothered the stuff all over themselves and their hair, filling the house with fumes and almost choking the lot of us!

Now standing face on to me with her hands inside her coat pockets, Hindley had silently looked me up and down. My

1

senses told me she was about to say something, but as I had waited in expectation for her to speak to me, she'd said nothing. I'd returned her brief smile, letting her know I'd felt comfortable in her presence and was approachable and she'd then stepped a little closer with a bright wide smile spread across her face. To all intent and purposes she had not seemed to me any more interesting or different from the people I had met while out begging on the streets, with my brothers and sisters, with some people kindly taking us in to their homes and feeding us before sending us on our way with a few spare coppers in our pockets. So when Myra Hindley had invited me to go with her to her Grandmother's house in Gorton for some *Bread and Jam* it had been nothing out of the ordinary to have been asked and for me to have agreed. And so, I had set off on my journey following her through the ever darkening streets on the edge of Longsight heading back into Gorton, with Ian Brady following just a short distance behind us, to a house where I had believed was a place of safety and a bite to eat. Though in reality, I was in fact walking in the mist of two evil child killers who'd had other ideas for me.

Before I take you on that particular journey and share with you the intense emotional atmosphere which had wrapped itself around me, as I had sat inside the old terraced house in Bannock Street, let me first take you to the beginning of 1963, so you may walk with me through that one particular year leading up to my encounter with the most reviled evil killers, Manchester will never forget. There is no set plot to this book, just fading memories of a bygone time, when the streets of Manchester, were the playgrounds of their children.

2

-ONE-

I am seven years old. I have three older brothers: Paddy, Shamie and Martin. And I also have four older sisters: Mary, Rose, Elizabeth and Maggie. I have three younger brothers and two younger sisters: Michael, Nabby and Gosson, Bernadette and Kathleen. I am Tommy, making thirteen Rattigan's in all - unlucky for some!

Most of my family, save for Michael, Gosson and Kathleen, were born in the Republic of Ireland. Daddy was known as a Tinker or a Tinsmith, or a dirty feckin' auld Gypsy, depending on who he was dealing with at the time. He mended or made pots and pans and sharpened peoples knives for a living as we travelled along the roads between Athlone, where I was conceived, and Dublin. And despite having served with the Military Police, out in India, during WW2, he had not been able to hold down a proper job since leaving the British army. And so, with no prospects in Southern Ireland, he decided to uproot and better himself over here in England, taking the whole family off across the Irish Sea to a new life in Hulme, Manchester, where he had signed up at the Labour Exchange.

Martin, Bernie and I, usually spent all our time together, while Nabby, if he hadn't been minded to be off doing his own thing, would come along with us at times. He was two years younger than me and three years younger than Martin, while Bernie was a year younger than me and two years younger than Martin, though she looked older than her age, on account of her height. She was at least six inches taller than Martin and me, and a foot taller than Nabby, and she never stopped eating. Daddy called us, the *four stooges,* because we were always getting up to all sorts of mischief. Sometimes he would have to come from the pub to fetch us from the police station. And while there, he'd pretend he was so pleased to see us, as any concerned parent would be, only to beat the living daylights out of us with his leather belt, once he'd got us home.

I was the fastest runner out of us all, so I would be the one to grab a purse, or any lose money left lying around. Even the odd unmanned cash till wasn't safe and if ever the opportunity arose, which it had done from time to time, my grubby little hands would be in it! The last till snatch was in Marks and Spencer's, a few months back, when Martin had ran past it, banging down on the keys to cause the drawer to shoot open as I'd followed a split second behind him and snatched up a handful of paper money, stuffing it down the back of my jumper, before heading for the main exit. We'd got caught before we'd managed to get out of the doors and were taken back to the custody room by two of the women cashiers. On the way, I'd noticed in one of the mirrors, I had this weird looking hump on my back and so I had rounded my shoulders and stooped slightly lower, looking slightly deformed in the hope no-one would notice the fact, the money was hidden there.

"Just hand back whatever money you took and we'll say no more." one of the two uniformed security guards, called Dave, had promised us.

"We didn't take any money. Look!" keeping myself slightly bent over, I'd turned out my pockets to show him they were

4

empty. Martin did the same.

"You were seen running away from the till?"

"Only because we were looking for someone to tell! Honest!" said Martin, pretending to cry, before going on to tell the security guards some cock-and-bull story about us seeing a young lad stealing money from the till.

"Can you describe this young lad?"

"If yah take us around the store, we could point him out ta yah. If he's still in here?" suggested Martin, and to our amazement, the security guards agreed with the idea!

Walking down the first aisle we'd came to, we'd spotted a young kid of around eight-years of age, with his mother, walking up in our direction. "That's the kid!" Martin suddenly pointed an accusing finger down the aisle.

"Are you positive about this?" asked Dave,

"That's him!" I'd backed my brother up, "I'd be able ta spot him a mile off with that pink patch on them glasses he's wearin! An' his mammy saw him, an' never said a word!" I'd added for good measure!

"Right. Wait there with these two, Roy, while I go and have a word with them."

"How dare you!" Jasis! The woman had gone mad and began beating the burly security guard over the head, with her handbag, at first, and then anything else she could lay her hands on!

"Help me Roy!"

"You two wait here."

Yeh-right! We were on our way before Roy had got halfway down the aisle to help his mate!

5

Martin was the best actor in Manchester, and was so brilliant at acting out an epileptic fit. If there'd been anyone showing any interest in us, or there'd been a time when we needed a distraction, Martin would suddenly go into a fit. Like a child possessed by the devil himself, he'd writher on the ground with his eyes rolled back, to show the whites of them, as well as frothing bubbles of spit from his mouth, just for good measure.

Bernie, on the other hand, was very special to us. And a different kettle of fish altogether. Daddy said, the doctor said, our Bernie has two people living inside her. One is Bernie herself, and the other, though to all intents and purposes, is still Bernie, it was a different Bernie altogether. Though he have a clue who the other Bernie was! It didn't make much sense to any of us, how Bernie could be living inside herself, especially when we could see her every day, though I had wondered, if the reason why she ate a lot, was on account she was eating for two!

Daddy also said, the doctor said, the other Bernie, living inside Bernie, was a very angry person, which was the reason why she could be the nicest person in the world one minute, and the wildest of Banshees the next! But we only saw the wild side of our young sister when she was hitting someone with a lump of wood, or throwing large duckers at them, to protect us, or herself. Up to a point, and besides eating for two, she could do almost all the things Martin and I could do, though not as well as us. But if there was one thing we were all equally good at, then that would have to be lying. We were so good at lying, we often convinced ourselves, the lies we told, were the truth!

6

Once, the police had caught us riding Danny McCarthy's horse and cart through the streets. Danny McCarthy was the local rag and bone man - though we had never seen any bones in his cart, only old rags and scrap metal, along with other odds and sods, which no one had any use for. Last Friday, we'd tried selling him some huge bones we'd stolen from outside the local butcher's shop. But he'd just laughed in our faces and told us to *fuck off*, before he gave us a bone of his own.

McCarthy would always leave Goliath, a giant amongst the carthorses of Manchester, tethered to the lamppost outside the Red-Rose pub, which was just around the corner from Stamford Street, where we'd lived. He'd go to the pub every Friday afternoon, without fail, and wouldn't show his face again until closing time, when he'd be carried out by his friends, drunk and unsteady on his feet, to be thrown onto the back of his cart, before Goliath is given a smack on the arse and shooed on his way, obediently taking his master all the way back to his yard.

Bernie had got this notion into her head, she knew how to ride the big beast. 'It's just like riding a donkey,' she'd said, inviting Martin, Nabby and me, along for the ride. Without questioning her ability to do this, we'd hopped up onto the cart and sat back, waiting for the ride of our lives.

"Only up to the other end of the road and back again," she'd said, "No one will ever know."

Grabbing hold of the leather reigns, our sister had giddy-upped the horse, but Goliath had just given her a sideways glance, before sticking his head back into the maize bag hung round his neck, and continued to munch away. She tried

7

shooing it a few times, but the stubborn black stallion still refused to budge an inch, no matter how loudly we'd shooed it. Picking up the horsewhip, Bernie had given it a few taps, gently at first, and then more vigorously, until the other Bernie inside Bernie, had suddenly made an appearance. Standing up in the cart, she'd whipped the horse, screaming at it to, "Feckin' move yah poxty ting! Or yer for the knacker's yard!"

Any other horse being flogged in such a manner, would probably have been on their way by now, but not Goliath. He wasn't budging for love nor money, and certainly not for the Devil child whipping his arse. He'd held his ground and had turned his huge head to glare back at Bernie, with his big dark bulging eyes, before snorting snot out of his wide nostrils, as if to tell her, 'You can beat the shite out of me all day long, little girlie! But I'm not moving from this spot!' At least, not until the moment Martin had taken it upon himself to jab the pointed end of McCarthy's umbrella right up Goliath's hole, causing the stubborn beast to give out a loud long whine, before rearing up on his hind legs and bolting off down the street at great speed!

It didn't matter, how much the three of us had sworn our apologies to the giant horse, or how hard we'd pulled on his long leather reins. The beast wouldn't stop and had turned into Dale Street, at breakneck speed. All Martin, me and Bernie, could do, was to hold tightly onto each other and pray to the Divine Virgin Mary, Saint Martin - that's our mammy's favourite saint-he's a Blackman - and every other saint, Father Murphy had brainwashed us about, to save our sorry souls, or at the very least, send us all to heaven instead of languishing

8

in purgatory, if this should happen to be our last day on the earth.

By all accounts, purgatory is a place where dead people had to wait until they were purified from all their mortal sins, before being allowed to join all the other purified dead people, in heaven. And if there was any truth in Father Murphy's account, then it looked likely, with the amount of sins we'd committed, we would be floating around in the dark for a long while to come!

The police had joined us along the Stretford Road, just as we'd passed the Town Hall, where a fat policeman, in the leading car, had leaned out of the car window and screamed at us, "Pull over you fucking little bastards!" But we didn't know how to pull over. Martin had even screamed back, advising the policeman, he'd have to shoot the horse dead!

For at least ten minutes, traffic and people had frantically dodged out of the way, as Goliath had hurtled towards them. And it was only after he'd done two circuits around Piccadilly Circus, did he finally come to a standstill, before lifting his long hairy tail and having a good shite.

With no time for us to thank the Divine Virgin Mary, Saint Martin, or any other saints, for saving our wretched souls, we'd quickly jumped from the cart as an army of policemen headed in our direction.

I'd led the way, as we'd dodged down a couple of side streets before dashing across the busy high street, into Woolworths, and heading straight up the escalator to the toy department, where we'd quickly stripped naked, swapped our filthy clothing for the new range of cowboy and Indian outfits on display, before boldly ambling past the posse of policemen, scouring the place for three filthy urchins.

We were almost at the main entrance doors and freedom, when we were stopped in our tracks, by the loud shout of the keen-eyed, nosey store detective.

"Stop the cowboy and Indian's!"

Well. We might have been surrounded, but we were not going down without a fight, as the three of us had stood facing the long line of red-faced coppers, in a standoff. Dressed as Big Chief Sitting Bull, complete with the head of feathers, I'd raised my plastic tomahawk high above my head, threatening to scalp the first copper who came near us, even though the nearest copper to us was already as bald as a cooty. Martin, dressed as the Lone Ranger, had drawn his two silver revolvers and was threatening to shoot the bollocks of anyone who'd dared to come near him. And Bernie, dressed as the Lone Ranger's sidekick, Tonto, already had an arrow in her bow and was taking careful aim with it.

Of course, we'd been outnumbered and easily overpowered. But not before Bernie managed to get an arrow off, pulling off a spectacular shot and catching the snitching store-detective in his right eye, causing him to howl like a baby.

Taken prisoners, we were frog marched out of the store and carted off to the City's police station, still dressed in our stolen outfits, where we'd stubbornly insisted on giving our names as, the Lone Ranger, Tonto and Big Chief Sitting Bull, to the annoyance of the overweight desk sergeant, who'd gave all three of us a clip round the ear, before threatening to throw us in a cell and chucking away the key!

We'd told the fat bastard, he could do what he liked and had retaliated with our own threats warning him of the dire consequences of what he'd done and swearing, "As there's a Jasis in heaven, our mammy and daddy, along with all our Uncles and Aunties and our Cousins and Nephews, will come down ta the police station and beat the living daylights out of yea an' all your coolies, before settin' the station ablaze!"

We'd agreed to call a truce on the offer of, sausages, eggs and chips, and steaming hot cups of sweet tea, which we'd eagerly tucked into. But once our bellies were full, we'd continued with our intimidation tactics right up into the early hours of the morning, when we'd fallen asleep.

It wasn't until the following afternoon that we were reunited back with mammy and daddy, when they'd suddenly realised we were not at home! Woolworths had allowed us to keep the stolen outfits, on account that they'd slung our stinky clothes away. Daddy's attempt to have the store charged with the theft of our clothing, which he said, were only bought for us a few weeks earlier, had fallen on deaf ears. The store-detective had dropped the complaint of assault against Bernie, who'd insisted she'd not deliberately fired the arrow at him, and was in fact aiming it at one of the policemen! As for Goliath. Though he was none the worse for his adventure, I swear, he always raised his trotting pace whenever he caught a glimpse of us walking along the streets.

-TWO-

Hulme was probably one of the largest slum-cum demolition sites in the whole of Manchester, with its blighted wastelands, Victorian slums, dark streets and derelict houses and factories. Every day, we would watch the heavy bulldozers hard at work, doing what the blitz of the 1940's had done to the city of Manchester but had failed to do to Hulme and the neighbouring towns. There seemed to be a sense of urgency-a keenness, to eradicate all evidence of the Victorian era and innumerable smoking chimneys which blocked out the sun and poisoned the air and our lungs. And so the mills and the factories and the slums, would constantly meet with their fate, as day after day the blighted landscape around us, steadily changed and became even more blighted by the high-rise curved tower blocks and their concrete pedestrian walkways above the streets. This new regeneration plan for Hulme, had an ugliness about it, which the grownups would say, was all too reminiscent of a Communist country, though they'd never said which country they were talking about. The neighborliness, inherited from a bygone age, had been slowly deteriorating for a long while, along with its sense of community, as a new concrete jungle steadily rose up, as did the new and more sinister culture of *the Crescents!*

It seemed the sky was always grey and it rained a lot, with the winters made much the worse by the blistering harsh chilly winds which would hit you from all sides of the compass. This year's freezing winter had lasted all the way up until March, which the older neighbours said, was the worst they'd ever witnessed in their whole lives, with the canals and the sea surrounding the country, freezing over!

Every street we had walk down, we'd be met by row upon row of empty houses, standing mute in their solemn silence, as they waited for the huge ball and chain to mercifully come knocking on their walls and putting them out of their misery. And every day, we would watch people piling their furniture and rugs and other personal belongings into the big removal trucks, before they'd drive off, never to be seen again.

Some people would stand for a short while, looking back on their home in silent thoughts. Perhaps, reflecting on past decades of memories they were about to leave behind them. These were the people who closed their front doors behind them, as if locking the echoes of their past away. While others, just hurried off without bothering to close their doors, or even take one last glance backwards, only too pleased to be given a second chance in life. Where are they going? We hadn't a clue. Nor did we really care. By the time a removal truck had got halfway along the street, a rush of grubby faced children would suddenly appear out from their shadowy hiding places and descend upon the empty property. And there, like scavenging rats searching out a meal, we took anything and everything that wasn't bolted down, because anything and everything had its value.

I was always the first one down into the dark coal cellar. With Martin and Bernie, we would stand guard over the wrought iron manhole cover leading down into the dark cellar at the front of the house. To the unsuspecting eye, we had looked just like any ordinary, run of the mill scallywags, watching the progress of the removal men, as they'd gone about their business emptying a house. We'd always ask, if we could lend a hand, knowing full well, the owners of the property would decline our kind offer, too busy keeping an eye on the removal men, to have to worry about us stealing from them, as well! But it all added to our ploy to stop any of the other children, hiding somewhere in the shadows, ready to make their move and getting down into the cellar before us.

I was small for my age, and with a little push from Martin, I could just about squeeze my skinny body, head-first, through the small hole, before sliding down the concrete chute into the cellar below. Martin would then throw the small hessian bag down after me, and I'd scavenge around with my bare hands for any remnants of coal, hurriedly filling the bag, as my brother and sister peered down at me through the small hole above my head, offering words of encouragement.

With most people not bothering to take their coal with them, at times there'd be enough to keep the fire going for a few days or so. And so, once I'd filled the small bag, I'd offer this back up to Martin, who'd tip it into one of the two larger hessian coal sacks, we'd bring with us, along with our bogie to carry the coal home on. We'd repeat the process, until we had taken whatever coal there was, or until the two larger sacks had been filled.

Next; unless there'd been no coal, then this would have been my first task, I'd use the small crowbar passed down to me, to force off the small lock on the gas meter, if it hadn't already been broken into by the leaving occupants, or the removal men.

Which often happened.

Sometimes, I'd find the odd shilling inside the cash box, though never as much as the change I'd find in the gas meters, daddy would make me break into, after he'd pushed me down into the blackened coal chutes of an occupied house! But he'd always checked the house out first, just to make sure there was no one at home, or the occupants, were either too old or too infirm, to give chase, if they had caught me in the act.

My daddy was an expert at robbing people's houses. He had a knack of being able to weigh up people's vulnerabilities. Just one knock on any door, and he could tell by how long it took for someone to answer, whether the job had any potential or not. If the door wasn't answered after a few good loud knocks, then either no-one was at home or the occupants were totally deaf! If anyone did come to the door quickly, daddy would look them up and down, always able to spot any potential weaknesses. If it was a no-go, he'd just make up some cock-and-bull story or invent the name of a person he was trying to trace.

Early one evening he'd knocked on a front door, which had been answered by an old woman, probably in her eighties. She'd taken one look at daddy and had thrown her arms wide open.

"Is that you, Jim!" she'd excitedly asked, peering out through a pair of thick bifocal spectacles hanging off her nose.

Daddy had been stunned into taking a backward step, almost falling over me in the process, when she'd suddenly called him by his first name.

"Oh! And look at you, little David!" The auld woman had

15

smiled down on me with her stained dark brown dentures. "My, aren't you growing into a handsome young man! Come in! Come in, and make yourselves at home!"

Glancing over my shoulder, I'd half expected to see, Jim and little David, standing behind me, but there wasn't another living soul around, barring myself, daddy, and the old woman herself. I was just on the point of telling her, "My name isn't David." When daddy had suddenly stood on my left foot, before pushing me in through the open doorway, ahead of him, following after the blind old bat.

There were a number of birthday cards on the mantelpiece above the lit coal fire, and daddy had quickly read a couple of these, discovering the woman's son was called Jim, and her grandson David. I'd then had to endure the next ten minutes or so, sitting next to the auld biddy on the small sofa by the coal fire, with her fussing over me and asking me all the usual sorts of questions, a granny would ask of her grandson. How was I getting on at school? Was I keeping out of trouble? Why hadn't my sister, Teresa, accompanied us? It was a wonder she was still alive, with the amount of illnesses she'd told me she'd suffered with. And I'd suspected, if she'd known what daddy was up to it probably would have killed her. It was no wonder, she'd hardly seen much of her real family, with the way she'd gone on and on. And the stench of piss!

I'd hardly been to school in my whole life, but I couldn't tell her this. And so I'd used my imagination and had told her, I was top in my class at spelling, history, and math's. In fact, I was tops at every subject in the school, including one they didn't have, lying!

She must have thought I was a feckin genius! Though I was grateful, she'd not asked me a question on any of these subjects, otherwise I'd probably would have to have had one of Martin sudden fits!

"So. Have you had a nice birthday, then, Mammy?" daddy had suddenly reappeared back in the lounge, where he'd plundered the woman's handbag and purse.

"All the better for seeing you, son," she'd smiled over at the empty chair by the table.

"I'll just go and make sure you've plenty of coal in the cellar, then." he'd thrown me a wink, "If not, I'll have the coal man bring you a few bags around in the morning."

When we were finally leaving, the auld biddy began to cry. Daddy, with his pockets laden with the contents of her jewellery box, the gas meter and her purse, promised he'd come back to see her again, soon. She'd fumbled in her handbag for her purse so she could give me a few shilling to buy myself some sweets, but daddy was having none of it, and had told her, 'He gets enough sweets, as it is." and instead, he'd insisted on giving his new mammy a ten-shilling note, for her birthday.

-THREE-

We'd lived in one of the older Victorian slum areas of Hulme, at twenty-four Stamford Street. The house was a cold damp dump, and that was the best part! The only pattern on what was left of the peeling wallpaper, was the damp stains and greenmold growing on it. The floors were bare and there was no bathroom. The toilet was outside in the back yard, where small squares of old newspapers hung off the piece of string, hanging off an old rusty nail, which we'd pull off one at a time to wipe our dirty arses with. The shiny magazines was the worst! The large tin bath we were washed in, was chained to the outside wall underneath the backroom sash window, so an eye could be kept on it, in case any thieving bastards tried to steal it for scrap.

Mammy would fill the tin bath once every second Sunday, scrubbing all of us clean to the bone, one by one. In the winter months, she would bring the bath inside the house and scrub us in front of the open fire, in order of age, the eldest going first. Paddy, Shamie, Mary, Rose, Elizabeth and Maggie, all went to the bathhouse up on Leaf Street, so I'd got to go second in line after Martin. And although the water would just be hovering on lukewarm, by the time it came to little Michael, the youngest of the family being scrubbed, the water would be filthy.

Barring Paddy and Shamie, who'd shared their own bedroom, the other five boys shared a tiny box bedroom between us, which was just big enough to fit a small bed in, but too small to fit any other piece of furniture in. We'd slept like a tin of sardines, Martin and me at one end of the bed, with Nabby, Michael and Gosson down the other end. My six sisters shared the front upstairs bedroom, which had a double bed and a small single bed, including a small sideboard and a wardrobe. Mary had the small single bed to herself and the others all slept in the big bed.

I'd liked their bedroom, because the light from the street Gaslamp, which stood directly outside our house, lit up their room with a soft yellowy orange glow. Sometimes when our two eldest sisters had stayed away from home – which had become more often now - Martin and me, would sneak into the girls' room and sleep in the big bed with our other sisters, while Elizabeth slept in the single bed. Mammy and daddy had their own bedroom downstairs at the front of the house.

Stamford Street was a long street with two rows of Victorian terraced houses running down both sides of the street and lit up at night by the Gaslamp's. Unlike some of the streets in Hulme, most houses along our street were occupied, but the few that were not, had already been vandalised and stripped bare, with all of their windowpanes smashed, either by us, or the other local children taking pot shots at them. It was inevitable, now and again a ducker would miss its intended target and smash the window of an occupied house, causing all sorts of rows with the owners; if they were in. It was also inevitable, we'd all deny it was our ducker that had caused the damage, usually blaming one another.

Daddy used our back yard to breed chickens. He'd built a small run and roosting box for them along the side wall next to the outside toilet, poor things! My favorite chicken, was a big grey cock, about the size of an Alsatian dog, which mammy named 'King Dick' who'd spent most of his days chasing chicken's around the yard and humping them!

Unlike mammy and daddy, we'd never got to eat chicken eggs, though we did have a roast chicken dinner on St Patrick's Day and Christmas day. And if Daddy was not minded to kill a chicken when one of his regular customers called to the house, he'd send me or Martin out to kill one. I'd loved chopping their heads off on the chopping block and letting them run around the yard, scaring the others chickens half to death, as they'd bump into all four walls, until they'd suddenly realised they'd no head on their body's and would keel over, dying with the shock of it!

Sometimes we found dead chickens that had died overnight for one reason or another. Daddy would sell them chickens to the yellow skinned men who wore the turbans around their heads, in the belief they'd be none the wiser if they'd got the scutters after eating them, as they always had the scutters with the kind of food they were used to eating!

Now and again we'd see a colony of cat-size rats scurrying out into the back ally from the empty houses in Dunham Street, which backed onto Stamford Street. A flock of around eighty pigeons had set up home in one of the empty houses, and although people had complained to the local council about the stench and the birds shitting everywhere, especially on all the clothes hanging out on the washing lines. The man from the council said, the council were far too busy to be dealing with the like of pigeon shit and rats, with all the demolition and rebuilding works going on in the area. He'd also said, it wasn't going to be long now before the whole of Stamford Street, Denham Street, along with the rest of Hulme, was demolished, and we'd all be moving into new houses. Which wasn't a big help, when it was constantly raining pigeon shit every day!

One weekend, someone had taken it upon themselves to get rid of the problem once and for all, and had tried to smoke the vermin out of one of the empty houses in Denham Street. Only, they'd set Mrs. Whitmore's house alight in the process! The roof of her house had thick grew smoke belching out from it, but lucky for her, my daddy was in the alley at the time, and had barged his way through her back door, rushing in to save her.

Ten heart-stopping minutes later, he reappeared out through the front door, carrying the unconscious old woman over his shoulder, in one of those fireman's lifts, to the loud applause of the neighbours gathered outside, just as the two fire engines, closely followed by an ambulance and a police car, had come screeching around the corner, nearly killing Mrs. Donnelly and her mongrel son, Billy-the-kid ambling across for a peek.

Billy was known to everyone in Hulme as, 'Billy the Kid,' which might have had something to do with the fact, day in-day out, he'd always wore his cowboy outfit along with the two holstered guns hanging around his waist.

"Come away from there, Tommy!" my hero daddy, for the first time in my life, had suddenly showed concern for my safety. Picking me up off the ground in one swift movement, he'd carried me back along the street and around the corner into Stamford Street, without saying a word. I could smell the distinct smell of petrol and smoke on his clothes and hands, as he'd plonked me down near the entrance to our back alley.

"Get to the house straight away! Here! Give these to your mammy, and be quick about it!" he'd suddenly snuck a purse and pieces of jewellery out from his inside coat pocket and stuffed them down inside my jumper, before walking off back around the corner in the direction of Dunham Street.

When Mrs. Whitmore was discharged from the hospital a few days later, she'd came around to our house in the middle of the afternoon to see daddy. She'd brought a large box of Dairy Milk chocolates with her and had given them to daddy, as a token of her gratitude, for him having risked his own safety to save "a helpless old woman who'd not long on this earth, and who didn't deserve to be saved." She'd told him, she would have rewarded him with something much more substantial, only someone had stolen her purse, robbed her gas meter and taken her priceless jewellery, whilst she'd been laid up dying in the hospital. She'd believed the culprit might have been one of the firemen, who'd risked life and limb to save her house from burning down to the ground! She'd informed daddy, she'd written a formal complaint to the Chief Officer of the Fire Brigade, as well as a letter to Her Majesty the Queen-giving him a mention!

"Good on yah missus." said mammy, shaking her head with dismay, "Sure they're all thieving heathens! The feckin' whole lot of them!"

She'd offered Mrs. Whitmore a cup of brewed tea, which the auld lady had been on the point of accepting, before suddenly having second thoughts, declining mammy's kind offer. She'd probably remembered the last time she'd had a cup of mammy's tea, and how, when she'd taken a swig, she'd almost choked to death swallowing the large mouthful of tea leaves resting at the bottom of the cup!

Daddy had been keen to know how much the stolen items of jewellery had been worth as he had sold the lot to someone he knew, for four pounds and ten shillings, though he'd tried to haggle for a fiver. When Mrs. Whitmore had told him, they'd been worth at least, one hundred and fifty pounds. It had suddenly brought on a severe coughing fit from daddy, which he'd blamed on the tea dregs!

Not long after Mrs. Whitmore had left the house, two detectives had called around. Daddy had told Bernie, to answer the door. "If it's the milkman, the rent collector, or anyone else wanting money. Tell them I'm not at home," he'd told her.

"Daddy said to say, he wasn't in." we'd heard Bernie, telling the two detectives, standing in the open doorway. But they'd invited themselves in anyhow, so he had to come out from hiding under his bed.

They'd not brought any chocolates with them, but instead, told daddy, they'd not been wholly convinced the small tube of petrol, he usually carried in his pocket to refill his lighter, had split when he was carrying Mrs. Whitmore, out of the smoking building. Which had been the reason daddy had given, to explain why his clothing, had had a strong smell of petrol on them, when the police had first spoke with him at the scene.

They'd also informed Daddy, that Mrs. McKinney, who'd lived further down in Dunham Street, said she'd been out in the alley putting the bin out, when she'd seen someone hurrying up it, carrying, what appeared to her, to have been a large petrol can, not long before the house had gone up in flames, believing the person she'd seen, was him!

As well as telling the two dectectives, he doesn't possess a petrol can, which he'd hidden down in the cellar, he'd told them, Mrs. McKinney was a blind auld bat, a mischief maker, and last but not least. A lying feckin' heathen Protestant, who'd hated all the Irish Catholics. He'd gone on to tell them, "We were a family of God-fearing people!" and to prove the point, he'd gone to the side cupboard in the backroom, and had taken out the large family bible, which had all the family names and dates of birth written in it. And kneeling before the two bemused detectives, he'd sworn on the holy bible, and on the lives of all the names written in the book, that he was telling the truth. "Otherwise. 'God strike the lot of us down dead!' It was a wonder any of us were still alive!

The coppers had had enough and had left us in peace, but not before warning daddy, they'd be keeping a close eye on him in the future. Daddy had thrown them a smile, telling them, they could keep an eye on him for the rest of eternity and they'll not catch him putting one foot wrong, as it wasn't in his nature. After seeing the detectives out the front door, he'd hurried back into the back room fuming.

"Quick, boys!" he'd spoken to me and Martin, 'I want yah to nip out the back and down to Mrs. McKinney's, and break every feckin window of the auld whore's house! Hurry now! And watch out for them coppers!'

-FOUR-

It was Martin's birthday. And better still. It was Saint Patrick's Day! The day when all the Irish Catholics joined together to celebrate their patron Saint. Daddy had been cussing earlier in the morning about a dozen chicken eggs having disappeared overnight from the back yard, until Mammy had told him, she'd given them to Bernie yesterday, for the school's food stall.

"But the eggs have probably been lyin' around for months upon months! I'd found them underneath the roosting box!"

"Well that's no trouble. I don't feckin' eat them anyhow!" was mammy's reply.

This year, St Wilfrid's school were putting on a school fête in celebration of the big day. And we didn't have far to walk from St Wilfrid's Church across to the school, to get at the free buffet. The only downside to all this was, we'd had to go to church and listen to the boring priest drone on about, glorious St Patrick, and how he'd commanded all the snakes to get out of Ireland, and they'd just upped and left! Though daddy, was minded to believe, "It wasn't only the snakes he'd told to feck off out of it, but the feckin' rats too! Though, only as far as Northern Ireland, where all the feckin' snakes and rats live!" We all had to wear large fist-size clumps of shamrock, which our Uncle Oliver, one of daddy's younger brother's, had fetched over from Ireland, a few days earlier.

When Paddy and Shamie, had come down the stairs, looking half dead, and telling mammy, they were not feeling too good,

and probable wouldn't be able to make it to the church, though there was every chance, they might be able to make it to the fête. Mammy had cursed the pair of them and told them, "Ye'd better be at the feckin' church, by the time the rest of us get there, or else the auld man's belt will be at yer arses!"

As the sulking pair had headed off out the back door, she'd warned after them, not to be showing her up like they'd done last Sunday, when they'd been competing against each other to see who could fart the loudest, during Father Murphy's sermon.

The noise, as their farts had skidded of the wooden pew, was loud enough, but the stench was overbearing! Especially for the people sat in the pews behind us, who'd held handkerchiefs to their nostrils throughout the whole service, like we'd had the plague! Somehow, mammy had managed to convince the half-drunk priest, none of her children were responsible for such a thing! And she'd complained, the only reason why the stench had given out around the family, was because of the stink bomb thrown in our direction, from the vicinity of the boy scouts group, sitting in the pews at the back of the church. Resulting in the priest, rushing angrily over to 'Skip' the scoutmaster, and berating him about the behavior of his boys.

It was teeming down with rain, and mammy said, she hadn't the time to be lighting a coal fire or bringing water to the boil, so we were to make do with standing out in the back yard to wash ourselves. It was brilliant! I'd loved the heavy rain! Especially standing bollock naked in the open air as the heavy droplets pricked every part of my body into life. And when I'd close my eyes, I could have been anywhere, but Stamford

Street. And the water was clean for us all!

Yesterday. Mammy had taken, Maggie, Martin, Bernie, Nabby, Michael, Gosson, Kathleen and me, off to the social services clothing store, to have us kitted out with second-hand clothes, which she would do every three months. The two social services women on duty that day, had stood peering down their snooty noses at us, from behind the safety of the tall counter, as one of them had marked off our names and dates of birth on her forms.

I don't think mammy liked them very much and kept referring to them under her breath, as, "lesheens."

Sizing us all up and down for a minute or so, the two women had set about plucking items of clothing off the rails and putting them down on top of the counter, along with an assortment of clean socks and underwear, for us to fight over.

Nabby had bagged himself a Victorian-style child's navy blue sailor's outfit, complete with the large white square collar that hung down at the back. Martin and I had bagged ourselves matching grey corduroy outfits, consisting of a white shirt, a grey jacket and matching pair of short grey trousers. The two women had turned their noses up to the ceiling, as we'd hurriedly undressed in front of them, throwing our dirty rags in a big heap on top of the counter, followed by our smelly socks and skid-marked underwear, which they'd swiftly picked up with their large wooden laundry tongs, before throwing them into the large brown paper waste sack.

They'd put some black slip on plimsolls and girls sandals on the counter, but no proper boy's shoes. And as none of the pumps would fit Martin and me, we'd each had to make do with a pair of the girls brown sandals! Not that we'd minded, as they'd been more comfortable than the Wellington boots we'd been given the last time we'd came here.

One of the women, remarked to mammy, how smart we'd all looked. She said, Martin and me, had reminded her of Tweedle-Dee and Tweedle-Dum, in our identical matching outfits. We'd scowled up at her, but she had ignored us and said to mammy, "If you are minded to, you might like to make a donation in the poor box, at the other end of the counter." But mammy wasn't minded to, and had declined the kind offer, on a technical point.

"As I'm one of the poor people that collection is intended for. Then there's no need ta be putting me own money in the box, seeing I'd only be getting back the money I'd given ta meself, when I already had it in the first place! Which is a feckin' waste of time, if yah asked me!"

Making our way through the busy waiting area, towards the main exits of the building, there was a loud clattering noise, just like the sound of a collection box being dropped on the ground, as the collection box hidden under Nabby's new duffel coat, had clattered to the floor.

"Jasis, Mary an' Joseph!" mammy gave out, hitting me around the head because I was nearest to her, as an army of accusing eyes had stared at the collection box, before fixing back on us, "Yer going to get us all corrupt!" she'd scolded Nabby, before bending down and quickly scooping up the full collection box in one movement and slipping into her large bag, before hurrying out through the main swing doors, with the rest of us hurrying after her.

Mammy had spent a while pinning the big clumps of shamrock to the lapels of our new outfits, we'd got from the social services the previous day. She'd asked daddy, if he was coming along to the church service, but daddy said, it was too much for him, with his bad back-an-all, and he'd feel better just sitting in the pub celebrating in the warm.

She'd said nothing, knowing he'd only start another blazing row with her, if she'd tried to push the point to the fact, him being an Irishman, and so should be at the church respecting his Patron Saint. She herself, tried to get to the church on most Sundays, or any other special day. It gave her the opportunity to meet with family and friends and to catch up with any gossip she might have missed out on. Though it seemed to me, she always knew everything that had been going on around Hulme.

The rain had slowed to a drizzle, by the time we'd set off for the church. But it hadn't dampened our spirits, or stopped us from singing *'Glorious Saint Patrick, dear Saint of our Isle'* which was the only hymn we'd known that mentioned the auld saints name.

We'd followed mammy as her high heeled shoes clippety clopped along the pavements in the direction of St Wilfred's church, with her having her cut out trying to stop her broken umbrella from turning inside out and her hollering at us to stop splashing in the puddles, threatening us with the auld man, if we didn't give up with the shenanigans. And by the time we had reached the church, the lumps of shamrock had already withered through lack of water, while our sandals and socks were soaked through, from too much water!

"Good morning' ta, Mrs. Rattigan!' The scowling face of

Sister Mary, had greeted us at the entrance doors of the church. Her evil looking lob-sided eyes behind large bifocal glasses, gave us the once over, while her lips stayed permanently pursed, like a dogs arse.

"Mornin, Holy Mother." Mammy bowed her head to the auld dragon.

"Ah, will ya get a look at those fine children of yers," she'd scowled at us. "All washed and dressed like little angels. They're a credit ta yah for sure-so they are, Mrs. Rattigan!" the patronising auld hen suddenly shoved the wooden collection box right up under mammy's nose.

Slightly turning her back away from the auld nun's beady eyes, mammy had carefully fumbled inside her purse, so as not to let the loose change rattle. "I've only the ten shillings to me name,' she'd said, pulling the ten shilling note out and showing it to Sister Mary, while tipping her purse over to show she'd had no change. "I'll put a few extra coins in the plate on Sunday," she'd lied.

"Ah sure, that'll be fine." said the auld nun, suddenly snatching the ten shilling note out of mammy's grasp. "You're a saintly woman an' yah don't even know it, so yah don't. An' with all those mouths ta feed as well!" the thieving hen had quickly slipped the ten shilling note into the side pocket of her starched black habit, before mammy could snatch it back.

We'd all waited with baited breath, for mammy to give the thieving auld hen, a box on her warty hooter, but to our shocked surprise, mammy just gave the smiling nun another bow of the head, angrily smacking Martin around the ear as she'd ushered us into the packed church, where we'd joined our older sisters, alongside Paddy and Shamie, in the pew which they they'd kept empty for the rest of us.

Father Murphy had droned on and on so much about St Patrick, anyone would have been forgiven for thinking, he was a close relative of the heavenly saint! He'd gone on to mention lots of other Irish saints, but forgot to mention our mammy's name! I'd supposed, there'd been so many saints to remember all in one go, it was understandable, he couldn't remember all of them.

-FIVE-

Cathy McCarthy had been sitting in the pew in front of us. She had glanced over her shoulder at me and had thrown me a big smile, and I had thrown a smile and a wink back at her. But Mrs. McCarthy had to go and spoil the moment, telling her daughter to turn round the other way, before she'd given me one of her evil glares. I'd pretended I'd something in my eye and I'd keep winking at her, to the point where, she must have been thinking I'd been afflicted with a twitchy eye. She'd just looked right down her long haughty nose at me, before swiftly throwing her head back, aiming her snooty conk up in the air, as if the smell of my skid-marked undies had suddenly hit her nostrils. I'd retaliated, throwing her one of my sweetest dribble smiles, letting the spit run down my chin, causing her to turn away in total disgust.

Mr. McCarthy was glaring over his shoulder at Bernie. It was difficult to see most of his facial features on account of his large bristly grey beard and long sideburns, which covered most of his face, so all you could see, were his wide dark unblinking eyes peering from his large bushy eyebrows, resting just above his big purple-veined hooter. He'd not forgiven my sister for terrorising his horse. And even had the cheek to call at our house not long afterwards, with a vet's bill, demanding daddy should pay for Goliath's sore arse! But daddy had told him, "That feckin' horse should have been for the knacker's yard, years ago! And if yah don't feck off pronto, I'll be shoving that bill up yer hole!

Bernie, had asked Mr. McCarthy, what he was gawking at, before poking her tongue out at him. He had still kept glaring at her, so she had given him two of her best V signs. Only then, did he turn away, shaking his big shaggy grey head in utter despair.

As the wooden collection plate was passed from one row of pews to another, Sister Mary would stand at one end of the pew, keeping her beady eyes on the offertory plate, as it passed from one person to the next. While the keen-eyed, Sister Gertrude, stood at the other end, ready to take the plate and pass it to the first person in the next row of pews, and so on. Paddy and Shamie were in fits of giggles, desperately trying to suppress their laughter, as they'd stared at Sister Gertrude. She was a strange-looking nun, with a hump on her back, furrowed eyebrows, and a leg shorter than the other. The sole of her left shoe was at least a foot thicker than the sole of the right shoe, stopping her from toppling over altogether. It seemed all the nuns we came into contact with, were afflicted by one sort of thing or another. Whether or not they'd been sinners, like Sister Mary, that was a secret only they held unto themselves.

As the plate had reached mammy, the natural instincts of the whole family standing either side of her, had suddenly kicked in, and we had all suddenly contracted a serious bout of whooping cough, causing us to move backward and forwards, blocking the plate from Sister Gertrude's view for the briefest of seconds. But those brief seconds, were all the time mammy needed, to screw up a couple of ten shilling notes into the palm of her hand, before blessing herself and passing the plate along!

33

I had thought, with the look on Sister Gertrude's face, she must have cottoned on to mammy, especially when she stood staring down into the collection plate, with her lips silently moving, as if she'd been mentally adding up the notes still left on the plate, before she had taken a sudden backward step, the thick sole of her left shoe holding her steady, probably from the shock of seeing there were a few notes missing. She had suspiciously stared into mammy's eyes, searching for the slightest sign of guilt. But mammy never felt guilty about anything and just threw the inflicted nun a smile back, blessing herself again with the sign of the cross as the auld hunchback hobbled off to the next row of pews.

After the church service, mammy had spent a few minutes outside the main entrance doors, talking with Father Murphy, and telling him what a beautiful service it had been. Though it had been hard for any of us to have heard a single word he'd droned on about. She'd told him, she was looking forward to hearing him again, this coming Sunday, and asked him, if he would give the family the honour of a blessing, to which he'd obliged in an instant. Cutting the air with a swift sign of the cross with his fat podgy hand, while muttering some strange Latin words. And we were all purified!

With mammy feeling a lot holier, and richer, we took the few minutes' walk to St Wilfred's school playground and the fête, where the distinct sound of Irish music could be heard filtering through the air. The whole of the school playground had been packed with all sorts of stalls, selling second-hand clothes, toys and other bits-and-bobs, as well as homemade jam and cakes. Martin and me, made a beeline for the free buffet stall, but when we'd got there, the vultures had already eaten most of the food, save for the one large plateful of smelly egg sandwiches which no-one, so it had seemed, wanted. I'd found myself cursing mammy, for wasting precious time, asking Father Murphy to bless us! And as for his preaching, of how the blessed were the most fortunate of God's followers, and us children inheriting the earth! When we couldn't even get to inherit a slice of poxty cake!

Sister Joseph, our form teacher, was running the church stall, with Sister Rosemary. They were selling rosary beads, religious medallions and pictures of Jesus and St Patrick. As well as other kinds of religious paraphernalia. She'd glared at Martin and me, as we'd loitered around her stall, picking up the odd picture or odd medallion, hoping she'd be distracted for a few seconds, so we could steal them. But she wouldn't be distracted, and her hawkish eye had stayed firmly fixed on us, as she'd whispered into Sister Rosemary's ear, loud enough for us to hear, "Keep a good eye on those two thieving heathens!"

Like most of the other children in our class, I didn't like our form teacher. She was a miserable tallish fat Irish nun with a big hairy chin, who used her size and big gob, to frighten us to death. I'd thought she was about two hundred years old, and if her black habit were made into a tent, the whole class would probably have been able to fit inside it! She had a big wart on the left hand side of her nose, and a strange look in her half-closed left eye, as if she was forever studying the hairs growing out of the wart, as her other eye looked in the opposite direction. I'd wondered if God, had given her that face to punish her for all her wrongdoings. Wondering too, what it must have been like for her to look in the mirror at herself, day in day out. If she could bare it!

"If ye've no money ta be buyin' anythin' then there's no point in hanging around here now, is there, boys? So get away with yah before yah feel the back of me hand!" She'd shooed us away to the strains of 'Oh Danny Boy!' emitting from the gramophone's loudspeaker.

Paddy and Shamie, seemed to have put their past arguments aside, at least for St Patrick's Day. They were standing over by the far wall of the playground, talking to a couple of girls, when Shamie had gestured, with a wave of his hand, for us to come over to him.

Making our way straight over to them, he'd asked us, if the sour-faced auld dragon, Sister Joseph, was still giving us grief.

"That she is." said Martin.

"Wouldn't it be a grand miracle, if for once in her miserable life, she'd liven herself up a little" smiled Shamie

"It would for sure." I'd agreed

"Well. We've somethin' that can make miracles work." Shamie suddenly emptied the small lemon-coloured tablets, six in all, into the palm of his hand, 'These'll put a smile back on her sour miserable auld puss!' he'd said, as the two girls with him and Paddy had giggled. "Do yah want ta see the biggest miracle, St Wilfred's has ever seen?"

"We would that!' we both agreed"

Handing the tablets to Martin, Shamie told us to slip them into Sister Joseph's tea, when she's not looking.

"What if she's not drinkin' tea?" I'd asked.

"Well slip them in ta whatever she's drinkin'."

"But what if she isn't drinkin' anythin'?" said Martin.

"Then get the feckin' auld hen a poxty drink of somethin! Just stop asking me feckin' questions! Will yah!"

Looking forward to the biggest miracle, St Wilfred's School had ever witnessed, Martin and me, made off in the direction of Sister Gertrude's tea and biscuit stall. On the way, I'd suddenly felt this terrible pain rise up in the pit of my stomach, which had built up to a crescendo, forcing me to let out a silent fart which rushed down the legs of my short trousers. Martin had suddenly stopped and cocked his left leg in the air, as his face had contorted, turning a shade of red, while he'd squeezed out a loud smelly fart, before we'd rushed away from the stench.

"And what can I do for yea boys?" Sister Gertrude had greeted us with her usual suspicious furrowed eyes, as she'd slurped at her cup of tea, making loud gulping noises as she'd swallowed it down.

"Sister Joseph, sent us over to fetch her back a cup of tea.' said Martin.

"Did she now!' said the nun with the hump and the one leg shorter, or longer, than the other, depending on which way you looked at it, "Sister Joseph, has never touched a drop of tea in her whole life!" she'd said, before going on to suggest, we must have misheard her, with all the excitement of this beautiful St Patrick's Day festival! "It was probably a cup of coffee she'd wanted."

"Yeh! That's it!" Martin eagerly nodded his approval.

"Yah might as well take along a cup of coffee for Sister

Rosemary as well. Oh, and some biscuits.'

While she'd had her back turned to us, Martin had slipped two of the six yellow tablets into her tea, thinking two miracles would be better than the one. Perhaps they'd make her hump disappear and her shorter leg grow to the same length as her longer leg, or vis-versa.

Sister Gertrude placed the two matching china tea cups and saucers on the tray, along with a small plate of creamed biscuits, which she'd handed to Martin to carry, as he was the eldest. We'd paused for a moment, watching her take a big slurp of her tea before noisily gulping it down, not knowing what we were supposed to expect to happen. We'd only ever heard about the miracles Jesus had done, and had never seen one happen in real life.

"Well go on then! Before the coffee gets cold.' The auld nun shooed us off on our way, with her suspicious scowl still unchanged, as her eyes, like little round brown buttons, stared out at us beneath her thick hairy eyebrows.

Heading in the direction of Sister Joseph's stall, Martin slipped two of the tablets into each cup as we'd scoffed down the plate of biscuits.

"Sister Gertrude, told us to fetch these over ta yah." said Martin, swallowing the last remnants of the dried creamed biscuits, as he'd plonked the tray down on top of the stall.

"An' I suppose she sent yah over with the plate of biscuit crumbs for me as well, did she?' snarled Sister Joseph.

As none of her eyes were looking directly at me, I'd not been sure whether she'd been talking to me or Martin, so I'd opted to say nothing. Martin too opted to say nothing either and we'd let the gibbering nun, gibber on! I'd known by the look on my brothers reddening face, what the nuns didn't know he was about to do, and seconds later when he'd let a silent one off, Sister Joseph had suddenly stopped gibbering as she and Sister Rosemary, all red faced themselves, had attempted to break the world record for holding their breath the longest.

We'd moved off, just as the auld dragons had gasped for air, hurrying across the playground, where we took up a good vantage point on the corner of Mrs. McCormack's homemade cake stand, where we could keep an eye out for their faces to crack into a smile. Once they'd gotten over the pong!

It hadn't taken too long for the tetchy Mrs. McCormack, to tell us to 'Keep our thieving hands in your pockets, where I can see them!' Martin had asked her, how it was possible for her to be able to see our hands, if they were in our pockets. But she'd snapped at him, not to get smart with her!

"If you're not buying anything, why don't the pair of you just bugger off out of it!"

"How much for a bag of yer broken biscuits?" asked Martin.

"More than you can afford, I expect!"

"We might be able to."

"Tuppence a bag! If you really want to know!" which was tuppence more than we'd had. Trying one of daddy's tricks, I'd asked her, "Is it possible yea can put the cost on a slab of sorts, to pay off at another time?"

"I'll put the pair of you on a bleedin' mortuary slab, if you don't piss off!" It had never worked for daddy either! And so we'd rushed off to the toilet block before we shat ourselves, creating a no-go area for some while.

-SIX-

We'd come across mammy, talking to Mrs. Reilly; Bridget Reilly's mammy, at her stall. Mrs. Reilly teaches Irish dancing once a week and she sells second-hand dancing shoes and kilts to those who can't afford to buy new ones. Martin and I had always fancied ourselves as Irish dancers! Sure, we'd learnt to jig just by watching our mammy and daddy, along with Uncle Paddy and Uncle Oliver and the rest of our aunties and uncles, dancing many an Irish jig in the streets, after staggering out from the pubs at closing times.

Mrs. Reilly was only too happy to snatch our sixpenny pieces, out of our hands, when we'd turned up for one of her lessons wearing Scottish tartan kilts, which our Granny Liz - mammy's mammy - had thrown together from a dress she'd said, she'd not worn since the beginning of WW1, and we'd given the class an impromptu exhibition of our jigging skills. To our surprise the class had seemed well impressed with us, considering we'd never had a lesson in our lives!

We'd jigged and spun around and around, getting the biggest applause from the other children, when we'd lifted our kilts, to show we were *real fellas,* which Uncle Oliver had told us we had to do, to be the finest of Irish dancers.

But it seemed the appalled looking Mrs. Reilly hadn't been that impressed. She'd said, she was having none of it and had ranted and raved at us about how disgusting the pair of us were, and of how we both should be ashamed of ourselves, banning us from dancing lessons before the first lesson had even begun!

"Yer not ta come here ever agin, unless yer scrubbed clean to the bone! And yea can hire - on second thoughts-yea can buy, proper Irish kilts from me. I've a few nearly-new ones for sale! And yea can make sure yer wearing underpants before daring to show yer faces in here again!

Martin told her she could go and hump a donkey! He also said, we wouldn't want to be coming to her dance lessons anyway, because she knew nothing about proper Irish dancing! At least not like how mammy and daddy and all the rest of our aunties and uncles knew! Before we'd rushed out of the church hall, we'd given her another encore and lifted the front of our kilts high up to our faces, causing her face to turn scarlet, while she'd turned the air blue, and the kids screamed their delight – we think!

As we'd strode up to mammy, Mrs. Reilly was in the middle of telling her about her fine troupe of Irish dancers, she'd turned out especially for St Patrick's day, going on about how the tears of joy had always welled up in her proud red cacky-eyes, whenever she'd watched her beautiful children dancing, bringing back memories of her own dancing career - which had been brought swiftly to an end, when she had drunkenly staggered off the pavement just as the bus into Manchester City Centre, came along and gave her a sideways glance. She'd somehow managed to escape with only the three broken ribs, two broken legs and a fractured hip.

"I could dance on a sixpence, so I could, Mrs. Rattigan, so I could."

"Well. Yah feckin' had enough of them!" I'd been about to remind her, but instead had asked mammy if she could spare me and Martin a couple of coppers, so we could buy ourselves a bag of broken biscuits from Mrs. McCormack's stall.

"I haven't even a couple of coppers ta spare for meself!" Mammy had glared at us as if we'd just asked her for the whole world, "So feck off an' get yer own biscuits! Jasis! The kids nower days don't know they're feckin' born!"

It had seemed Mrs. Reilly's dancing troupe were not the only ones that could bring a tear to her greedy eyes, as another involuntary exodus of wind, had rose up from my trouser legs to linger around her big conk, causing her to stagger back while her big hotter had shot up in the air as the terrible stench of rotten eggs had passed her wide nostrils, threatening to render her unconscious. It was strange how the putrid smell hadn't any effect on us, or Mammy?

We'd spent a short while wandering around the fête, being shooed from pillar to post whenever we'd loitered at a stall for more than a few seconds at a time. I'd began to wonder if there had been a conspiracy against us, and all the stallholders had mug-shots of our faces hidden under their stalls!

Martin said, "It must be our sour puss's that's drawing people's attention to us." He said, we should smile more often. But I'm not the best of smilers. I'd hated smiling because of my gappy teeth. So the best anyone could expect from me was a tight-lipped grin. But I'm not too clever at keeping up a false grin either, which usually turns to a quivering grimace as my facial muscles and lips go into spasm.

When we'd approached Mrs. Moses' toy stall, I'd given her one of my best smiles. Mrs. Moses was the head dinner lady, at the school. I'd not known whether she'd been a nun in the past, but she'd also had an infliction with a permanent smile on her face. Only, her smile just went up the one side of her face while the other side remained miserable, depending on which angle you'd looked at her from. So, I never really knew whether or not she'd be throwing a smile or an angry look at me. But I couldn't have cared less! It had been more than what we'd received, from all the other miserable auld goats put together, at the fête.

"And what can I do for you two lads?" Mrs. Moses had politely asked. "Is there a toy that takes your fancy?"

Feck! What a question to ask two thieves! Sure, there were lots of toys on her stall that had taken our fancy, if only we could have stolen them! I'd felt my false smile slipping, though I had desperately tried to keep it going, but one side of my face began to twitch violently.

Mrs. Moses - I hadn't been sure whether she was smiling or not – had suddenly leaned right over her stall and had angrily asked me through gritted teeth, "Are you trying to make a fool out of me, sonny!"

"Sure. I'm not!" I'd told her, but my attempt at throwing her a proper smile was doomed to failure, as my twitching mouth had suddenly gone into quivering spasms.

"Don't you be making a fool outta me you mother's curse, you!" she'd suddenly snatched up her walking stick, hooked over the edge of her stall and had taken a swipe at me, just missing me by a cats whisker as it had whooshed past my left ear.

Hurrying away from the mad woman, we'd decided to give up on the idea of looking around the rest of the stalls, for safety reasons. And with no miracle happening as yet, we'd headed over to the crowded dance area by the main entrance doors of the school, where Mrs. Reilly had already assembled her dance troupe, and was giving them their final instructions before they took to the floor. It wasn't hard to have noticed her big hooter, instinctively sniff at the air, when she'd seen us standing close by, before she'd ushered her troupe into position, a safe distance away from us.

"Are yer dancers ready to begin, Mrs. Reilly?" asked Mr. Reilly, the fête organizer and father of Bridget Reilly.

"They are that, Mr. Reilly," said Mrs. Reilly, his wife.

"Then let the show begin!" said Mr. Reilly, gently placing the needle arm of the gramophone down onto the spinning record and the dancer jigged. And that's when the miracle we'd been so eagerly waiting for to happen. Happened!

As we'd watched the dance troupe get into full swing, it was impossible not to toe-tap to the rhythm of the Irish jig echoing out across the schools playground. Martin and me, along with a hundred other feet, had joined in, the toe-tapping and clapping, as we'd all got into the spirit of the Irish music. And that's when I'd first noticed, the dark shadowy figure, swiftly appear out from the corner of my right eye.

It was Sister Joseph! But not the haughty tight-lipped, miserable auld warty dragon, as we knew her! This Sister Joseph, had a wild glazed look in her big bright watery-blue crossed eyes, along with the widest of grins spread across her face, with the corners of her gob almost touching both her ears. It was grotesque! Skipping like a teenager, without a care in the world, she'd hopped into the dance area with her habit hitched high above her knobbly knees, hidden by her woolly black long-johns, and she'd danced a jig, the likes of which I'd never seen before, nor I'm sure had anyone else in the watching crowd, by the looks on their faces!

Like a nun possessed, Sister Joseph's long legs jigged fast and free, with her bringing her knees up so high, at times, she'd almost kneed herself in the gob.

Neither mammy, daddy, nor any of my aunties or uncles could have jigged, the way Sister Joseph had jigged. And if that wasn't enough of a miracle for one day, Sister Gertrude got in on the act too! Suddenly lurching into view, yelling, *'Halleluiah!'* at the top of her voice, she'd hopped around in a circle, while her prosthetic foot stayed on the one spot, like a demented Indian, doing a war dance, as she'd flailed her arms in the air.

For a few minutes, we'd all toe-tapped and clapped louder, as the nuns had danced and howled, and seemed to have been enjoying themselves, until the moment Sister Gertrude had accidentally kicked Sister Joseph right up her hole with her six-inch high prosthetic shoe, which had caused the drug-crazed nun, to turn on her heels and box the hobbling nun on the chin, causing her to stagger backwards into the gramophone player, before she'd hurled herself on the top of her.

"Sister Joseph! Sister Gertrude! Have yah no shame on yea!' Father Murphy, had suddenly appeared on the scene, all red faced and wide eyed and bellowing at the top of his voice, as he'd pulled the warring nuns apart.

As we'd hurried off past the stalls, making our way to the main exit, we saw, the normally timid Sister Rosemary,

45

stroking the long bristly grey beard of Mr. McCarthy, while the unsmiling Mrs. McCarthy, standing with the love of my life, Cathy, was rooted to the spot, as the drug tripping nun was telling her, 'What a fine looking auld horse yah have here, Mrs. McCarthy.'

-SEVEN-

The city of Manchester survived on the success of its ethnic minorities and their diverse cultures. And it was those ethnic minorities which ran the boutiques, the shops, the restaurants, the coffee houses, the strip joints, the whore houses. All owned by the Indians, the Chinese, the Pakistanis, the Jews, and every other nationality, barring the Irish.

I'd once overheard my auntie Mary, asking mammy, "Why is it, the feckin' Irish fella's don't own any of the big businesses in Manchester?" and mammy telling her, "The Irish fella's only know about religion, beer an' humpin'. And that's why, some of them have given their lives up to the church, and the rest to the pubs, to get away from all the children they'd bred!'

Martin, Bernie and me, had been begging in the city since nine o'clock on the Friday evening, right up until the early hours of Saturday morning, as we'd do every Friday, without fail. We'd start off with a penny, spending hours asking passersby, if they could change the penny for two halfpennies, and so on. With most people giving us the two halfpennies, and taking the penny, there were the few people who'd tell us to keep it, and we'd accumulate this until we'd managed to collect ten shillings, or more in coppers, which was the target, daddy had set for us. The alternative, was usually a good hiding with his leather belt.

It was much harder to beg in the earlier parts of the evening, more so, because of the higher number of coppers out on the beat at that time, in search of the drunks and the prostitutes, and the homos, hanging around the public toilet blocks. They'd ignored the down-and-outs unless they were causing a big scene. Sent the whores on their way. But they always arrested the homos, giving them a good beating in the process.

If they'd ever managed to catch us begging, they'd just take all our hard-earned pennies and tell us to fuck off home. Thankfully it was only on the rare occasion we'd got caught. But we'd still had to play a cat-and-mouse game with them, until the midnight hour came along. That's when their presence walking the streets would wind down. Leaving it to the car patrols to take over.

With the cafés and the nightclubs closed, it left most of the streets empty, save for the odd staggering drunk and the groups of alcoholic down-and-outs, gathered close to the Central Plaza, where they would lounge and sleep beneath the huge statue of Queen Victoria, sitting on her throne, scowling down her long hooter at them.

An old drunk had suddenly staggered from a side street in front of us and had asked Bernie, "How much for a gobble!" Bernie asked him, to show us his money, first. And we'd watched him like vultures, as he'd fumbled around in his trousers, with me at the ready to snatch any money from his hand, and run. But instead, he'd suddenly flashed his mickey at us and had chased after us, as we'd ran off down the street.

Running into Market Street, with the drunk still staggering in persuit, he'd suddenly tripped over his own feet and fell arse over tit in a heap.

We'd cautiously, made our way back up the street to him,

with every intention of robbing every last penny he might have had, if he'd not already spent the lot on the booze. But just as we'd got to within a foot of him, the drunk had suddenly rolled over onto his back and started singing, *'I'm singing in the rain-I'm singing in the rain!'* as he'd pissed high into the air, sending a fountain of piss cascading down all over himself!

We'd ran off in fits of laughter, stopping further along by the statue of Prince Albert, who was looking in the opposite direction toward City Hall. And after counting out our takings of eleven shillings! We hurried off home, happy as we usually were, in the knowledge that there would be no beatings for us.

In the afternoon, dead on twelve o'clock, me and Martin, were peering in through the display window of the Hippodrome Bingo Hall, just as the odd looking fella wearing a tight pair of red drainpipe trousers and a yellow frilly shirt, had carefully placed the huge Chocolate Easter egg on top of the tall mahogany display stand. We'd watched with drooling mouths, as he'd placed the wide purple ribbon around the middle of the egg, before tying a large neat bow to it.

On either side of the tall mahogany stand, stood two smiling female mannequins, each wearing a different designed flowery pattern summer skirt. We'd curiously watched the fella as he'd turned his attention to these and had gone about straightening down the hems of each skirt, before taking a backward step, where he'd paused for the briefest of moments with both hands on his hips, admiring his handiwork. And then, satisfied, he'd walked off into the inner part of the Hyperdrome, out of sight.

At five minutes past twelve, in the same display window of

the Hippodrome Bingo Hall, a tall mahogany stand stood devoid of its huge chocolate Easter egg, with the big purple bow neatly tied around the middle of it. On either side of the display plinth, the two female mannequins were still happily smiling, despite the fact, they were now as naked as the day they'd came out of the mold!

"Quick, Tommy!" Martin's voice was urgent, as he'd held the main entrance doors of the bingo hall wide open, for me to rush out onto the damp street, carrying the huge chocolate egg, which was now hidden from view, wrapped inside the two summer skirts.

Outside the usual light drizzle of rain had drifted across a miserable grey sky, as Martin's skinny legs had set of running down the long street, in the direction of the bombed-out derelict Radnor, picture house. He'd stayed a safe distance ahead of me, keeping a sharp eye out for any coppers, as I'd followed, struggling to see over the top of my heavy burden. It was always better only one of us carried the ill-gotten gains. That way, and in the unlikely event of getting caught, then only the one carrying the stolen booty, carried the can. While the lookout would just walk on by, without a second glance. And since Martin had wheeled the large four-wheeled baker's trolley, which had been loaded with freshly made cakes and baked bread rolls, away from the bakery, the previous day. It'd been my turn to carry the goodies today.

The Radnor picture house, had stood derelict before I was born. Some parts of the floors had fallen in on themselves, but underneath the debris the ground floor still remained intact, though the auditorium had been completely stripped bare of all its fixtures and fittings, with the middle section having caved into the basement, causing it to slope in on itself, resembling a huge bomb crater. In one of the basement rooms a small hole had been cut through the wall in to one of the adjoining empty shop cellars. Here, during most of the days, and far away from prying adult eyes - and the police – a world thriving with gangs of children co-existed.

One of our favourite past-times, and an escape route, if the police did call, was to hurl ourselves out of a top window of the building onto the street lamppost, standing some three feet or so away from the building, which we would slide all the way down to the pavement. Some older, and much braver kids, would launch themselves from the rooftop! And it wasn't just the fellas that got up to this kind of thing. The girls too were just as daring, especially a girl called Catherine, who would have been around ten or eleven-years-old and probably tougher and more daring than most boys of the same age. She would just step up onto the windowsill and launch herself out the window, without pausing to see if the lamppost was still there! Her younger sister Marian, like a lot of the kids around, would always step up on the windowsill, but it didn't matter how much coxing her sister Catherine and the rest of us gave to her, she just couldn't bring herself to launch herself out. Which was hardly suprising, considering the long drop we had to the pavement below, if any of us had slipped or missed the lamppost!

When we'd reached the back of the picture house, Martin, had pulled away a loose board across one of the exit doors, allowing me to crawl in through the gap, still struggling with the huge chocolate egg. And it was only after he'd followed me in through the gap, did he relieve me of my burden, before handing the two flowery skirts back to me and quickly scuttling off over the mounds of debris into the dimly lit auditorium.

"Where'd the feck did yah get that feckin' ting from!" Shamie, our older brother, had asked Martin. He'd been standing at the top of the bomb crater with a group of other lads and three girls, all of them around the same age as himself.

For a twelve -year-old, Shamie, had been renowned for his toughness and could beat the crap out of almost anyone. Even lads much older and twice his size. There was only two ways our brother knew how to fight, and that was, *one way* or the *other*. Which was beating the crap out of someone, fair and square. Or beating the crap out of someone with the first object that came to hand! But, *one way* or the *other*, we were proud of him, and only too glad he was our big brother, because nobody dared pick a fight with us, while we were in his presence.

"Found it," I'd lied.

"Stole it," said Martin, at the same time!

"Found yerself some skirts as well then, did yah Tommy? They suit yah down to the ground, they do!' scoffed Shamie, causing me to go all bright red, as a barrage of guffaws and wolf-whistles resounded from his friends standing around him.

"Yah big Nancy boy, yah!' laughed my toothless cousin, Paddy Ward.

"Don't call me little brother a feckin' Nancy boy! Yah gummy twat yah!" Shamie had swiftly turned on his heels to eyeball Paddy. "Call him a Nancy boy and yah call it me too. Is that right?"

"Ah. I was only joking with him, Shamie!"

"Then say, sorry, before I knock those last few rotten teeth of yer's down yer long skinny neck!"

"What?"

"Tell Tommy, yer feckin' sorry!"

In the briefest moments that followed, as the quietness had suddenly descended upon the auditorium, I'd looked directly into Paddy Ward's eyes, sure that I'd detected a slight hint of defiance in them. Half expecting him to show his hand and put up a fight, I'd taken a couple of backward steps, to be sure I wasn't going to be in any harm's way, if it all were to kick off.

Shamie though, had already read the threat and his hands had turned into great big fists, clenching tightly, until the knuckles had turned white, ready to pummel cousin Paddy's broken nose into the ground, if the need had arose. But unfortunately, the moment had passed without incident, and Paddy had got to keep his last remaining rotten teeth.

"I was only kidding yah, Tommy." said Paddy, throwing a gummy smile in my direction, though he'd deliberately not used the word, '*sorry.*'

"That's alright, Paddy." I'd accepted his apology with a sense of power over him, though I'd known, if he had wanted to, he could have kicked the living daylights out of me, if he'd had no arms the one eye, and only the one leg to stand on!

With the brief, but tense atmosphere gone, I'd made up a story about stealing the giant Easter egg and the two skirts from Woolworths. Getting my version in, before Martin could tell Shamie the truth, especially when our eldest sisters, Mary and Rose had worked there! They'd only been in the job a few weeks, and if they'd found out we'd stolen from their place of work, our lives wouldn't have been worth living.

Taking the large Easter egg and the two dresses off us, Shamie slipped a hand into his pocket and gave us two shillings for them. Not that we had any choice in the matter. He'd banged the egg down hard against the ground, breaking a large hole in it, before snapping off a couple of good-sized lumps of chocolate, which he'd handed over to me. Reaching a hand inside the egg, he'd then pulled out a handful of assorted wrapped chocolates, which he'd handed to Martin. The rest he would sell on, along with the two dresses, making a few extra bob for himself.

We didn't mind how he did business, and in any case chocolate for Easter, was better than the treat of boiled duck eggs daddy gave us for the last few Easter's. Tap the top and lift it off, and the whole place would stink to high heaven! So much so, our noses would instinctively turn upwards in the direction of the ceiling, to seek out the last remnants of fresher air, before the stench had managed to suffocate us. Of course, the stench didn't actually stop us from eating the eggs. As mammy always said, 'Yah have ta be grateful for whatever scraps of food yah get, cos yea'll never know when the next lot is coming. And we were grateful for any scraps. It was just the smelly farting all day long that we found hardest to contend with, especially from Martin.

-EIGHT-

During the early part of Monday morning the rain had belted down in torrents, though it had felt slightly warmer than it had been for a long while, which daddy said, was a good sign the big freeze was finally over. Barring mammy and daddy, along with our two eldest sisters, Rose, and Mary, the rest of us had to go into town, to the Schools Health Clinic, for our usual monthly bath, before the nurse painted our naked bodies with purplish coloured liquid she'd had in a big red bucket. This, we were told, was supposed to stop us from catching the lurgie, scabies, nits and hundreds of other things lurking all over Hulme, just waiting to make a meal out of us. We were bathed in two's before having the thick purple liquid painted all over our bodies with an eight-inch longhaired paintbrush.

The long bristles of the brush always tickled me, and when the nurse brushed around my bollocks, I'd loved it, and couldn't help getting a stalk on! She would smile, telling me I was a dirty little fellow. Though it hadn't stopped her from tickling my bollocks for a little longer. When she'd tried to tickle Martin's, he'd come over all shy and would hold his hands over his mickey. So I'd asked the nurse, if I could have my brother's tickles instead. And she'd always oblige.

On the way out, I had crept into the staff's cloakroom, while the others had kept a sharp eye out in the hallway. Rummaging through the nearest handbag to me, I'd pulled out a large black leather purse, and with my heart pumping, I'd ran out of the cloakroom, through the main doors, with the others following after me, straight across the busy Stretford Road, and down into the nearest alley, where we'd scrambled out of sight into one of the bombed houses, to discover, when I'd opened the purse, it was full with ten shilling notes!

There was a mixture of excitement and panic, from most of us as we'd stared wide-eyed at the amount of money we had. Bernie's expression though, had remained calm. I'd often wished I could have been like her. She was so laid back, seemingly not afraid or too concerned about anything, unless the other Bernie showed herself! We we're all streetwise and clever, in as much as we knew most of the streets of Manchester, like the back of our hands, but Bernie, she seemed different, "Very intellectually clever." is what the education woman, had told mammy and daddy, when she'd came around to our house one morning, when we were all still lounging in bed, to inquire as to why none of us had been to school for the past three weeks.

Daddy, had gone through his usual ritual of swearing on the family bible, and our lives, that he'd always walked us to the main gates of St Wilfred's Junior School, every single morning, without fail! So we must be wagging off, when his back had been turned! Though in truth, education just wasn't one of daddy's favourite subjects, having no financial benefit to him. And so, he'd make us go begging for money on the streets, or go searching through the empty houses for scrap metal, or wood for the fire. Which, to be fair, was more adventurous for us than going off to school, the dinners being the only good reason to go.

There had been just over five quid in the purse, which Martin had slipped into his pocket, for safe keeping. That it was a lot of money, we knew! Which was the reason why we had been shaking with the mixture of fear and excitement. We'd never seen-let alone touched, so much money all in one go. Though we must have brought home at least that amount every month, from our begging expeditions.

Martin's first thoughts were, we shouldn't bother with school today. Instead, he'd suggested, we should buy ourselves some broken biscuits and some sweets, and take the rest of the money straight home to mammy and daddy. But Bernie had this notion, if we did this, "It'll just bring nothing, but *more* trouble for us! They'll just spend the whole lot on fags and more booze and then, when the rowing starts, we'd be the ones for the blame, and the fists will come flying, straight at us!"

She was right of course, and none of us could, or would, deny this.

"Its yer feckin' faults, there's never enough food on the table to go round! It's yer feckin' faults, we have ta live in a dump like this! If it wasn't for yea lot of fuckin' bastards, we'd be livin' a better life than this! It's yer faults, we've been driven to the drink, an' sufferin' terrible with our nerves! It's yer faults, we're a pair of uncaring fecker's, who only tink about ourselves!"

"I think we'll take Michael, Gosson and Kathleen, back home, like we always do." said Bernie, "And then go off to Bellevue Zoo, and enjoy ourselves, for a change.'

And with none of us objecting to the idea, I'd thrown the purse with the small front door key, and a couple of photographs which were left inside, into the old fireplace to keep the dead pigeon company, and we took our two younger brothers and sister back home, as agreed, leaving them in the care of Elizabeth, telling her, we were off to school.

The walk to Bellevue Zoo usually took us about an hour, from Hulme, depending how much ducking and diving we'd usually have to do every time we saw a police car heading along the street, or if we became distracted by something else.

The Zoo, wasn't just a zoo, in the ordinary sense of the word. It was also one of the biggest funfair attractions in the whole of Manchester, with its amusement arcades, theatres and boating lakes, hotels and bars. And the Funhouse! One of my favourites!

The rain by now had stopped, and the light breeze had begun to ease away the dull grey clouds, to reveal a blanket of blue sky high above us. And there were puddles galore! Dotted all over the place, like liquid silver, glistening in the morning sun. How I loved my puddles! Martin, Nabby and me, were always competing with one another to see who could make the biggest splash. Bernie, would always refuse to join in, telling us we were feckin' eejits!

One at a time, we'd take long run-ups to each puddle, before launching ourselves into the air and landing with an almighty splash in the middle of them. It was great fun! And we were all just about as equal with our splashes. However. There was one large puddle which we'd avoid at all costs! It was originally a large garden pond, which, Martin found out, to his detriment, a few weeks back, when he'd taken a long run and jump before landing right in the middle of it, and suddenly disappearing out of sight, beneath five feet of filthy black water.

On the way, we'd met up with our cousins, Paddy and Martin Ward, searching through the debris at the side of the road. They too, came from a big Irish family like ours, but there were eighteen of them, not including their mammy and daddy. Their mammy — our Aunty Helen, one of our mammy's sister's — was expecting another baby to drop any day. Daddy said, her and Uncle Bernard, "Were like a pair of feckin' sex-starved rabbits, forever humpin' each other! And if they carried on humpin' at the rate they were humpin', they'd be taking over the whole show!"

"Hi Bernie,' our eight-year-old cousin Paddy, had greeted my sister with one of his charming big watery-blue-eyed smiles, as well as showing off his dirty teeth. "Why aren't yah in school?"

"Why aren't yah in school yerself?" Bernie threw the question back at him. She was good at throwing questions back at people who'd asked her questions.

"Our school is closed for the day, isn't that right, Martin?" Paddy prompted his younger brother.

"That's right." said Cousin Martin - unconvincingly.

"And why is it closed?" asked Bernie.

"Ah, well...' Paddy gave it some thought before answering, "Our Headmaster had suddenly dropped dead, for no reason at all. "Isn't that right, Martin?"

"That's right, Paddy,' his brother agreed - unconvincingly.

"That's funny!" said Bernie. 'Our school's closed for the day as well, because our Headmaster suddenly dropped dead, for no reason at all. It much be catchin'" she'd added, without the need for a prompt from any of us, to back up her lie. "Isn't it a small world?"

"Liar! Liar! Knickers on fire!" Paddy, goaded her.

"They can't be on fire, cos I'm not wearing any-so there!"

"Prove it!" Paddy swallowed hard.

"I've nothing ta prove ta the likes of yea, Paddy Ward."

"Come on! Let me see!' said Paddy, moving a step closer to my sister and attempting to lift the hem of her skirt to take a peek.

"I heard, yer mammy's goin' ta have another rabbit soon!" said Nabby, coming to Bernie's aid, as well as saving Paddy from losing a tooth or two. We'd all fell about laughing, except Paddy.

"If it wasn't for Bernie here, I'd beat the shite out of yah for that, so I would, Nabby." Paddy threatened.

"Are yah afraid of me sister then, are yah, Paddy?' Martin smirked.

"Yah couldn't beat the shite outta a lump of shite!" I'd scoffed at him.

"Paddy's in love with Bernie.' cousin Martin, had suddenly given away his brothers big secret.

"No I'm not, yah feckin' liar yah!"

"Yea are! Every time yah see her, yah tell me, yea'd like to give her a big kiss and take a peek at her budgie!"

"Yer a feckin' big liar, so yah are!' Paddy went as red as a tomato. "An' if yah don't want yer gob busted yea'd better shallup!" he'd warned his smirking brother.

"Anyways,' red-faced Paddy changed the subject, "Where are yea going?"

"There and back to see how far it is," said our Martin, "An' if it's too far to go, then we won't be botherin!"

"Can we come with yah?' Paddy asked.

"I'm not sharing our money with them two!' said Nabby.

"We've our own money," said Paddy, pulling out a handfuls of shilling pieces from his pockets, "We robbed our granny's gas meter!" he'd confessed, "Ah go on, Bernie. Let's tag along, will yah? Please! We'll be no trouble ta yah?"

"Only if yah can make a bigger splash than our Martin can," said Bernie, throwing a wink in Martin's direction, before throwing a sly glance over in the direction of the pond!

"We'll go for that one over there," said Martin, pretending to ready himself to take a long run and jump.

"I'm older than yea, Martin," said Paddy, suddenly pushing himself in front of my brother, "So I'll go first.

Putting up no argument, our Martin, had stepped to one side, letting Paddy ready himself. And we'd all watched on with baited breath, as Paddy, with a few words of encouragement from his brother Martin, had rushed across the street, took one mighty leap into the air, before disappearing out of sight beneath the smelly surface of the water. And with that, we were on our way, leaving Cousin Martin to rescue his drowning brother, as we'd headed off in the direction of Bellevue Zoo.

-NINE-

We hadn't been in the Belle Vue Fun park for all that long, when we'd came across Billy-the-Kid, dressed, as usual, in his cowboy outfit and holstered guns hanging down off his waist. And although he must have been in his middle twenties, we'd called him, *Billy-the Kid* for no other reason than it being the name everyone knew him by! He was with another group of retards, and we had started taking the mickey out of them, pulling ugly faces, and trying to mimic them. But, thinking we were playing with them, they'd just laughed and had thrown ugly faces back at us, while Billy gave us a wave, before doing a quick draw with both guns, like it was all a big show to him!

Still pulling faces and making grunting noises, as the group of retards had climbed onto the big wheel, the man in charge of the ride, had suddenly turned to the three of us and had shouted, "Hurry up you gormless gits! Or you're going to miss your ride!" And so we'd hopped onto the big wheel, without a second invitation, ending up tagging along with Billy-the-Kid, and our new found friends, for most of the day, sharing our stolen money with them, on hot dogs, candy floss and ice creams. What a day! We still had to pull the odd face and make grunting noises, just to fit in with the rest of the group, which hadn't been too difficult for us! Though, we did have to tell Nabby, a few times, not to overdo things or he'd draw too much attention to us! Especially when, he'd started jumping up and down and making monkey noises at the group of black kids, from another school of misfits, who'd starting taking the piss out of us, as we'd walked up the slope towards the entrance to the big Funhouse.

It had taken a short while for Billy, and the rest of the group to calm down, as they'd copied Nabby, nearly causing a riot, until the teachers had taken back control and had moved us on up the slope and into the Funhouse.

Our drunken granny, once had a good old moan to mammy, when Granddad had come back home, three weeks after running off with, *That whore-mans-bastard!* "Nothin' good ever lasts forever." and our fun, in the Funhouse, soon came to abrupt halt, when smoke was spotted high above us!

There'd been a mad rush for the exit, as panicking children and adults had rushed around just like our chickens did, when they were headless! And we had not been aware of exactly what the problem had been, until we'd noticed the billowing black smoke quickly descending down towards us from the roof space!

We'd grabbed hold of a ginger-haired retard lad called Robby, who obviously hadn't a clue as to the seriousness of our situation, as he'd ran around in circles with his arms spread out wide, pretending to be a fighter airplane! After we'd convinced him he'd shot the German enemy down! We'd led him out of the Funhouse and back down the slope following the others before deciding to go our separate ways, spending the next hour or so, watching as the fire crews had worked on the blaze, sadly to no avail and our the Funhouse, my favourite place, became a blackened shell, destroyed before my very eyes.

With five shillings to our name, which we'd agreed to give

to mammy and daddy, we'd made a detour on our way back into Hulme. And it was just as we had approached the corner of Warwick Street, and the nearby Hippodrome Bingo Hall, when we'd heard a loud commotion going on outside and we'd gone over to have a nose.

It was hard to get a good look in, because of the nosey crowd gathered outside the place. But when we did eventually find ourselves a small gap in the crowd and got a good peek. I was stunned to see my distraught sister, Rose, sitting in the back of a police car, crying hysterically! A few seconds later, a couple of uniformed coppers came out through the main entrance doors of the Bingo hall, standing either side of our other sister, Mary, who'd been wearing a patterned summer skirt, just like the one, Shamie had taken off our hands a few days earlier! The odd looking fella we'd seen putting the giant Easter egg on display and then straightening down the hems of the dresses, was standing off to one side, talking with a third copper. And that's when it had suddenly dawned on Martin and me, the skirt Mary was wearing, was in fact, one of the two skirts we'd stolen from the bingo hall! Worse still! Rose had been wearing the other one!

"When I get me poxty hands on you, Shamie! I'll feckin' swing for yah, I swear it!" our sister Mary, all red-faced, had screamed over at our redder-faced brother, standing at the front of the crowd.

"Yah should have told Shamie the truth." said Martin, looking fearfull.

"And let Mary and Rose, kill the pair of us?"

"What have yah done, Martin?" Bernie had thrown the

question at him, accompanied by her usual frown, when she knows we're in deep shit.

"Nothin'." I'd assured her.

"We stole the skirts, from the bingo hall." Martin, owned up.

"Jasis! The ones Shamie sold to Mary and Rose!"

"Aye! The same feckin' ones!"

"Looks like Shamie will probably be killing the pair of yah, as well, I wouldn't wonder." said Nabby.

"Well don't be wondering," I'd scolded him.

"Quick! Hide!' Bernie had warned us, "Shamie's heading this way!"

Getting a glimpse of our angry looking brother hurrying away from the crowd and heading across the road in our direction, I'd just manage to duck down alongside Martin, and follow him, on all fours, underneath the parked lorry, as our big brother had approached the others.

"Have yah seen them pair of gormless gimpy-eyed fuckers?" he'd angrily growled.

"Yah mean, our Martin and Tommy?' said Bernie.

"What other gormless gimpy-eyed, fuckers, would yah know, besides yerself?'

"Saw them today in school" lied Bernie.

"Today in school me arse!" scoffed Shamie, "None of yah's have been ta school today, yah liar yah! The truant man was around at the house asking after all of yah - again! An' the auld man's going up the wall! So be fuckin' warned!"

"And how would yah know all this, if yah were supposed ta be in school yourself?' Nabby threw the question.

"Cos I was hiding under me feckin' bed! That's how, yah

cheeky little twat! An' don't yea be telling the auld man that!"

"What's happening with Mary and Rose then?"

"The pair got arrested for stealing the two skirts and the big fuckin' Easter egg them two humpy bastards said they'd stolen from Woolies, when they'd feckin' stolen them from the feckin' bingo hall! The poxty little bastards!" Shamie had raged on. "When yah do see them. Tell them, they'd better be getting' to confession because their last rites are comin' an' I'll be feckin' killing them after!"

We'd watched from under the lorry as Shamie's stocky legs had hurried past and we'd waited until he was out of sight, before we'd dared crawl out from our hiding place.

"It wasn't me that told Shamie, we'd stolen the tings from Woollies!" Martin had protested his innocence to the others, as he'd got to his feet. "It was Tommy."

"Well. I had to tell him that! Otherwise Mary and Rose would have murdered us, for sure."

"Well. Now they're going ta murder yah for sure." said Bernie,

"After Shamie kills yah first. I wouldn't wonder" said Nabby.

"Will yah shallup wondering before I box yah one in the gob!" I'd given my little brother such an angry look, his big watery blue eyes stared back at me with a hurt expression. And for a second, I'd thought he was going to burst into tears.

Instinctively putting a consoling arm around him, I'd assured him I would never have really boxed him in the gob. Even if he'd carried on wondering about the things, he shouldn't have been wondering about, in the first place. He'd accepted my apology with a bright smile, before suddenly bursting into tears.

As it turned out. I had got five beatings in the one day! Which was a record! I'd been expecting the three. But the fourth and fifth had come as a complete surprise to me and had never been on the cards, as such.

I'd spent the first couple of days, after my sister's arrests, avoiding the pair of them like the plague. And if they had happened to be around the house, I would make sure I had been in mammy's sights all the while, because the pair of them wouldn't have dared done a thing to me, in front of her.

Mammy, had wondered, why it was, I'd not been able to keep still in the one spot, for a minute, and she'd asked me, if I had worms up my hole. I'd told her, I had not been feeling well. And when Mary, had suddenly suggested, I come over and cuddle up to her on the sofa and she'd make me feel better! I'd opted to run out the back way and off up the alley, just as Churchill our cat had done when his arse had been scorched!

Besides both my sisters losing their jobs and having to pay for the two stolen skirts and the giant Easter egg, out of their wages they'd had coming to them, which I'd overheard them complaining, didn't amount to much anyhow, they'd both agreed to the police caution, and were warned, they'd be sent to prison if there was to be a next time.

Daddy ignored their pleas of innocence, telling them, they were inconsiderate greedy feckin' pigs! He'd said, they could have at least, brought the Easter egg home to share with the family instead of keeping it all to themselves" This had incensed my two sisters even more, with them promising me, they were just biding their time to get a hold of me!

It hadn't taken too long for that *time* to come along, and for me to let my guard down. And they'd finally got me on the Thursday evening, outside on the toilet, while I was in the middle of having a good shite. I don't think it was anything I had particularly eaten. I had always seemed prone to frequent bouts of the scutters; as did the whole family come to think of it! But there I was, in the middle of my biggest scutter to date, when the unlocked toilet door had suddenly swung outwards, to reveal my two angry sisters, standing there like a couple of hungry lions, who had cornered their prey and were now ready to devour it.

Steeling myself, for the promised beating, I'd been stunned to have felt the few feeble slaps around my head, and the threats of having my bollocks cut off, next time! As my two sisters had avoided coming right into the toilet, probable on account of the stench. It had all been over and done with in a flash, and I'd wondered, why the feck, had I gone through all that bother to hide from them in the first place!

The following evening at around six o'clock, Martin, Bernie, Nabby and me, had been sitting at the dining table, playing snap, when Shamie, had suddenly walked in from the back yard, into the back room. Mammy and daddy were sitting on the small sofa near to the fireside, having their usual few bottles of ale, before going out for the rest of the evening. Mammy was already merry and giving us a rendition of her favourite song, *'The Forty Shades of Green'*. she was singing the line, *'an' most of all I miss me girl'* when Shamie had gone to walk past the table, at least that was the impression he'd given to me, with a wide grin on his face. Which at the time, seemed a little unusual, considering, he had two black eyes and a swollen lip! We'd seemed oblivious to him and he had made no eye contact with me at all. And I'd been halfway through breathing a heavy sigh of relief, while wondering, if the good hiding he'd got from our two sisters, had made him lose his memory. When his fist made contact with my gob, the momentum causing my chair to topple backwards, knocking over mammy and daddy's half empty bottles of ale, standing on the fireside hearth. My third, fourth and fifth beatings of the week!

-TEN-

St Wilfrid's Catholic School wasn't too long of a walk from Stamford Street. It would normally take us around ten minutes to walk there, if walking at a brisk pace. Which was something we had never felt minded to do unless we'd stolen something from a shop and the shopkeeper or the police were on our tails!

The journey through the streets of bombed houses had too many distractions for the kids like us. And unless a mammy or a daddy, or both, took their kids to school, it was rare any of us made it on time for morning the assembly. On those odd miraculous mornings when we did make it on time, then this would have been a particular special day such as, All Saints Day or St Patrick's Day or a day a group of pupils were going to be making their first Holy Communion. These special days meant a party after the church service! And you could be sure, we would always endeavor to get there at the earliest opportunity for any party! Otherwise we'd amble through the streets of bombed-out houses with our keen eyes darting to and fro sniffing out anything that might be of some value to us.

Ten o'clock in the morning and we'd still not reached school, though we'd only been a few streets away. We'd found a huge discarded lorry tyre on one of the crofts. The tyre was about a foot taller than us and as Martin was the eldest, he was the first to hop inside it, while Bernie and I had rolled him along the street in the direction of the school. I'd let Bernie have her turn before me, while Martin and me had pushed her along. But after travelling only a few yards, she'd screamed for us to stop because it had made her feel dizzy! So I'd hopped in for my turn.

It had been a strange sensation rolling over and over at a slow gentle pace, and seeing the world from different angles. And I'd been minded to thinking, it was just as good a ride-if not better, than some of the rides, at Bellevue Zoo. Round and round I'd gone, without a care in the world, as the tyre had gradually begun to pick up speed, only realising something was not right, when I'd heard Martin and Bernie, screaming, "Jump, Tommy! Jump!"

"This is the quickest yea'll ever get ta school, yah little fucker yah!" I'd heard the demented laugh of my big brother, Shamie, as he'd given the tyre a final push down Rutland Street, heading directly towards St Wilfrid's school further down at the bottom of the long slopping street.

I know I'd not lived on this earth for that many years, but whatever life I'd lived up to that moment, along with all the sins I'd ever committed, had flashed before my very eyes. I couldn't jump out of the tyre, because of the speed it was travelling, which had kept me pinned inside! And even if I'd wanted to jump out of the poxty thing, I couldn't even tell which way was up or which way was down! Let alone how I'd survived unscathed, as the tyre had flown off the pavement and onto the road where it had continued down the middle of the street, with a few cars missing me by inches!

To my relief, the huge tyre had eventually slowed enough for me to throw myself out of it just outside the main entrance gates to the school. I'd staggered to my feet, dizzy, shaken, but otherwise unhurt. And though I'd had plenty of strange looks from parents standing around, gossiping near the school's entrance, I had ignored them, as one would do when arriving on ones mode of transport, and I had nonchantly brushed myself down, as if arriving to school inside a tyre had been nothing out of the ordinary for me!

Thankfully, Bernie and Martin had arrived at my side a few moments later and I was able to throw an arm around my brother; pretending I'd not seen him in ages, to support my shaky legs. "Sham. Get me away from these feckin' lot-will yah." I'd said, "I feel sick!"

"Are yah all right, our Tommy?" Bernie asked, in between deep breaths, as she'd swept her tatty long blonde hair off her pale-face, "Only yah look as if yea've seen a ghost!"

"It was feckin' great!" I'd assured her, my head still spinning and a false quivering grin etched across my face as I had puked my ring up.

'Jasis! Yah could have been killed!' said Martin, walking me through the gates into the playground and deliberately making the lump of green snot, dangling from his left nostril, go up and down like a yoyo, as he'd breathed in and out through his nose, to the disgust of the group of women it was intended for.

"A car just missed yah by that much!" he'd demonstrated the distance with two fingers, gleefully smiling, as the three of us had headed across the yard into the school.

Like the majority of the kids in our class, I too didn't like Sister Joseph. Still none the wiser as to what had come over her at the St Patrick's Day celebrations, she'd gone and blamed her unruly behavior on stress. She'd seemed a little taken aback, as Martin and me, had strolled into the classroom, much earlier than was usual for us, and she'd called us straight over to her desk, glaring suspiciously at us for a moment or two.

"Here yea are. Take these ta yer parents." she'd handed us a small envelope each, with the letters **O X F A M** written across the top in bold black lettering. Underneath this was a picture of a bald-headed black child of about two years of age, with a belly as big as hers! There were smaller words below the picture of the boy, which had meant nothing to me, because I couldn't read. Not that it had mattered, because she'd gone on to tell us, all the money we collected in the envelopes was for a good cause and would be used to help the starving orphans of war-torn Africa. Though we hadn't a clue where Africa was, and she hadn't bothered to tell us where Africa was. So we were still none the wiser.

As I'd followed Martin to the classroom door, the auld hen had suddenly stopped us in our tracks, and hollered, in her sternest voice, 'Where on earth, do yea two urchins tink yer goin'?"

"Yah just told us to take these envelopes home, to our mammy an' daddy, Sister." Martin reminded her.

"Yah did say that, Sister." I'd backed up my brother.

"Are yah tryin' ta show me up in front of the whole class, Martin Rattigan, are yah?" Sister Joseph's face had gone all purple.

For a big woman, she was very quick on her feet and she'd cuffed the pair of us around our heads, before ordering me, to get to my desk. She'd then grabbed Martin by his left ear and had frogmarched him to his own desk. "I meant at home time, yah blitherin' eejit, yah!" she'd bellowed down my brother's ear while she'd still held on to it, making it go all red, to the amusement of the rest of the class. "Sit there and don't speak until yer spoken ta! And wipe that filthy green nose!' she'd growled.

Looking over at my brother, staring across the classroom at me, we didn't need to say anything to know what we were thinking. Throwing a smile in my direction, he'd wiped away the lump of green snot dangling from his nose, with the dirty sleeve of his jumper. And in that moment, without having to say a word to each other, it became common knowledge between the two of us, Sister Joseph, and the rest of the class, were going to get their comeuppance, one way or the other!

Lunch times, would see us marched off across Rutland Street, and around the corner to the annex, near Cooke Street, where we'd have to stand in the long line, which slowly moved forwards at a snail's pace, towards the serving hatch and Mrs. Moses, the head Dinner Lady. I'd say, she was roughly around the same age as Sister Joseph, though, unlike the nun's miserable scowly auld face, Mrs. Moses, had a permanent smile on hers. Even when she was telling us off, she always smiled about it! Word around the school was, she'd been inflicted with a stroke from God! A stroke from the headmaster, Mr. Coleman's strap, had never put a smile on my face! So I didn't know, whether a stroke from God, was a good thing, or a bad thing, for Mrs. Moses. She didn't seem the sort of person to be committing big sins. And so I supposed, as it was a good thing to be smiling all the time, the chances were, her stroke must have been a gift from the Almighty himself.

It was difficult to know if she was being serious or not,

because of the smile. But at least a smile was far better than the permanent sour scowl from Sister Joseph, which daddy, had likened to a gawking barracuda, with her pouting lips and eyes looking in opposite directions. Though mammy had stuck up for the auld witch and said, she wouldn't have much to smile about herself, if she'd a face like Sister Joseph's.

Every Sunday in the church, when Father Murphy, asked the congregation to take a minute in silent prayer. I'd look over at the auld hen, and pray to the almighty God to give her miserable-looking face a stroke, so as she could have a permanent grin like Mrs. Moses. But he never did answer my prayers!

The head dinner lady had splattered a couple of huge dollops of over-heated shepherd's pie onto my dinner tray, which smelt lovely. The peas I'd loved, the carrots-not so much. Cabbage! I'd hated the stuff! Just the mere thought of putting that shite into my mouth, made me gag and want to vomit. Mammy cooked it for us, when daddy, managed to steal them from the allotments. And if there wasn't the tiny worms or the slugs to contend with, there was always the grit, crunching against my teeth! Mammy too, would go on at me to eat the stuff, "As its good for yah." But when her back was turned I'd slip it onto Bernie's plate, as she loved the stuff!

Mrs. Moses also told me, I had to eat up all my greens, because they were good for me and would make me big and strong. And I'd told her, I'd rather remain small and weak for the rest of my life, than eat that shite! But the smiling cook had still managed to slap a large dollop of stewed watery cabbage next to my shepherd's pie, before I could move my tray away, causing me to heave. And just as I was on the point of picking up a handful of the disgusting stuff and throwing it back into her smiling face, she'd been saved, when Bernie had walked along the dinner line and had nudged me forwards, telling me, she'd have it.

Outside in the playground, the new boy, Paul Morgan, had hit another boy in the belly, winding him to the point, the boy had doubled up on the ground in tears. Paul Morgan, was a sly little bastard. He'd not been at the school all that long and had been putting himself about as a bit of a hard nut. Of course, he'd had the advantage over the rest of the boys, because his right hand was false. The fingers were fused together like a plastic dolls hand, and turned slightly inwards into a half-clenched fist, which seemed pointless, because the hand was just a solid lump of hard plastic and couldn't do anything. Not even wipe his arse! I'd seen him use the hand to good effect, only ever needing the one sly punch to win his fights.

As usual, Martin would go off to play football, and I'd sneak into the girls' playground to find Bernie. Sometimes ending up in a game of kiss-n-chase, which I'd liked playing. Especially when I'd got to chase after the rag and bone-man's daughter, Cathy McCarthy! She had the most beautiful Irish blue eyes imaginable and when Mammy was drunk and sung 'W*hen Irish eyes are smiling.'* I would always think of Cathy McCarthy. Two years older than me, the age gap hadn't mattered. We were in love and we're going to get married, when we got older.

I'd not told her this at the time, but I'd known she'd felt the same way about me, as I'd done about her, because I didn't

76

have to put much effort into chasing her, before catching her. And she would instinctively close her eyes and purse her lips ready for mine. And when we kissed, our lingering kisses, I'd always got this strange warm tingling feeling inside me, causing my mickey to go all funny, just like in the mornings when I'd first woken up. Or when the nurse, down at the clinic, tickled my bollocks with the bristles of the large paint brush.

Cathy's best friend was, Bridget Reilly. They were both always together and seemed inseparable. I wouldn't have called Bridget ugly, but I wouldn't have said, she was pretty either. I suppose pretty-ugly would have been the fairest way of describing her. With her small freckled pixie looking face, with the tip of her dainty little nose pointing skywards and light hazel coloured cacky eyes, encircled by red rims. And all sitting atop of her unusual long skinny neck, topped by her red hair, reminding me of our chickens! And another one that smelt of piss. Jasis! She'd not leave any of the boys alone, and seemed to have had taken a shine to me. Always asking for a kiss, even when we we're not playing Kiss-n-chase!

Just like me, she too was a fast runner and would chase me all over the school yard! I could always tell if she'd nearly caught up with me because of the piss smell! The good thing was, she couldn't climb, so whenever she'd got to within a foot of me, I'd be up the drainpipe of the toilet block, and there I'd stay, with the other lads, until she'd found someone else to chase, or the bell rang out for the end of playtime.

-ELEVEN-

"A penny for the starving children of Africa!" said Daddy, as he had blown a plume of smoke from his rollup, into the air. "An' here's me! With not even two halfpennies to rub together!" he'd moaned. "An' she's given yah two envelopes!" he'd pointed the fact out. "So it's more than a penny, the greedy auld cow is after! More like a penny for her an' a penny for the darkies, if yah ask me!" Daddy had screwed the two Oxfam charity envelopes up, before throwing them onto the open coal fire. "There's more starving children in Manchester, than the whole African tribes put together!" he'd moaned on, "Starving Africans me feckin' arse! It doesn't stop them breeding like feckin' rabbits in their straw huts, does it? No it feckin' doesn't!" he'd answered his own question. "They should cut off their feckin' bollocks, then they wouldn't be having all those children to starve in the first place! Tell Sister Joseph, if she'd like to hand some envelopes out an' collect some money for the starving Rattigan's of Hulme, I'd very much appreciate it!"

"Sure, aren't most of the Africans over here anyways?" Mammy had asked, as she'd stood with her back to the fire, with the back of her skirt hitched up so as she could warm her arse on the flames; a habit Daddy kept warning her, will give her chilblains, or something worse, if she didn't put a stop to it. But she'd never listen.

"Jasis! The feckin' whole of the African nations are over here, I've no doubt." said daddy, blowing another plume of

78

smoke into the air. "An' if it wasn't for me bad health stopping me from getting a job in the first place. Sure I wouldn't be able to find a feckin' job anyhow, because the Zulus, have taken all of them! Listen to me, the two of yah." he'd looked both of us straight in the eyes, with his serious face on. "If yah happen to see any of them envelopes lying around the school, bring them home - I mean the feckin' full ones! D'ya hear!"

In the evening, mammy had sent me and Martin on an errand to the corner shop with a hand-written note, for a packet of five Woodbine cigarettes, a loaf of bread and a bag of sugar, from the corner shop, where the shopkeeper, always let mammy have things on the tick, which mammy had to pay back, once a week, when daddy collected his money from the labour exchange.

Daddy wrote the note with a pencil and had given it to me. He did all the writing, because mammy couldn't read or write to save her life. She wasn't able to even spell her own name, and would have to draw a big X, instead.

As she'd seen us out of the front door, she'd suddenly remembered to tell us, old Ma Collins, who'd lived just around the corner from us, at number thirty-six, had been taken into hospital the previous evening, with a suspected heart attack, and might not have come home yet. "So if the milkman has left her bottle of sterilised milk on the doorstep an' no thievin' bastards have stolen it yet. Bring it home with yah. There's no point in lettin' it go ta waste. Get off on now! And don't be there til yer back! And if yah fall, don't wait to get up!" she'd hollered after us, as we'd hurried off down the street.

Making our way down and around the corner of Stamford

79

Street, Martin had suddenly stopped and asked me for the written note, which I'd handed over to him without question and watched in silence as he'd taken the small pencil out of his trouser pocket, licked it, like daddy always did, and began writing more letters under the words that daddy had already written. When he'd finished writing he'd handed the note back to me, without a word.

"You keep hold of the note." I'd offered.

"No! I mean that's okay." Martin declined the offer. "Anyhow, daddy gave it to you, to give to Ma Turner. She likes you better than me." he'd quickly added. And so I'd slipped the note back into my pocket, as we'd headed off to the corner shop.

Ma Turner was a small plump grey haired old lady and though I hadn't thought she was as old as Sister Joseph, or Mrs. Moses, I'd bet she wasn't too far off their ages! You could just about see the top half of her grey curly head and bespectacled eyes peering out over the top of the shop counter, and for some odd reason we couldn't understand, she would always greet me and Martin, as 'Laurel and Hardy.' It wasn't as if we'd had an ounce of fat on us, let alone between the pair of us put together! We we're always scratching our nit-infested heads, mind! So I could only assume, that might have had something to do with it! Unless we came across as a pair of feckin' idiots!

When I'd placed the note down on the top of the counter, she'd picked it up and studied it for few moments before reaching behind to the cigarette counter and getting down a packet of five Woodbines which she'd handed straight over the counter to me. "Get them into your pocket, before anyone sees them." she'd warned me, before walking off to the shelf to get the bread and sugar, tilling this up before packing it into the large brown paper bag. She'd spent the next few moments studying the note and shaking her head at the same time. I'd watched her lips moving, as she'd tried to decipher the words Martin had written underneath daddy's words, and I'd noticed too, how my brother had edged his way closer toward the shop doorway.

"What's the meaning of this?' Ma Turner had suddenly asked, causing me to almost jump out of my feckin skin and run out the of shop door, which Martin was already standing closer to! Clasping her beady eyes on me, she'd asked. "What in heaven's name is *derry*?"

"I can't read!" I'd shrugged, "So I can't help yah there, missus. But me Brother Martin can. He wro-I mean, he's able to read and write." I'd smiled over at Martin, scowling across the shop at me.

"I tink it's supposed to say "Dairy," Martin was forced to answer, An' I tink the other word next to it, says milk-but I'm not sure as I can't read an' write properly meself." he'd quickly added.

"Milk?" muttered Ma Turner, squinting her little eyes while staring at the note, "Ah yes! I understand now! So what milk does your mother want? Sterilised? Full -?'

"A box of Dairy Milk Tray. It's our daddy's birthday!' Martin had suddenly blurted out, before taking another backward step on to the shop entrance door mat.

"A box of Dairy Milk Tray?" she'd studied the note and eyed Martin and me, for a moment.

"Who wrote this note?" she'd asked none of us in particular.

"Me mammy," I'd said.

"Me daddy," Martin had said, throwing yet another scowl in my direction.

"Daddy wrote the first bit!" I'd heard myself saying, "An' mammy wrote the second bit. Daddy's teaching mammy how to write!"

"Mammy can't write an' daddy's teaching her." said my brother, which was cue for me to scowl at him, which he'd totally ignored.

"Ah!" smiled Ma Turner, "That would explain the difference in the style of writing-and the bad spelling!" she'd quickly added. "Your mammy didn't say, how big a box she'd wanted?" she'd peered over the counter at the pair of us, but we'd been too shocked for words, thinking we'd actually got away with it! And all we could do was shrug our shoulders.

"We'll start off with a small box and if it's the wrong one, then you can always bring it back and exchange it for the bigger one." she'd suggested.

We'd happily agreed with her suggestion and I'd cautiously took the small box of chocolates from her, while keeping a close watch on her eyes, which stared straight at me from behind her thick set glasses, not too sure as to whether or not the old woman had been codding us along all the while, just so as she could get close enough to box me one around the ear. But no! She'd given me the box and the bag of shopping and had cheerfully waved us on our way, telling us to wish daddy a "Happy Birthday." from her, as she'd jotted the items down in to her I.O.U. book.

Hurrying out of the shop and off down the street, taking the longest route home, we'd greedily scoffed down the whole box of chocolates before getting rid of the empty box over the wall of someone's backyard. When we'd reached old Mrs. Collins' house, we could see no *thievin' bastard* had stolen her bottle of Steralised milk, which was still standing on the top of the concrete steps leading up to her front door. And so I'd ran up the steps and stole it!

Reaching the house we saw the lamp-man was lighting the street Gaslamp directly outside. He'd greeted us with his usual "Hello you little rascals!" before suddenly asking us if we'd been stealing the milk again! We hadn't a clue how he could have known this or if he'd just been joking, but we'd looked down our noses at him before hurrying into the house, which had seemed quieter than it had, prior to us going on the errand for mammy. Bernie had suddenly appeared from the coal cellar carrying a full load of coal in the metal scuttle, which Martin took from her, tipping half the load onto the glowing embers of the fire and putting the scuttle at the side of the fireplace. When mammy came through from the kitchen, she'd angrily snatched the packet of fags out of my outstretched hand, immediately lighting one with her trembling hands while bemoaning the fact, she'd almost died of her nerves, having to wait so long for them! Taking the shopping bag off me, she'd disappeared back into the kitchen.

Bernie, told us, Michael, Gosson, Nabby and Kathleen were all asleep in bed. Our elder sisters had gone out. Paddy and Shamie had another row and daddy had kicked the pair of them out of the house and told them not to show their feckin' faces in the house again, until the pair of them could get on together. There had been no need to tell us daddy has gone off to the pub around the corner, because daddy always went off to the Red-Rose pub around the corner at the same time every evening.

Mammy came back out of the kitchen with a lit fag dangling from her mouth. 'Here yah are.' she'd plonked the plate of three slices of bread covered in dripping, down onto the dining table top, before dragging herself back off into the kitchen again.

We were all eyeing the thick knocker of bread on top of the pile, but Bernie had been too quick for Martin and me, and her hand had shot out and snatched the knocker up off the plate, in the blink of an eye! We'd scolded her when she'd taken a huge bite out of it, telling her, she should have let the eldest of us take the pick of the bread first.

"So. Which slice would yah have taken first then, Martin?" she'd asked, chewing on the mouthful of bread and dripping.

"Well. I wouldn't have snatched the knocker, that's for sure," lied Martin.

"What about our Tommy, then?"

"I would have taken one of the other slices and left the knocker for Martin. As he is the eldest." I'd also lied.

"Well, as yah would have left the knocker for Martin, and Martin didn't want it in the first place. I'll keep it." She'd sunk her teeth back into it.

Mammy had reappeared a few moments later with three mugs of sweet hot tea. Daddy didn't think much of mammy's tea and often said, "It looks like feckin' gumwater!" because she would water the milk down so much, making it possible to

84

see the dregs of tea leaves at the bottom of the cup! But we didn't care as long as it was sweet and hot and we'd gratefully swigged it down, sugary tea leaves and all, before she'd sent the three of us out to collect wood for the fire.

We'd left by the back way and up along the alley, bringing the large pram with us, taking it in turns to be pushed in it along the dimly lit streets, where the air was damp and heavy with the putrid smell of smoke from the coal fires spewing out from the chimney tops. The derelict houses nearest to Stamford Street had been completely stripped bare and so our searches took us further afield. But wherever we went, it never seemed to hold any fear for us. We'd felt comfortable in our surroundings, be it night or day. And were confident, as well as streetwise enough to know how to look after ourselves and each other. The fact we'd lived in Manchester for some time while roaming the streets up until the early hours of the mornings, without any harm coming our way, might probably had filled us all with a false sense of self-confidence, bordering on the point of totally indifference to the perils and dangers, that we could possibly encounter.

-TWELVE-

As the empty streets had forever grown darker, so we had walked further into the uninhabited areas of Hulme. And despite there being the odd Gaslamp reflecting what little light they could off the damp ground, as well as the tiny glints of lights far off in the distance guiding us on our way, we had often found ourselves walking in relative darkness for the best parts of our journey.

It had been Martin's turn, after Bernie's, to ride in the pram, and it hadn't taken long before he had fallen fast asleep. And as I had looked down on his peaceful dirty face, I had wondered to myself, just where he might have been in his dreams. Perhaps like me when I was fast off, he'd be far off in some distant land, where the sun always shone and the air was always fresh and clean and where there were no filthy smoking chimneys or smog to suffocate on. Somewhere, were he hadn't needed to be going off late into the nights, scavenging for firewood or scrap metal or begging on the streets for something to eat, or *a penny for two halfpennies.* Where mammies and daddies danced and sang all their Irish songs, without having to be drunk and violent towards each other and their children.

There were no sounds along these dark empty silent streets, save for the noise from a couple of loose spokes softly clattering on the front wheel of the pram, as the wheels had endlessly turned. Me and Bernie, didn't usually have a lot to say to each other when we were out at those late hours of the night. It wasn't that we didn't speak to each other, we did. But as there wasn't much going on in our lives, our conversations were limited, and we would be lost in our own thoughts, whatever they might have been at the time.

As we had walked, I had constantly kept my gaze fixed straight ahead of me. I'd always found it easier to take in my surroundings when looking straight ahead, as I'd seemed to be more conscious of those dark shadowy areas to the left and the right of me. Just like when I stare up at any one particular star in the night sky and see other stars further away out of the corners of my eye, which I'd not been able to see looking directly at them. Daddy once told us, the bogeyman only lived in places where people lived. And so we shouldn't worry about encountering him in these empty streets. But that didn't stop me from conjuring up those imaginative and invisible threats, which might possibly be lurking in the dark shadows of every derelict building, just waiting for us to pass by.

"Look! There's a fire further up!" said Bernie, bringing me out from my thoughts. I'd strained my eyes, searching in the distance, but couldn't make out a fire against the backdrop of distant streets lights away off in the distance. Bernie pointed her long finger and I'd closed one eye and looked down it, as if looking down the barrel of a rifle, until the dim orange glow of a fire far away, had suddenly dropped into my sight. "I see it!"

"Yah should eat more carrots, Tommy. And yea'd have eyes like a rabbit and be able to see in the dark!" Laughed Bernie. But I hadn't wanted to see in the dark, if it meant I'd have to have eyes like a rabbit! Especially if they were pinky-red eyes, like Richard Smart's two white rabbits! I'd rather go blind!

Shaking Martin awake, he'd jumped straight out of the pram, like he hadn't been asleep at all, and we'd quickened our pace in the direction of the fire, which had taken us a short while to reach it. Discovering, there wasn't anyone else about, though there had been a good amount of copper wiring, which had been burnt off from its layer of protective flex, lying next to another pile that had yet to be burnt off!

"They look like the dying embers of an old fire." said Martin, "Someone left in a hurry."

"That's clever Martin!" Bernie, couldn't resist the dig.

"Do yah think someone's tried to steal their stuff and frightened them off?" I'd asked. Immediately wishing I'd kept my gob shut!

"Don't yah think, the one's doing all the chasing off would have taken the copper with them? If they'd come ta steal it in the first place' my brother threw me one of his, *yah eejit,* looks.

I had been about to suggest, perhaps someone else could have come along to chase off the first lot of chasers. But I'd held back with that suggestion, just in case Martin had an answer for that as well, just to make me look an even bigger eejit than I already was. And in any case, he had a good point!

With no owners around, to claim the fire or the scrap copper, we'd instinctively set about picking up small pieces of wood lying about the croft and began to feed the fire back up. I could feel the warmth from the burning wood brushing against my bare legs, as the tiny flames had flickered back into life, before rising up and licking around the pieces of damp wood we'd thrown on to feed it. Standing in silence around the fire, I had stared into the hypnotic flickering flames dancing to and fro, as each one wrapped itself around another, like lovers or long lost friends meeting again. I loved staring into the flames of a fire and I could happily have done so forever! Providing they were not the flames of hell!

Martin pretended he'd had a cigarette in his hand and had put it to his mouth before taking long drags and blowing plumes of his warm breath into the air. I'd bet him, a sweet Blackjack, he couldn't blow smoke rings like Shamie could, and he'd had me and Bernie in stitches, as he'd pulled all sorts of funny faces in his attempt to win the bet.

We'd eventually set about collecting up larger pieces of wood scattered around the outside of the derelict houses, which, as a rule, we would never enter during the nights, because it would have been impossible to have spotted any potential danger in the darkness. I'd noticed the small wooden gate leaning up against the side wall of a house and I had made my way to it, as Martin had thrown the pile of unburnt flex onto the blazing fire. I'd caught a glimpse of Bernie loading an armful of wood into the pram and I had been on the point of calling her over to give me a hand with the gate, when I'd been suddenly gripped tightly and a big hand had gone around my mouth.

"Don't make a sound, or I'll squeeze the living daylights out of yah." I could smell the stench of stale tobacco and beer on the man's breath, as he'd grabbed me from behind and lifted me off my feet in one swift movement, before heading off with me into the derelict house behind us. I had tried to scream a warning to my brother and sister, but no sound would come out. I'd tried kicking my legs, in the hope the man might loosen his grip enough for me to wriggle free. But it had seemed the more I had kicked out as I had been carried off into the darkness of the house and out of sight, the tighter the grip around my mouth and my chest had become.

Taken in to the empty room at the front of the house, I'd been able to see through the dirty broken windows panes, the high flames of the fire dancing across the damp walls and ceiling as the man had put me down, still with his hand tightly over my mouth.

"I'm not going to hurt yah," he'd spoken into my ear in a low whispery voice, "I'm going to take my hand away from your gob and I don't want to hear a peep out of yah-or else. Just do something for me and then yah can go back to your friends," he'd promised, "But if I hear one peep, yah won't see them again," he'd quickly added, before turning me around to face him.

The flickering shadows distorted the man's face as he'd knelt in front of me and I'd felt the fear of God running through my whole body, as he'd stared straight into my eyes. And though I couldn't make out all of the man's facial features, I could have sworn he was the devil himself. Dumbstruck with the fear, all I'd been able to do was nod my head and let my warm piss run down my legs.

"That's a good boy," he'd slowly taken his hand away from my mouth, "Not a peep." the devil had whispered. "Get down on your knees," he'd pushed me down by my shoulders forcing my bare knees to the hard gritty surface of the floorboards.

"Are we going to say a prayer to Jesus?" I'd asked.

"Yah can say a prayer to who yah want, as long as you say

them in yer head."

I'd started with the *Hail Mary,* as the man had turned me back away from him, so he was kneeling behind me, and he'd pulled down my piss soaked trousers, before pushing me forwards and down onto my hands. Moments later I had felt something hard pressing up against my hole, just as Bernie had called out my name. I couldn't see her, but I had been able to see Martin through the broken panes of glass, as he'd stoked the fire with a long piece of wood and the flames had suddenly rose up. For a moment, I'd thought my brother had made eye contact with mine, as he had briefly glanced over in the direction of the window. And I had been on the point of calling out to him, when the man's big hand was back around my mouth, stifling my cry. All I could think at the time was, daddy was completely wrong, when he'd said the bogeymen only lived where people lived.

The man had been leaning right over me, shushing in my ear and telling me he wasn't going to hurt me, while trying to push his big mickey up me! And it had seemed my prayers to the *Virgin Mary* and the *little Flower of Jesus,* were not going to help me out of this one! Not that I could recall them helping me out at any time! I'd never found myself in this sort of situation before and so, nothing had automatically come to my mind as to how I could get myself out of it. There I was, knowing what it was like to have constipation and struggling to get a large turd out as the tip of it pokes out, but the rest of it stubbornly doesn't want to follow and I don't want to squeeze, because of the pain! And now it's going in the opposite direction! Feck this! I'd kept the cheeks of my arse closed tightly for as long as I had been able to and hoped the devil would realise he was trying to push a pencil into a needle hole! But this had only caused him to push even harder against me, until I'd no choice other than to give in, and I had relaxed.

The loud scream must have spilt out of every broken window pane and echoed across Hulme, if not further, as the devil had suddenly leapt up in the air and danced across the room, after Martin had appeared behind him, carrying the long stick with the pile of burning electric flex and hot copper wiring hanging off it, which he'd dropped straight onto the man's arse!

"Run Tommy!"

"Where did yah get ta!" the look on Bernie's face, had been a genuine one of despair and anger as I'd held up my pissy kecks and had rushed from the empty house past her, following Martin, "An' who's doin' all that hollerin'?"

"Just run!" said Martin.

Managing to fasten the hook of my kecks as I'd hurried across the uneven ground, I'd reached the pram and began to push it along the street as Martin and Bernie hurried to catch up with me.

"What about all the copper wire!" Bernie asked Martin.

"Someone else has it!"

"He tried to shove his mickey up me hole!"

"Who? Martin!"

"The feckin man!"

"What man?"

"The man doin' all the hollering with his arse on fire! Did yah see the way he'd leapt in the air, Tommy?" Martin had suddenly let off a long fart, which instantly brought the pair of us out in fits of laughter!

"Yer a pair of feckin' eejits, yea's two!" Bernie had shook her head at us.

-THIRTEEN-

On Saturday morning, mammy had told me to go off to Aunt Rosie's, to see what was taking daddy so long. "Sure. He'd only taken half a dozen chicken eggs to her not laying the feckin' tings!" she'd snapped.

Aunt Rosie lived in Collins Street, which was, the next street across on the opposite other side of Stamford Street. She wasn't our real Aunty as such. We just called her that because she was always nice to us. She was married to Uncle Mike, who also wasn't our real uncle. It seemed as if all the women neighbours got on well with Uncle Mike, but not with Aunty Rosie. We'd often hear them talking about her and saying things, such as, "He's too good for the likes of her!" or "She's as common as muck that one!" Once, when I was stealing from the corner stores, I'd heard Mrs. Mosley, from Philips Street, saying to Mrs. Kelly, from Collins Street, that Mrs. Tanner; Aunty Rosie, "Doesn't have enough time in the day to keep her drawers hitched up to her waist, because of what she gets up to, while her husband is out working all the hours of the day!" and I'd heard Mrs. Kelly say, "She makes Mary Magdalene look like a saint!" There were lots of other things I'd heard the neighbours saying about Aunty Rosie, but I think they were all just jealous auld goats, because Aunty Rose had a nice big pair of tits. That's what I'd heard my brother Paddy tell Shamie, on one of those occasions when they were on speaking terms with one another.

Paddy, the eldest of my brothers, was a *'Rocker'* and

94

supported Manchester City Football Club! While Shamie, the second eldest brother, was a '*Mod*' and supported the greatest team that ever walked the earth, Manchester United! I could only suppose, this was a good enough reason for the pair of them to have a mutual dislike for each other.

If I'd to pick a favourite out of the two I would pick Shamie every day of the week. Paddy was far too sullen and secretive and didn't pay much attention to any of us, unless he had wanted us to run an errand for him. At fifteen-years old, he'd worked as a labourer during the day and would be out most nights of the week, often staying away from home all night. So we hardly ever came into contact with him. He was really handsome, "A cross between Elvis Presley and James Dean." people had told him - *he'd* told us! With his swept back jet-black greasy hair, tight drain-pipe jeans and size nine winkle-picker shoes, topped off by his black leather-look plastic jacket with the large iron-on transfer of a tiger's head on the back of it.

There was always girls hanging around the front of the house when Paddy was at home. Mammy was forever telling him, "Get them who-ers away from the house before all the neighbours start tinkin' we're running a brothel!" When Paddy was going out and he'd not wanted the girls waiting out the front to see him, he would sneak out through the back way and zoom off on his bike at breakneck speed, up along the back alley, dodging dustbins as he went, while keeping the toe ends of his winkle pickers pointing skywards so as not to scuff them, as he'd peddled like mad!

Shamie, on the other hand, was the complete opposite. He

had lots of time for us and sometimes would even keep a *lookout* for us when he took me and Martin out to burgle a house for him. Unlike Paddy, Shamie didn't have a job on account of his bad back-just like daddy's! The doctor said, "It must be an inherited thing." though daddy's thoughts were, "Shamie is just a feckin' lazy bastard who should be out working to pay for his keep, instead of hanging around with gangs all the day and doin' nothin' but scratchin' his hole!" But mammy would always defend Shamie on this point, and she'd tell daddy to leave Shamie alone as, "He's out all the hours of the day and night robbing to pay his keep. And so doesn't need to get a proper job!"

Unlike Paddy, Shamie was outgoing, loud and forever fighting with anyone and everyone he didn't like. Which was mainly most people! And unlike our Paddy, he never turned his back on any of us in the street, always acknowledging us as family, if and when we'd called out to him when he was with his gang. Sometimes he would let us tag along with him, and on the odd occasion he'd even encouraged us to have a few good kicks at the head of one of his defenseless victims, which he'd hold down on the ground for us. I can only think of the one time when he hadn't acknowledged me. That was the day when he'd rushed out through the back gate of Aunt Rosie's house, with a wide grin spread right across his face, almost touching his ears, and his eyes distant and glazed with a look of bewilderment about them. He hadn't said a word to me and had just nodded as he'd carried on walking past me in his trance-like state. At the time I had wondered whether he'd had an extreme shock of sorts. Such as, Aunt Rosie giving him something special, like a big bag of sweets! Which in a way, I supposed would cause extreme shock considering she was as tight as a ducks arse, in the giving sense of the word.

Sprinting across Stamford Street, I had made my way down the back alley leading to Aunty Rosie's house. I'd ran as fast as my legs carried me, hurdling over piles of discarded rubbish and dodging overflowing rubbish bins. And in those briefest of moments, I had been transformed into, 'Hayes Jones' the black American one-hundred-and-ten yard hurdles champion! Mammy had once moaned about it always being the darkies that won all the races." and daddy said, "It's no wonder, when they get plenty of training running away from the starving lions chasing them, all over Africa!"

Hurrying through into Aunt Rosie's back yard, I'd opened the back door of the house leading in to her kitchen, where my keen sense of smell had hit on the odour of greasy fried food, which had made my belly groan loudly with the hunger. "Daddy!" I'd called out before inviting myself in.

Just as in our own house, Aunt Rosie's kitchen was dark and damp and just small enough to swing a cat in it. I knew this to be a fact, because a few months back, daddy caught hold of Churchill, our old ginger moggy up on the kitchen worktop, sniffing at the plateful of fried bacon and eggs he'd just cooked for himself. He'd grabbed hold of the overweight mangy-haired cat by the tail and had swung him once around his head, hitting the cat against all four walls of the kitchen, before holding the half-unconscious animal over the high flames of the gas ring, singeing its arse. "Get out yah fuck!" he'd drop-kicked the smoldering animal out through the open back door.

On the sink's wooden draining board there were two plates, one on top of the other, with scraps of fried egg and bacon fat on them. I'd helped myself to the leftovers before licking both plates spotlessly clean and dropping them into the sink of murky greasy luke-warm water. On hearing low murmuring noises coming from the front of the house, I'd called out to daddy once more as I'd made my way from the kitchen through into the back room, where I was met by the sight of four sets of Aunty Rosie's frilly underwear dangling over the clothes horse, by the open coal fire. It had surprised me, how tiny her frilly knickers were, in comparison to the size of her huge braziers. And I'd gone over to have a closer peek and a feel and was just on the point of imagining her huge knockers hanging inside the bra cups, when I'd suddenly heard Aunt Rosie angrily call out, "Take me, Jim, take me yah bastard!"

Where she'd wanted daddy to take her to? I hadn't a clue. She'd not mentioned the location, but she did seem very determined to be taken to wherever it was she'd wanted to be taken to! And I couldn't help thinking, If mammy had been that impatient to go somewhere and had put out like that, daddy would have probably told her she'd have to "Feckin' wait til I'm ready! Or feck off and take yerself!"

"Oh fuck! Oh Jesus! Oh fuck-fuck! Oh fucking Jesus! Take me." she'd hollered obscenities at him.

If Father Murphy could have heard all that blasphemy, I'm sure he would have been shocked! Especially by the use of the Lord's name in vain! I was on the point of calling out to daddy once again, when he too had suddenly joined in all the blasphemy, "Ahh Jasis! I'm coming! I'm feckin' coming" he had shouted. He hadn't sounded very happy and I wasn't sure whether it's because Aunt Rosie was putting out about going out somewhere, or because mammy had sent one of us to fetch him home. So I'd hurried back out of house, up the alley and home, telling mammy, "Daddy said, he's coming."

The sky was still full with large black clouds, though the heavy rain, which had been with us for most of the morning, had gone off to soak another part of Manchester. Not that it had bothered me. I loved walking in the rain, which had not only cleansed my clothes and my skin from the days grime, but also gave me a strange exhilarating feeling of freedom, with so many wonderful thoughts, so personal only to me, they defy definition. I'd often wondered how, when looking down into the puddles, the colour of the dim yellow glow of the streets Gaslamp's clearly reflected back. And yet, the rest of my surroundings reflected back a drab black and white picture of a true reflection of the place I'd lived in.

In the evening, Martin, Nabby, Bernie, and me, had made our way to the main car park, near the derelict Radnor picture house, where once a row of shops had stood and the streets had buzzed with everyday life, as the people out shopping and meeting friends, gossiped about what the day might be bringing for them. And there we would wait, along with other kids, hiding in the shadows as the delivery trucks had parked up and made their deliveries, for our opportunity to steal something and run while the drivers back was turned.

Now fenced off, by the local council, to provide more parking spaces, the land would be packed with cars during the weekends, for those people who, as Father Murphy would say, had enough money to waste on alcohol, bingo, drugs and whores. When it could have been better spent on his church. Strangely enough, he never did mention anything about his starving flock.

Whenever a car arrived, we would follow it to its parking spot and wait for the driver to park up and get out, before we'd ask him-or her, if they would like us to keep an eye on it, while they were off enjoying themselves. The small jagged pieces of metal, we'd openly carried in our hands, usually prompted the drivers to hand over a few coppers or the odd tanner. But, just as you get in all walks of life, we always got the odd fella - always the fellas, who would tell us to feck off before they ram the piece of metal up our arses!

"Look!" Bernie had squealed. "It's the Queen!"
We had watched as the gleaming black car had turned in through the wide entrance of the car park and had silently glided past us.

The woman sitting in the back seat, wore a glittering diamond tiara on the top of her dark hair. She had turned her nose up at us, ignoring the best curtsy, Bernie had ever done in her entire life. To the point where I'd thought, she was about to kneel down on the wet graveled surface. As we'd hurried after the car, following it to its parking spot, I'd asked Bernie if she'd ever met the Queen to know the haughty woman sitting in the back of the car was the Queen. Only Martin and me, thought she had looked more like Elsie Tanner, from off Coronation Street!

"Yah don't have to meet the Queen, to know she's the Queen, Tommy!" said Bernie. "Yah only have ta look an' see what she's wearing to know she's the Queen. I mean. How would yah know a copper is a copper or a soldier is a soldier, if they're not been wearing uniforms?"

"Father Christmas isn't real, an' he wears a uniform," I'd said.

"He is real, isn't he Martin?" Nabby looked to him with a pained expression written all over his face.

"Course he's real, Nabby!" Martin reassured our little brother, "Pay no mind ta Tommy! He wouldn't know his arse from his face.

"Then how come Father Christmas was a big fat Pakistani, this year! And a skinny drunken Irish fella last year?" I'd asked, "And the woman looks more like Elsie Tanner than the Queen!"

"What would Elsie Tanner be doing in a dump like this?" Bernie scoffed at the idea. And though that same point could have also counted for the Queen, I couldn't be bothered to argue with my young sister. She'd only have an answer!

Skirting around the large puddle in the middle of the path, Martin had disappeared for a moment or two before coming back dragging a large piece of old tarpaulin behind him. He had placed this across the puddle by the side of the car, so her majesty wouldn't get her feet wet when she got out of it. So there we had stood. All four of us in one line, watching as the driver had got out of the car first and had stood on the tarpaulin, while opening the back door for the Queen to step out.

"Can we look after your car, missus?" Martin gave her a bow.

"And why would I want you to do that for me?" questioned

the haughty Queen, as she'd sniffed at the air while looking down her hooter at the four of us. She wore a stunning figure hugging blue silk dress with matching coloured high heeled shoes, along with a furry-white dead fox hanging around her shoulders. And she'd smelt beautiful! Her perfume filling the air all around us and helping to disguise our smelly bodies.

"To stop anyone from scratching the paintwork." said Martin.

"With something pointy," I'd added, letting Her Majesty get a good glimpse of my jagged piece of metal.

"Shall I give the little fuckers a slap?" The Queen's driver had taken a step towards us.

"Leave them" the Queen's haughty attitude had suddenly turned into a wide smile, "Cheeky little bleeders aren't you! Here." she searched inside her small silver chain purse before pulling out a crispy ten-shilling note, which she'd handed over to Bernie, who'd given her another curtsy. Martin and me had bowed our heads to her while Nabby, just looked on with a big scowl on his face.

When we had noticed the heels of the Queen's shoes had gone straight through the tarpaulin and the dirty water had begun seeping up through the holes, we'd rushed off and hid behind another parked, as she had turned the air the same colour as her wet blue shoes.

Making a beeline to the new customer in the Austin Mini, which had just parked up, we didn't even get a chance to say anything as the demented Chinaman had hurriedly got out of the car and had produced a large meat cleaver, threatening to chop all of us into little pieces and make a curry out of us, if he had so much as found a dirty fingerprint on his car when he got back to it. This had been our cue to move on and ply our trade elsewhere. But not before Martin had left his calling card. And the minute the Chinese man had walked out of sight, he was back at the car sticking little pieces of discarded matchsticks into the air valves of each tyre, before we'd hurried on our way.

-FOURTEEN-

We'd arrived home at around nine o'clock in the evening, having collected three shillings and thrupence. Elizabeth and Maggie were at home, looking after Gosson, Michael and Kathleen, who were fast asleep on the old wooden-framed sofa, with its broken springs covered with a thick bed of flattened cardboard underneath the thin cushions, preventing the old springs from poking through and sticking in us.

It had been a long while since the whole family had been in the house, all at the same time. And only then, if there had been a funeral, wedding, or some feud with another Irish family! Mammy and daddy had been in their usual place, at the pub, probably drunk with our aunties and uncles, grannies and granddads, keeping alive the old Irish tradition of carrying their feuds over from the last wedding or funeral, when the lot of them had been at each other's throats. As usual, daddy would come home on his own leaving mammy to stay away overnight with one of her brothers or sisters.

"Did yah bring home any wood for the fire?" Elizabeth had asked, in her soft voice.

"No," the three of us had guiltily replied, in unison.

Elizabeth was fourteen-years-old and Maggie had just turned ten, though they had both looked older. Elizabeth took over most of the chores around the house when mammy and daddy had gone off for days on end and whenever Mary and Rose ran away from home, which became more often as time had passed us by. And on those very few occasions when Elizabeth had also ran away, Maggie would take over from her.

Elizabeth was the quieter of the two and had often seemed to be far away in her own world, staring into the flames of the fire, or just sitting on the sofa with the two babies, Michael and Gosson in her arms and Kathleen laying at her side. All three fast asleep, while she stared at the one spot in the fire or on the floor. Her skin too was pale, on account she didn't get out that often. Which had made her watery blue eyes her most striking feature. I had always loved it when she gave out a smile, because her facial features would dramatically change, and she would radiate a genuine warmth, which seemed to wrap itself around me in an instant. And I had felt I could easily have curled up on her lap and had gone to sleep forever and ever, and not wake up again.

Maggie, on the other hand, was forever telling us off in the way a proper mother who cared for her children, would do. And I guess she had cared for us in the best way that she possibly could-or knew how to - Both of them had. But when daddy was around, they would hardly speak to us at all. It was as if they had been trying their very best to become invisible to everyone around them, including him.

Though the whole family were blue-eyed. Elizabeth, Paddy and little Kathleen, were the only ones in the family who had jet black hair. The rest of us were fair. Mammy and daddy, once got into a fight over us, in the Rob-Roy pub, when the drunken Gordon McKinley, had announced to the packed bar, "If Adolf Hitler, had chosen all the blue-eyed fair-haired Irish children for his *Master-Race*. The whole world would now be full of gormless thick idiots!" The pub had erupted in laughter, which had incensed the Irish drinkers, with the inevitable riot erupting and the war of words and the usual threats going on and on for months afterwards, only coming to a truce after Gordon McKinley's eldest son, Connor, had been stabbed in both his thighs, when the warring families had come together again.

Taking the money which we had collected, out of his trouser pocket, Martin had placed this up on the mantelpiece in case mammy and daddy were to come home later that night. If not, Elizabeth would use it the following day to buy something for all of us to eat. We never did have a clue as to when they would be coming home. And it hadn't been that unusual for them to be away for days on end, after having gone off to the pub for the one night! Sometimes, one of them would stagger in the house on their own, for one reason or another. But mainly for rowing with each other. Which again, wasn't all that unusual once the alcohol has taken hold of their senses. There had been many occasions, when the pair of them came back to the house in the early hours of the morning with Aunties and Uncles in tow and all of them blind drunk and singing their Irish songs about missing the '*Land of their birth*' or leaving a loved one behind. Or how they'd like to take up arms and murder the feckin' "Murdering Black-n-Tan bastards!" for what they'd gone and done to the likes of Kevin Barry and all the other Irish Martyrs long since gone. And they'd sing and they'd dance and they'd reminisce on the good old days back in Ireland, *Land of the Free!* When there wasn't enough spuds to feed all the starving people because of the potato famine and those blue-nosed bastards over in the North, hogging all the food to themselves!

Inevitably. Someone would say just the one word out of turn, which someone else would always have to take offence to, or take it the wrong way. And they would be at each other's throats again! Punching, kicking and biting, before staggering off out of the house beaten and bloodied and swearing, "On the, *little flower of Jesus!* I'll never be speaking with yah agin, as long as I've a hole up me arse!" Until the following weekend, came along!

Nabby had told us, he'd been too tired and didn't want to come out with us to collect firewood. And so, Martin, Bernie and me made our way out into the back yard, where we made ready the large pram. Bernie had bagged first ride, and once she'd climbed into the pram, settling herself back in to it, we had set off out the gate and made our way down the alley into the dimly-lit streets, making our way down towards Stretford Road, where the electric streetlights smothered the area in bright light.

On our way, we had passed an old woman sitting on the fifth concrete step leading up to a private bar. The night shadows had cast a strange eerie look upon her face, as if she had just been on the point of squeezing out a long fart, before suddenly falling into a deep sleep, with her left arm reaching upwards as her tiny frail hand had held onto the handrail of the ornate metal fencing running up along the side wall of the steps. It looked as if the old woman had just pissed herself, as a line of dark-stained liquid had slowly flowed from underneath her, and ran all the way to the bottom of the steps, forming a small dark puddle on the pavement below. Probably she'd drank too much of the stout and couldn't hold it in? Just like our granny would sometimes do, when she'd drink herself into a drunken stupor and suddenly drop off to sleep in the chair.

We had spotted the small red purse nestling in the old woman's other hand, which had been resting on her knee and Martin had taken it upon himself, to see if he could steal the purse without waking the old biddy up. I had woken Bernie, and she had hopped straight out of the pram just as Martin had dashed up the steps and had grabbed the purse. But the sleeping woman had a firm grip on it, and it didn't come out of her hand as easily as Martin had expected it to. Gripping the purse even tighter, he had given it another tug and to our utter horror, the woman had suddenly toppled headlong down the steps after Martin, and had landed on her back in a heap, still firmly holding onto her purse, and oddly hadn't made a sound, as she'd hit the deck!

"Jasis Martin!" Bernie had cried out. "Yea've gone and killed the auld biddy! They'll hang yah for sure!"

"I never laid a feckin' finger on her!" cried Martin, which made me cry, because I didn't like seeing him crying.

"For God's sake! Will the pair of yah shallup crying like a pair of feckin' sea lions!" Bernie snapped, "Or ya'll bring the whole show down on us!"

But it had been too late! We'd been seen by the two young women coming out of the main entrance to the private bar. And now Martin, it had seemed, was surely going to hang after all! And that thought had made me cry even louder.

"Oh Lord! What has happened!" the blonde-headed lady of the two had asked, as she had rushed down the steps with her dark-haired companion closely following behind her.

"She just fell." I had said.

"She dropped dead right in front of us!" Bernie said.

"I didn't kill her!' Martin cried.

I had been taken by complete surprise, when the blonde lady had suddenly got down on to her knees in front of me and flung her arms around me, pulling me tightly into her. I was so gob smacked, I didn't know what to say or do. "Is she your nanny, luv? Oh, you poor kids!" she'd pulled me even closer in to her, as I had got to thinking, if I told the lady, the auld woman wasn't my nanny, then she would probably stop hugging me. But on the other hand, if I said, she was my nanny, I would probably have been digging us into deeper trouble. So I'd said nothing, and let the woman think whatever she wanted to think and pushed my face deeper into her soft warm bosom, taking another whiff of her beautiful perfumed smelling skin, which for some reason had me imagining myself walking through a field of wild flowers - not that I can recall ever having set eyes on a field of wild flowers, let alone walking through one!

I hadn't been one to feel the cold that much. But I was surprised to feel the heat from the woman's body creeping through my thin layers of clothing to touch my bare skin. And for the briefest of moments, as I had held on to her, I had felt what it was like to be held in the affectionate warmth of someone who had genuinely cared for me. Albeit us being complete strangers to one another. And in reality, if it had not been for strangers such as her. Life would have been much harder for us.

Martin had stopped crying, and I had taken a quick peek over the woman's shoulder, to see him looking back at me with his big cheeky grin, spread right across his face! Happily wrapped in the arms of the dark-haired woman, he'd thrown me a wink, before pressing his nose right down into the cleavage of her breasts, while Bernie, had gone all agitated, and had stood there scowling at us.

It had not been long before a large crowd had gathered around the dead woman just lying there frozen in time and still gripping on to her purse for dear life. A man, said he was a doctor, and had bent over the prone woman to examine her for a minute or two, before he had stood up and announced to the crowd, "She is dead." which to all intents and purposes, was plainly obvious, to an idiot, let alone people with no medical knowledge! Even we had known straight away!

"She has been dead for quite some time now. Probable Heart attack." added the doctor, to my utter delight! And I could see the relief on my brother's face, which had lifted my spirits because for sure, he wasn't going to face the hangman's noose after all!

"She hadn't looked all that good, when I had passed here, half hour ago, with the dog." A man had decided to volunteer the information.

"Why didn't you call an ambulance?" an angry woman had questioned him.

"I thought she was asleep!"

"Asleep?" On the pavement!"

"She wasn't on the pavement then! She was sitting at the top of those steps."

"And you thought she was having a kip, did ya!" said

someone else.

With all the attention of the crowd directed towards the man and the angry woman, arguing over someone they hadn't even known, we had silently slipped away into the shadows. And as I had taken one last look back on the scene I was leaving behind, I saw the fair-haired woman, who had held on to me so tightly, frantically looking through the crowd of people. Probably in search, of the dead woman's grandchildren.

We had made our way to the Town Hall, before crossing the Stretford Road and heading up along Lupton Street, to an area near St Wilfred's School, where the whole street had been boarded off from one side to the other, after the people living there had been moved out only days earlier. I would always get the same sort of feelings well up inside me every time I walked through the empty streets, which were once alive with the hum of everyday noises and people milling around. These streets, like most, were once the children's playgrounds. Hopscotch. Chalk drawings on the pavements. Racing their bogies up and down the middle of the street. Swinging on the ropes, tied to the gas lamps. Playing alleys. Football and all other sorts of games. Here the front doors were all too familiar, doors which we had knocked on countless times when pretending to be collecting for charity, using the empty OXFAM envelopes, or the books of Christmas raffle tickets or stamps, we had stolen from the school! And sometimes a door would open and the people would put a few coppers in the envelopes, or buy one of the raffle ticket from us, crossing their fingers and hoping, theirs would be the lucky ticket. With us knowing full well. It would be a feckin' miracle!

With it being much too dark to be scavenging inside the empty houses. We'd gone about collecting firewood scattered about the place, with me forever conscious about my encounter with the Devil, and making sure I'd stuck closer than I would normally have done, to my brother and sister. Just around one of the corners, we had come across an old grey-haired Indian man sitting on a small wooden box, looking into the flames of a fire. He was in the company of a young Indian girl, around Martin's age. The old man had ignored us, not even bothering to give us a brief glance to acknowledge our presence, while the young girl had continued to pull the exposed copper wiring out of the fire with a small piece of wood, leaving it to cool down, while she had thrown more of the rubber electrical flex onto the flames. She had glanced over at us, the hint of a smile on her face. And I couldn't help but notice her eyes fixing on Martin for a few lingering moments. Admittedly, he did have a much grubbier face than me and Bernie, and I had supposed she could have at first mistaken him for an Indian boy!

We were unable to understand what the young girl was saying to us. But, when she had offered out the small brown paper bag of rhubarb and custard flavoured sweets, we knew our presence had not been unwelcome. And so we had hung around by the fire, while Martin had helped the girl to burn off the rest of the electrical flex, with me suggesting to him, he should ask to take a peek of her budgie to see if she was normal like Bernie, which he had refused to do. Though he had shown her how to cool down the hot copper wiring quicker, by pissing all over it! Which had made her laugh, though the old man had seemed agitated by this, and had gibbered at the girl in his

112

strange language. I think Martin and the young girl had fallen in love! They kept throwing smiles at each other and as sign of his affection, when we were leaving, Martin had even given her his two small round brass doorknobs, which he had found in the debris, a short while earlier.

Back at the house, it had been in total darkness when we had pushed the heavy pram, laden with the firewood, in through the back gate and packed it neatly into the makeshift lean-to, daddy had built to keep the wood dry. We hadn't a clue of what the time had been. Not that time meant anything to us. But the streets had been empty and all the pubs we'd passed, had been closed and quiet. So it must have been late.

One of the chickens had jumped off the dividing boundary wall, startling us. Martin had grabbed the clucking bird by its neck and had slung it over the gate into the back alley. Quick to spot the flash of the torch light suddenly coming on in the back room of our house, we'd hidden in the shadows of the outside toilet, just as daddy had come up to the window shining his the torch out as his broken nose had pressed right up against the glass. We'd watched as the beam of light had slowly moved around the yard, holding our breaths, as it had snaked its way across the walls in our direction, before touching the outer edge of the toilet block and passing us by, missing us by half a foot. Only after the torchlight had gone out and we'd given it a few minutes longer, did we dare sneak in through the back door, before quietly making our way through the house and up the stairs to our beds, with me following up last.

"I want mammy." I had heard one of my sisters' whimper, just as I had reached the top of the landing. I'd tiptoed back

113

down the stairs and had stood listening in the dark, at the door of mammy and daddy's bedroom, where I was able to hear the soft muffled voices on the opposite side of the bedroom door, with daddy shushing my sister; I couldn't make out whether it was Kathleen or Elizabeth, wanting mammy. It hadn't been unusual, and always when mammy hadn't come home, to have heard one of my sisters cry out late in the night. Mary and Rose used to cry a lot too, before they had ran away from home, and I'd come down to listen at the door to hear daddy shushing them off to sleep. And I'd go back up the stairs and hop back into the bed with the rest of my brothers. Happy in the knowledge that at least he cared about Elizabeth and Maggie, if not the rest of us.

-FIFTEEN-

We had been begging in the city all the morning, collecting two shillings for our hard graft, which wasn't a bad morning's work, considering, we were having to compete against the likes of the Wards and the Gavin's, our cousins, as well as the other vultures who came trespassing on our patch, looking for easy pickings.

Daddy said, "If yah spent the whole while chasing off the little feckers, yea'd be coming back with only the penny yea'd started off with, in the first place," which had made a lot of sense. So we just put up with them trespassing.

The McKenna twins, Rory and Sean, on the other hand, were a different kettle of fish, altogether. They were a nasty pair of evil bastards and amongst our worst enemies. The whole tribe of them came from Scotland and had settled in Longsight, getting a reputation as the worst of our kind.

A few weeks back, we had a run in with the terrible twins, who had decided to chase Bernie and me through the streets of Hulme, for no other reason than my sister asking Sean, the older of the two, "What are yah gawking at!" Normally we would attempt to avoid this family like the plague. But on that particular day, Bernie had seemed to be in a bolshie mood about something or other, and she wouldn't tell me what is was. Not that I had asked her mind. It wasn't my place to be asking. And anyway. If she had wanted to tell me anything, she would have done so. In her own time.

The McKenna twins, four years older than me, had chased

the pair of us through the streets and across open wastelands of Hulme, before cornering us up by a row of derelict houses where they had forced us to stand up against the end wall of a derelict house, while they had taken it in turns to have pot-shots at us with duckers. Sean McKenna's first ducker had just whistled past my ear, as I had ducked out of the way of the fist-sized lump of masonry. Poor Bernie! She hadn't been as fortunate and the small ducker, thrown by Rory McKenna, which would have initially missed her, if only she had kept still and not taken the one step to her right as it had hit the ground in front of her, before bouncing up and catching her on her shin, making it bleed.

"Hey! Yah fuckin" Scottish bastards, yah!"

The sight of Martin and Nabby, running in our direction, was a glorious moment to behold! One of which I would never forget for the rest of my life. The twins had made a run for it, but only as far as the protection of a low wall just a short distance away, which they had scurried behind, before popping up their shaven heads and shouting at us, "Come and get us if yah think yer brave enough! Yea Irish bastards!"

The fact the odds were stacked in our favour two-to-one, made us feel brave enough to have a go. And for a few minutes, we'd fought a pitched battle with missile after missile raining down on each other, with all of them missing their targets, until Rory McKenna had stood up and screeched, "Up the Scots! All the Irish are fuckin ba -" he never did get to finish his sentence, as the slim shiny ducker had flown, at great speed, straight and true out of Martin's hand, catching Rory on the side of his shaven head which had immediately spurted blood!

We had stopped our onslaught and watched the cowardly brothers run off, only stopping when they were out of our range, to call us every name the could think of before swearing their revenge on us, and the rest of the Rattigan clan. We of course had retorted with our own insults, before heading off the other way into town.

All day long, Nabby had put out about us buying him an ice cream. Martin had lied and told him, he can have an ice cream when we got to the matinee, later in the afternoon. But Nabby had stubbornly insisted he had an ice cream, right then!

Martin's attempt to explain to our younger brother, we could buy a big bag of broken biscuits from the cake shop, back in Hulme, to share amongst the four of us, for the same price as a poxty ice cream, fell on deaf ears. And he just wouldn't stop going on and on about it.

On our way out of the City Centre, we'd decided to take a quick ganders around Woolworths, where we'd came across a group of people loitering around the jewellery counter. Making our way over to them, we'd pushed through the crowd to get a better look at the strange contraption standing on top of the display counter. This was basically a large claw hammer moving up and down as it banged down on the face of the, **NEW SHOCKPROOF WRISTWATCH** causing shocked gasps of amazement by the fact the second hand of the Swiss-made watch, was still ticking away nicely while the hammer was shocking it!

Looking over my shoulder, in Martin's direction. I'd silently mouthed the word "Fit." and he had immediately obliged me, by throwing himself to the ground and writhing around like one of our chickens in its last throes of death, with the whites of his eyes showing, along with bubbles of frothy spit dribbling out of the corners of his mouth. Bernie had screamed. The shoppers had turned to see the helpless little child, instinctively rushing to his aid. And that was about all it had taken for me to swipe the watch from under their noses, without the hammer even shocking me!

Miraculously, Martin; like one of the lepers healed by Jesus, had suddenly got up on his feet and walked out of the store, with Bernie and Nabby on each side of him, aiding their poor ill brother, with me following just a few yards behind them.

"Hang on a mo!" said Martin, suddenly leaving us standing on the corner of the street further along from Woolworths. We had watched him hurry across the road ahead of us, in the direction of the zebra crossing, where we could clearly see the two young chubby kids holding their ice creams as they had waited alongside their larger-than-life mammy for her to give the *all clear* to cross the Stretford Road.

"Look!" Martin had suddenly pointed his finger skywards, as he had ran in front of the two kids and their mammy, just as they had got halfway across the crossing. And as they had all instinctively looked into the sky, my brother had snatched an ice cream from out of the nearest boy's chubby hand and ran back in our direction. He was so quick, he was almost back to us, before the kid had even noticed his ice cream was gone. And when he had noticed, to our amazement, he'd instinctively snatched his brother's ice cream and had devoured it in one go, as his brother had looked on, bawling his eyes out!

"You greedy little pig!" The boy's mammy had scolded her

118

son, giving him a sharp slap around the ear for good measure, "Just you wait until your father hears about this!"

The three of us had hurried off around the corner, as Martin had reached us, with his usual big grin on his snotty face. Taking a couple of bites out of the ice cream, he'd handed it over to Nabby, who'd ungratefully refused it, complaining most of it had already been eaten! Handing it to me, I had gratefully taken it from Martin and had snapped off the bottom part of the cone, filled it with ice cream and handed it over to Bernie, who'd downed it in two bites. I'd done likewise, as we'd headed off along Jackson Street, to the *Popular Picture* house, where we had joined the long queue of chattering kids stretching all the way down the street, as they'd patiently waited for the doors to swing open, and the uniformed usher to come out and call us in for the afternoon matinee, with Flash Gordon!

Looking over my shoulder, I had spotted the love of my life, Cathy McCarthy! She was standing with her mother a few places ahead in the queue. When our eyes had met, we had instinctively thrown a big smile to one another, but the crabby-faced dragon, Mrs. McCarthy, had scolded her daughter, before throwing one of her deadliest scowls in my direction. I'd loved antagonising her and had given her a wave, before throwing her my best gappy smile. It must have been embarrassing for Cathy, not being able to come to the Matinee on her own, like all the other kids would do. Instead of having a mammy's fussing, like a brooding hen all over her. Once, I had called around to Cathy's house and had asked Mrs. McCarthy, in my politest voice, if "One may accompany your dearest daughter to the Matinee." I had heard words to that affect, spoken in one of those BBC radio plays a few weeks previously, and the mammy getting all excited and saying, "What a charming young man!" And how delighted she would be, for her daughter to be accompanied to the theatre by such a fine, upstanding young gentleman!

"Do you honestly think my daughter would want to be seen associating with the likes of you! You flea-ridden filthy little tramp!" Mrs. McCarthy had indicated her displeasure all in the one breath, before slamming the front door in my face.

Paul Morgan, had turned up outside the picture house with two of his friends. They had pushed their way into the queue in front of us, and Martin had told him to clear off to the back of it!

"You want to try and make me?" Morgan, had turned to my brother and had suddenly punched him in the pit of his stomach with his false hand, causing Martin to double over with the pain. Incensed, I had slapped the bully around the face from behind, which had stunned him briefly and had given me the advantage of surprise. And I'd grabbed hold of his prosthetic hand and ran around in circles, like an Olympic hammer thrower, with Morgan able to do nothing but follow me.

I was a little shocked when I'd found myself holding onto the false hand without Morgan being attached to it, as he had gone flying in the opposite direction, the sight bringing screams of horror from some of the kids, while others, who had known all along the hand had been a false one, had laughed their socks off.

Cathy's mammy had looked to be in a state of shock, with

her eyes all agog and gawking at me in utter disbelief, as she leaned against the wall of the picture house. Instinctively I had made growling noises, before pretending to take a bite out of the hand! She'd screamed herself back into reality, only to pull Cathy from the queue and head off up the road away from the picture house!

Throwing the false hand to Martin. He had thrown it to Nabby, who in turn had thrown it to another kid. And so on the hand went, down the long line of kids, with Morgan and his two friends hurrying after it. Someone then had the bright idea to throw the prosthetic hand skywards, causing a temporary moment of silence, as all eyes had fixed on the hand spinning high into the air before falling back to earth and landing straight into the passing rag and bone man's cart, just as the uniformed usher had thrown open the cinema doors. He must have thought all the applause was meant for him, as he had doffed his cap and given us a bow, only just managing to dodge out of the way as the herd of stampeding children rushed through the open doors, like a pack of wild horses.

The last I had seen of Paul Morgan, before I had made my way in through the doors, he was running up the road after the rag and bone man's cart! His two friends must have decided, *Flash Gordon* was more important than chasing after a false hand and they had joined the back of the queue

-SIXTEEN-

Mammy and daddy were having a blazing row. The cause of the row, was all about the cause of the last row they'd had in the Red-Rose pub, when daddy came home on his own and mammy hadn't. She'd had her big white *going away* suitcase, standing next to her feet and was telling daddy, she was bailing out of the house for good.

"It's all over this time, Jim." She had tearfully told him without spilling a teardrop. This would probably have been the twentieth time she had threatened to leave him for good, this year alone! And as usual, none of us had taken a blind bit of notice of her threats to leave, as she would usually leave by the front door and arrive through the back door a short while later, as if nothing had happened

Mammy had accused daddy, of pushing his hand up a floozy's skirt in the pub last night. She had told him, he was a "feckin' whore-man's bastard," adding, "Me eyesight might be bad! But I'm not feckin' blind!"

"On the little flower of Jasis and the children's lives." daddy had sworn, "I'd not shoved me hand up the floozy's skirt! I'd dropped fag ash on the auld whore's feckin' knee an' was just brushin' it off! And that was all ta it!"

"She must have gotten the fag ash all the way up ta her hairy budgie!' mammy had hit back, "because that's how far yer hand had gone up her skirt! I've had enough of yer womanisin' Jim. An' I'm not puttin' up with it any longer! I'm leavin' yah for good, this time. There's no stoppin' me!'

"What about yea wigglin' yer big feckin' fat arse at all the men in the pub! An' throwin' yerself at that gimpy queer lookin' fella, Danny Flanagan!'"

"Danny Flanagan! For fecks sake! Him an' his brother are little' feckin' midgets!" said mammy, "Sure the pair of them must be over eighty an' halfway in their coffins, if they'd not already died durin' the night! An' where'd yah tink the money came from for all them drinks? Not from your feckin' pockets! Yah, humpy bastard yah?'

"Well yah started it all! Midget brothers! Jasis yah must be feckin' desperate!'

"An' I'm finishin' it too, Jim! As there's a God up there, an' I'm on bended knees! I'm finishin' it for good!" promised mammy, still standing upright, 'An' another ting!" she had quickly added, "I'd have ta be desperate, ta be putting up with the likes of yea! An' where's them sheets off the bed?' she'd suddenly changed the subject.

"What?"

"The clean sheets I put on the bed yesterday morning."

"Ah-them - I had to throw them out in the bin.' daddy had lied, "The bed was full of bugs an' what-have-yah."

"Well they weren't my feckin' bugs!"

I had known daddy was lying about the sheet, because I had seen him, from our bedroom window, in the early hours of the morning, making his way out of the back yard, carrying, what had looked to me, like a crumpled up white sheet. I had watched him as he'd walked up the alley, before he had returned a short while later, empty handed.

As good as her word, mammy had given us all her usual fond

farewell handshakes and we had bade her our goodbye's like we didn't give a toss! And she was off out of the house, slamming the front door behind her.

I had stood watching daddy roll himself a cigarette and light it, before blowing a plume of smoke in the direction of the nicotine-stained ceiling. He didn't seem to have a care in the world and I'd wondered to myself, if mammy had really left him for good, would he have genuinely missed her or not. They seemed to get on well, at times, and I had loved to see them smiling and being happy and getting on with each other, which would rub off on us, changing the atmosphere inside the house, for a while at least. But at times it was like treading on egg-shells with them rowing about almost anything and everything with the real issue of them, "Not having two pennies to rub together."

Suddenly turning his attention to Martin and me, as if he had only just noticed we had been standing there, he'd asked none of us in particular where we had been.

"Out." I said.

"I know you've been out, Tommy! Jasis.' He had shook his head at me, "If yea'd half a brain yea'd be feckin' dangerous, I tell yah."

It had seemed, he must have spoken with Sister Joseph at one time or another, because she had said the same thing to me some while back! And while I'd appreciated the compliment, I'd been unable to understand the point he was trying to make, or why he'd asked the question in the first place. If he had already known, we'd' been out.

He'd told us, there was no feckin' food in the house and I'd felt a sudden urge to shout out to him, "The reason we've no feckin' food in this house is because yea and mammy waste all the feckin' money yah get off the feckin labour exchange, as well as what we bring home, on booze and tobacco! But the words refused to come out. So I had changed tact at the last minute and had told him, "Martin and me, were just on our way out to get something, to bring home."

Bernie had thrown a smile in my direction, appreciating the fact that I had said "Martin and me." which had meant, she didn't have to tag along with us, at least not yet. She'd looked tired and drawn, as we all were, from the endless hours we had spent on the streets, walking for miles on end all over Hulme, Moss Side, Longsight, Gorton, and the City. It was never ending.

"Here. Before yah go off." daddy held out a two-shilling piece and had placed it into my outstretched hand, bringing to my mind the thought that the drink from last night must be still in his head, because he was giving us a treat. The drink always made the grownups do things they wouldn't normally do and it had seemed, this was no exception.

Father Murphy had said, alcohol was the ruination of all those that participated in its evil. *The devil's poison* as he had called it. Though it hadn't stopped him from swigging it back during his Mass services, or when he visited people's houses.

"Fetch back two bottles of ale, an' be feckin' quick about it!" snapped daddy.

The Red Rose pub was, conveniently, just around the corner from us and had a tiny off-licence, so I hadn't long to wait at the counter, which I could barely see over for the landlady and

125

biggest scrubber ever to have walked in Hulme, to come out from the bar area and serve me. Mammy seemed to know everyone living in Hulme, including all the scrubbers, naming Maureen, the landlady, as one of the biggest in the whole of Manchester!

Maureen was a big lady, with a beehive of bleached dried straw hair sitting on the top of her head. She had greeted me with a big warm smile and hadn't really fitted the description, mammy had given her. She had long red nails, which had made me wonder how she could have kept them so nice and long with all the scrubbing she must have done all over Manchester. I had told her, the ale was for my daddy, Jim Rattigan, and she'd said "Oh, you poor thing!" as her eyes had rolled up in the direction of the ceiling. Taking the thrupenny piece change, I had picked up the two bottles of ale off the counter and was about to head towards the door, when Maureen had suddenly called me back.

"Here. Have these on the house." she'd leant across the counter and pushed the small pack of peanuts in my direction.

I'd politely thanked her, desperately trying to keep my eyes from gawking at her enormous knockers resting on the bar top. Jesus! I'd thought, Aunty Rosie's tits were big, but these must have been double her size. And when she had asked me, if there was anything else that took my fancy, with a big wide smile spread across her face, I had nearly dropped one of the bottles of ale as I'd turned and hurried through the door.

Outside the pub, I'd put the two bottles down on the ground before shoving the thrupenny piece change down my left sock, thinking Martin and me could buy some sweets when we went out later. I had thought, with the state daddy had seemed to be still in, the chances were, he would not remember the change. But if he did, I would just tell him, Maureen the landlady, didn't give me any change.

Pulling the cap off the beer bottle with his teeth, and spitting it over the fireguard into the fireplace, daddy had taken a long swig of the ale, which I could clearly hear glugging down his throat as the beer had gone straight down, before he had suddenly put his nicotine stained hand out. "Change?"

"I didn't get any change, daddy."

"What d'ya mean! Yah didn't get any feckin' change! I want me change! Now, Tommy!"

"I didn't get any change, daddy!" I had repeated the lie.

"Who'd served yah?"

"The auld scrubber."

"What auld scrubber?"

"The one behind the counter with the huge tits."

"Don't yah be talking about her like that!" daddy had snapped, coming to the landlady's defense, "Did yah tell her the drink was for Jim Rattigan-did yah?"

"I can't remember if I did, daddy."

"Yah can't remember if yah did! Yah lying humpy little bastard, yah!" daddy was straight off the chair in a flash.

Giving me a left hook to the nose, he'd knocked me straight to the floor and there, with the blood pouring from my hooter, he had suddenly grabbed me by the right arm and had dragged me out of the back room and out through the kitchen screaming like a madman. "The woman wouldn't have served yah with any drink, unless yea'd given her a name first!" he'd grabbed the small hatchet hanging on a hook by the backdoor, before dragging me out into the back yard. And there, with me on my knees and him holding my right hand down on the blood-stained chopping block, which we used for chopping off the chickens heads. He had raised the axe high into the air and had threatened to chop all my fingers off, one by one. Unless I had told him what I had done with his change.

Martin and Bernie were screaming at him to let me alone, but their screams fell on deaf ears, as daddy had glared down at me before stamping down hard on my legs.

"I'm countin' ta three Tommy! An' if yah haven't told me where me change is, your feckin fingers are gone. 'One!'"

I'd found myself looking up into the maddening eyes of this unrecognisable lunatic, seeing the hatred burning within them for me. I had been well aware that the chances of him carrying out his threat, was a real one. Just as I had known, if I had have told him the change was down my sock, there would have been an even bigger chance of him carrying out the threat. Probably worse.

"Two!"

"Jasis, Mary and Joseph! Jim! What the feck are yah doing?" Mammy had suddenly walked in through the back gate. "Have yah lost yer feckin' marbles?'

"Keep out of this, Lizzy! I won't be havin' any thievin' little bastard of mine stealin' from me! An' if he doesn't say where me change is, I'll take both his feckin' hands off his arms!"

"Come on Tommy," said mammy, attempting to coax the truth out of me, "Tell mammy where the money is yea've taken."

"I didn't take any money mammy! I swear on the '*Little flower of Jasis*, and on yers and daddy's lives!" I used one of daddy's lines, "I never got any change from her. I swear!"

"Three!"

"And how do yah know the auld feckin' whore, didn't give him the money Jim?' mammy had brought a sudden pause to the amputation, "She looks ta me like she'd steal the flea off a donkey's arse, if she'd half a chance, that one! And how would he be able to hump the wood or go beggin?" Have yah taught of that one?"

"He's a lyin' thievin' fecker is all I know!' said daddy, "like the rest of them! An' no! I'd not feckin' asked at the pub! There wasn't any need to be askin." Daddy had let the hatchet drop to his side, before giving me a swift kick up the hole instead.

"Get back ta the pub an' get me feckin' change! And don't dare come back to the house 'til' yah have it! Or I'll be chopping yer feckin' legs off along with the hands! D'ya hear me!"

"Yes daddy!" I'd ran past mammy and was out the back gate and up the alley without a second look behind me. I could hear Martin calling after me and so I had waited at the top of the alleyway for him. He had looked pale and worried and said, we had to go straight to the pub and ask for the change and despite whether we got it or not, we should smash all the pubs windows as well. But I had assured Martin there wasn't any need to be doing either. Taking off my sandal and sock, I'd shook the brass thrupenny piece out and into me hand.

-SEVENTEEN-

We'd spent daddy's change on a handful of blackjacks from the sweetshop just a few streets away, which had been run by a whole tribe of Pakistanis, who made it impossible for us to steal anything because, like mammy's mashed potatoes, there were too many eyes gawking at us and making us feel paranoid! It had seemed our faces were either becoming all too familiar in the shops closer to home or, like a lot of the kids living around these parts, we just looked like the sort who would steal from their own grannies! Even on those rare occasions when our intentions were honest, we were still banned from entering some of the local shops. Tesco's had just about tolerated us, and only then because they'd never caught us in the act. Though I did think, they might have had their suspicions about us by the very fact, once we had stepped inside their main doors, we would be met by a guard of honour in the guise of the three security guards, who would escort us around the store on every visit!

We would walk the slow march, and all three security guards would follow suit. Upping our pace to a quickstep, and they upped their pace as well. It had taken them a long while to cotton on to Martin's fake fits and the fact, while they were dealing with him, we were helping ourselves, before silently slipping back out of the store, unnoticed. When they had eventually cottoned on to our ruse, the guards had changed their own tactics, cruelly ignoring Martin's fake fits, and stepping over his prone body to hurry after us. And for a short while, this tactical change of theirs, had worked in our favour, because, while we were leading the security guards a merry dance around the store, Martin would suddenly make a miraculous recovery and get up to help himself, before legging it!

Once. Martin had devised this great plan to disguise ourselves, before going back into the store. How we ever thought we could hoodwink anyone, was beyond me! But as our auld granny had once told us, "Yea'll never know til' yah try! Otherwise, for the rest of yer lives, yea'll be forever not knowin' an' wonderin' what could have been. If yea'd never tried in the first place!" Which made a lot of sense to us. And so we'd decided to disguise ourselves as an adult!

In the mouth of the back entry which ran down the side of the Tesco store, I had slipped on the plastic, Groucho Marx spectacles, complete with the false hotter and moustache attached to them. I had borrowed Uncle Frankie's trilby hat, left at the house from his previous visit to see mammy, his favourite sister. And then between us, we had worn daddy's long raincoat, with Martin adding the final touches with, our brother, Paddy's, drain-pipe jeans and shining black winkle picker shoes, stuffing a pair of undies down the toes of each one to keep them on his feet. And hey presto! The two little kids had become, a fully grown man!

We had practiced Martin's crazy plan a few times over, prior to putting it into action, with me sitting on his shoulders and him getting used to walking about the backyard holding my weight. And there we were! Probably the weirdest looking gentleman in Manchester! Tall, skinny and handsome, with his hands not quiet able to reach his coat pockets and muttering directions to himself, as he had walked in to the main entrance of the store.

What a mind blowing feeling it was to find myself as tall as an adult sitting on Martin's shoulders. And I had felt the strange sense of confidence and power surge right through me, as I had been able to look down on people, instead of having to look up to them. And when six-year-old Joshua Lemon, and his little sister, Maura, who lived a few streets away from us, had both walked out from the inner doors, I had stared down at them, to see if they could recognised me.

"Hello children." I had attempted to speak with a deep manly voice, which had sounded like *'Punch'* with a strangulated hernia.

"Pervert!"

Brilliant! The pair of them had not cottoned on to us! And everything had gone downhill, from there!

Martin, staggered as he had walked across the rough surface of the floor mat just inside the main entrance doors. And for the briefest of moments, I'd felt that I was going to topple off him. But he had somehow managed to retain our balance.

"Keep calm and just act natural." he'd called up to me.

"If yea'd stopped staggerin' around like a feckin' auld drunk, I'd be fine!'

"It's these feckin' shoes!" I can't pick me feet up 'cos they keep slippin' off! Ah shite! One of them's come off!"

"Put it back on before we're corrupt!"

"I can't feckin' see it!"

Looking directly down to the ground, I wasn't able to see the shoe either and I had asked Martin to take a couple of steps backwards. Which he had done.

"It's just there, in front of yah." I said, watching with amusement, as Martin's foot, with the big hole in the dirty sock, had snook out from under daddy's old mac and had blindly searched around for the shoe. "Forward a bit! To the left! To the right! Too far. Go back a bit!" I gave him the directions, "Just a little more forwards! Too far! Come back a little – Afternoon madam! Would yah care for a dance?" the words had just sprung to mind, when the old woman coming out of the store, had taken a moment's pause to stare at Martin's left foot doing a jig, before she had looked up at me, shaking her head and telling me, I was a complete fool!

After a few more directions from me, Martin had slipped the winkle picker back on, and we had managed to get into the store and to the first aisle, before he had moaned again, "the shoes keep slipping off!'

"Just shuffle yer feet along.' I had advised, "Go to the left. Not a feckin' sideways shuffle! I meant, turn to yer left and then shuffle forwards! Jasis, Martin! Yer walking just like one of them China women with stumpy feet! Can't yah lift yer feet just half an inch off the ground and take a bigger step?"

"Ah feck!' said Martin. "I'll have to undo a button so I can see where I'm going."

That's when I had suddenly noticed we'd had an audience with old Mrs. McGinley and another old biddy with her, who were standing with their sour pusses gawking straight up at me. "Afternoon ladies!" I had spoken in a polite deep manly voice, which seemed not to have impressed the pair of them. And when I had followed their gazes downwards, to the point where their beady eyes had firmly come to rest at, I had been momentarily shocked to have seen Martin's finger poking out through the mac in search of a button, as if beckoning to the two auld hens to come to him!

It was unusual for the devout Catholic, Mrs. McGinley, to have been lost for words, as she was usually so full of herself, and wanting the whole world to know all about her life, past and present. What she had been up to, what she is going to get up to. Who had said this, who had said that? Who she had seen and who she had not seen! But when I had grabbed hold of Martin's little finger, her face had suddenly turned a scarlet red, as she'd turned and staggered away in utter disgust, having to drag her friend away, as the auld woman eyes seemed to have been transfixed by the wriggling finger I'd held in my hand!

With Martin now able to see where he was going, through the gap in the mac, we had managed to get around the store without further incident, save for the odd look from people as they had nudged each other to get a look at the strange looking fella.

With both shopping bags filled and hidden beneath the mac, we were heading back down the aisle, in the direction of the main doors, when I had spotted the security man's foot suddenly poking out as we had reached the end of the aisle. It had happened so quickly, I'd had no chance to shout a warning to Martin of our pending doom. And I had just managed to grab hold of the top shelf as Martin had fallen from underneath the mac, leaving me dangling there like a helpless, legless man.

Quickly dropping to the ground, I'd hitched up the mac and had legged it past the three confused security guards and over Martin's prone body, before dashing past the gawky-eyed Mrs. McGinley, and her confused companion and I was out the doors and up the high street to where Nabby and Bernie, had been waiting for us

It hadn't taken long for our smiling brother to appear, holding Paddy's winkle pickers in his hands. He had told us, the security guards had to let him go, on account, they'd not seen him load the food into the bags, along with the fact, the food hadn't left the store. As for the midget. Martin had told them, he'd never set eyes on him before.

We had only been out of the house for about ten minutes, since daddy had threatened to take my fingers off, when Martin had spotted the large hessian sack resting up against the back wheel of O'Neil's, scrap merchant's lorry. We'd dragged it off around the corner into one of the empty houses, and had waited until the scrap merchant had closed the yards large wooden gates before getting into his lorry and driving off. Once we were sure the coast was clear, we had hurried on our way in the direction of home, carrying the heavy bag of scrap metal between us down through the back alleyways, and out of sight of prying eyes.

I'd had this daft notion, that daddy would be so pleased with what we've brought home to him, he'd probably forget the matter of his thruppence change and let it drop. Hurrying down the back alleyway leading down to the back of our house, we had met Uncle Mike, coming up from the other direction.

"Hi. Uncle Mike."

"What have you there, lads?"

"Scrap,' I told him. We dropped the heavy bag to the ground so he could open the top of the sack and take a ganders inside.

"Where did it come from?"

"The bombed houses."

"You collected all this, today?"

"Yep" lied Martin.

"All on our own." I added.

"I'll give you ten bob for it?" offered Uncle Mike standing back and searching around inside his jacket pockets.

"Twenty shillings." I had heard myself say.

"Fifteen! And that's your lot." Uncle Mike, handed the ten shilling note and five shillings in odd change, over to Martin, before swiftly picking up the sack and humping it on his shoulder before hurrying back to his house.

Before opening our own back gate, we had agreed between the pair of us, to give mammy the five shillings in the odd change, after we had taken the thruppence out of it to give back to daddy, pretending that the Landlady had made a mistake. Deciding, we would hide the ten bob note and spend it over the weekend, on all of us.

Mammy and daddy were in the kitchen when we had walked in from the back yard. Daddy had suddenly thrown out his hand, asking me for his change. Frozen with fear I'd thrown a look over at Martin, almost pleading with him to quickly hand the money over, before he found any excuse to start knocking me around again.

Fishing inside his trouser pocket, Martin had taken out the small handful of change to give to daddy. As he did so, the neatly folded ten-bob note had slipped out and dropped to the floor! You could have almost touched the silence, as all eyes had stared down at the neatly-folded note lying on the hard stoned surface of the kitchen floor. And when I'd looked up in daddy's direction, I could see the coldness in his evil eyes as he had glared, first at Martin and then at me. It may only have been a fleeting moment, but in that moment, I had seen and felt his loathing, his hatred, the evilness of my daddy, who day by day, grew more and more, a stranger to me.

"We got fifteen shillings." said Martin, breaking the silence. Picking the ten bob note up off the floor, he deliberately handed all of the money to mammy, to daddy's obvious annoyance, "And your thruppence change" he quickly added, plucking the thruppenny piece out from the pile of change in mammy's hand and handing it to daddy.

He'd said nothing, but sucked spit in through his teeth, which he usually did when he was either using his toothpick or sucking out a bit of stuck food, or when he was annoyed, but isn't particularly wanting to say anything.

Putting the ten-bob note into her purse, mammy handed the loose change over to daddy, who'd counted it before shoving it into his trouser pocket. "Here." he suddenly flicked the brass thruppenny piece in my direction, which, like a lizard's tongue catching a fly, I had caught it in midair and slipped it straight into my pocket, before thanking him. The look he gave me in return, had told me, it was far from being a reward, but merely to serve as a reminder, that thruppence was probably about all I had been worth to him.

-EIGHTEEN-

Two truant officers called at the house in the early morning. Apart from Elizabeth and daddy, who were up and about, the rest of us, who were at home at the time, were still in our beds. I had slipped out of the bed and had lain down on the bare floor at the top of the landing where I had a good view of the front door without being seen, as Elizabeth had answered it to the man and the woman, standing outside in the rain.

"Me mammy and daddy, are not here." she'd told them. But like everyone else with an ounce of authority to their names, they had invited themselves in making their way into the back room, with my sister hurrying behind them.

Straining my ears to the muffled voices downstairs, I hadn't been able to make out what was being said and so I had quietly tiptoed down the stairs to stand on the bottom step, listening at the door.

"I swear on this holy Bible -" I heard daddy's muted voice going through his usual blasphemies, before Elizabeth had suddenly hurried from the back room and had gone straight into mammy's bedroom.

"Mammy! Mammy! Wake up mammy!" The truant people are in the house!" she'd called.

When she'd hurried back out and saw me, she had put a finger up to her lips and had ushered me back up the stairs, following behind me to the top landing, "Quick Tommy. Get the others out of the bed. Leave, Michael and Gosson, and come to the girls' room. Hurry!" she spoke in a low whisper, before hurrying off along the short landing into the girls' bedroom.

A couple of shakes and Martin had woken up. But I still had to resort to the usual tactic of dragging Nabby out of the bed by his arm and letting him drop to the floor, where, with his eyes still closed, he'd attempted to crawl along the floor and back into the bed before we were forced to pull him to his feet and guide him along the landing to the girls bedroom. On the way there, I had knocked a couple of times on Paddy and Shamie's bedroom door.

Giving Martin a tube of mammy's red lipstick, Elizabeth had asked him to help her dab little red dots on all our faces and hands. "Just like this Martin." She'd made a few dots on Bernie's face, just to show him how it was done.

Shamie had suddenly poked his head around the door, wanting to know, 'What the feck is going on! An' why are yah puttin' all that shite on their faces!"

"The truant people are down in the back room talking with daddy." Elizabeth had kept her voice to a low whisper.

"Why didn't yah feckin' tell us?" said Shamie.

"They'd only just got here. They want to know why none of us have been to school in ages. Daddy's only gone and told them we're all ill with the chicken pox! That's why I'm putting these spots on them-d'ya want some?" she had offered the lipstick to him.

"Over me feckin' dead body!" he'd declined, "An' if them nosey bastards ask where I am. Tell them I've gone."

"Ta where?"

"I don't feckin' know! Tell them I've died of whatever yea

lot are supposed ta be dyin' of!" he silently closed the door behind him as he'd returned to his own bedroom. "Wake up, yah green nosed bastard yah!" we heard him on the opposite side of the wall, calling Paddy awake.

"What's wrong?" Maggie, had suddenly lifted her head up off the big double bed.

"Elizabeth wants us to be clowns." said Martin, as he dotted red spots all over Nabby's face.

"Yer already clowns!" said Elizabeth, throwing a smile at Martin, "Little dots Martin! Give us a hand here, will yah." she'd asked Maggie, taking the lipstick off Martin, and handing it over to her, before going on explain to her about the two truant people talking to daddy, downstairs.

When Elizabeth had been satisfied we'd all looked diseased enough, she led us out of the bedroom and down the stairs, while Maggie had stayed behind to spot her own face in the mirror. And there we all were, standing in the back room huddled together like a group of lepers, staring at the two truant officers, who had suddenly taken a backward step, in the direction of the kitchen door.

"There yah are! Didn't I tell yah all me children were poxed! And yah didn't believe a word of it!" daddy had protested, looking just as shocked as the two shocked truant officers had looked. "Have yah ever seen a sight like it in all yer lives? Have yah, missus!"

"Well. No. I have not, Mr. Rattigan." Mrs. Burke had her hanky almost wrapped around her nose, though I hadn't smelt anything out of the ordinary. And if daddy had let one go, we all would have known about it, for sure! "It is very odd." She'd said, studying us from a safe distance.

"That all my children are ill at the one time! Well it's catchin yah know!"

"I'd meant, the red blotches are odd. There doesn't seem to be a set pattern to them."

"Well they're not feckin' paintings by numbers are they!" daddy growled at her.

"Mr. Rattigan! There is no need for that kind of language." Mr. Twyman, had suddenly interrupted, "What Mrs. Burke is trying to explain is the fact, none of the red blotches on your children's faces are uniformed. They seem to be in all shapes and sizes, which is very unusual indeed."

"Jasis! Me children are dying of an unknown disease, like the plague! That's livin' in this poxty dump the council call a home! It's the council's fault for all this!" daddy had gone on to blame everyone he could think of for our demise, naming them off one by one. The Rats, the Pigeons, the Police, the Social Services, the Government, the Pope, the Teachers, the foreign workmen, with a special mention for the, "Blacks and the Pakistanis, who've never seen a shovel till they came over ta this country!" Adolf Hitler for failing to blow the whole of Hulme asunder! And even the milkman got a mention, because he had refused to call at the house ever again, just in case he caught the lurgy! Though in truth. He had refused to let mammy have any more milk on tick, until she had paid her last bill.

"Jasis! Mary an' Joseph!" Mammy, had suddenly appeared in the doorway, wearing her flimsy nylon nightdress, minus her two rows of false teeth with a lit cigarette dangling between her lips, "The children Jim! They've been cursed!"

"They're not well, Lizzy."

"They don't look feckin' well either sham! What have yah done to them?" she'd accusingly glared at daddy only noticing we had visitors when she'd walked right in to the back room, giving us a wide berth as she'd done so!

"Who're the queer people?" she'd asked no one in particular as she had eyed the two truant officers up and down.

"I am Mr. Twyman and this is Mrs. Burke."

"Ooh! I'm dying-I'm dead!' Maggie had suddenly staggered in through the open doorway with her arms outstretched in front of her, causing the two truant officers to take another step backwards, while mammy had taken the few hurried paces to stand behind daddy and peer out over his shoulder at Maggie, while giving out to him.

"Jasis, Jim! Will yah get a look at her! She looks like one of them people that's died an' come back to life agin! What's the matter with her? Why's she walkin' like that! Ah God! The banshee's comin' after us!" mammy reached down to the fireside and had picked up the poker. "If yah come a step nearer ta me! I'll bourn this feckin' poker over yer feckin' head, God help yah, so I will!"

"Ah-feck! Lizzy!" daddy had suddenly screamed out, causing the lot of us to almost jump out of our skins, "Yer fags burnt a hole in me feckin neck!"

"I will be sending the health visitors around tomorrow!" Mrs. Burke had hollered, almost falling over herself, as she had rushed through into the kitchen after Mr. Twyman, following him straight out the through the back door and out the back

142

gate and up the alleyway, without bothering to shut the gate behind them.

'Did yah see the faces on them two!' daddy had burst out laughing and we had all followed suit, barring mammy! She wasn't smiling and had just stood on the spot glaring at us, wanting to know what the feck was going on. When daddy had explained how we'd been codding the truant people all along, mammy had started a row with him!

"Why didn't yah give me the wink, instead of lettin' them gimpy eejits make a show out of me!"

"How the feck, could I give yah the wink, when yea'd stood behind me burning me feckin' neck, an' threatening ta murder Maggie with the poker at the same time!"

"Jasis! What are yah goin' ta tell the health people when the nosey fecker's come breakin' the door down tomorrow!"

"Ah, don't be worrying yerself about a ting. I'll pop in ta the church on the way back from the labour exchange, and I'll ask Father Murphy to pray for all our sick children, and get him ta send a blessing.

"But there's nothin' wrong with any of them!"

"Aye. We know that! But the queer people don't know that! It's about time the good Catholics of Hulme, had a real miracle to talk about!" and from there on in, the rest of the day had gone further downhill.

Uncle Mike had called at the house a short while after the truant officer's had escaped, and daddy had gone off to sign on at the labour exchange. It was the earliest Uncle Mike had ever called at the house. In fact. It had been some months back since he called to complain to daddy that the chicken he had bought off him the previous week, to make a curry had been off, laying him and Aunt Rosie up for almost a week with stomach aches and the scutters!

It seemed likely Martin had mistakenly given him one of the chickens which had dropped down dead on its own accord! But daddy was having none of it. He'd patted Uncle Mike on the shoulder and had advised him, "Yah shouldn't be eatin' all that foreign Chinese shite!" before closing the door on him.

This time around, when Bernie had answered the front door to Uncle Mike, she had immediately slammed it back shut, before hurrying up the stairs to tell Martin and me, "Uncle Mike's at the front door! An' he looks ta be in a bit of a state!" As the loud banging on the front door had echoed along the hallway, we had hidden under the big bed in the girls' bedroom. Bernie had joined us. Just to share in our guilt.

We heard Nabby asking at the door, "Who is it?" and Uncle Mike's voice bellowing through the letter box, something about, "Stringing the pair of bastards up by the bollocks!" confirming our suspicions, he might have called because of us! Which had been a good enough reason to have been hiding under the bed!

"Who the feck is it!" we'd heard mammy ask Nabby and him telling her, "It's Uncle Mike come ta see yah mammy." before he had rushed up the stairs and into the girls room, "Uncle Mike's at the door!"

"What would we do without yah Nabby!" quipped Bernie, as he had joined us under the bed.

When we heard the front door open, and mammy say, "Jasis! What the feck has happened to yer face, Mike!" we had crawled from out under the bed and had taken up a good vantage point at the top of the landing, where we could see mammy, with her back to us, standing in the open doorway, with the frying pan in her hand

"Those two little fuckers of yours, Martin and Tommy, sold me a bag of scrap for fifteen shillings! They should have told me the truth and just said, they'd stolen it! Instead of lying and telling me they'd collected it from the bombed houses! I took the bag up to O'Neil's, scrap merchants, where those little bastards had fucking stolen it from! I thought it was a bit unusual, when the big gorilla had asked me where I'd got it from. And like a big fucking twat I'd told him, I'd collected it myself. Then he showed me the fucking little brass name tag sewn onto the bottom of the bag, and stamped with O'Neil's name and the number fucking 4, which tallied with the bag he'd noticed had gone missing! Not only did I get a few slaps, Lizzy - he's a big fucker that fella! But he took the whole lot back and made me pay four quid on top! Four fuckin' quid and fifteen fuckin' shillings I've paid out for nothing! What are you going to do about it, Lizzy?'

"They must have forgotten were they'd gotten it from. Yah know what children are like." said mammy.

"I know what your fucking children are like, Lizzie! Jesus! Look at the state of me face! You can't say, they'd forgotten they didn't collect it themselves, can you!"

"I'll chastise them later."

But Uncle Mike was not satisfied with mammy's promise to give us a good hiding; not that she would have done so, as we'd given all the money to her, but he had wanted her to repay him the four pound fifteen shillings it had cost him, as well as the pleasure of being able to give us a good hiding! Or he was going to the police, he'd threatened.

"Yea can put that wife yer's on the game if she's not already on it, and get double yer money back!" said mammy. "Now feck off!" we'd heard the loud bonk as she'd hit him over the head with the frying pan, before slamming the door shut on him.

The rest of the day had dragged on because we had not been allowed out of the house due to the family's mystery illness. Mammy had told us, she didn't want to be shown up if we're all dying the one minute and then out on the streets, causing havoc the next. Daddy came home in the late afternoon. He was in a bad mood and had the hump, telling us to get all the shite off our faces, as we'd been miraculously cured by the new priest, "A young darkie." whose name he couldn't recall. He'd told mammy, "The morning mass was commemorated to the family, along with the first church collection and I had to feckin stay and pray with the rest of the heathens just to get me hands on the money! The whole church was packed to the rafters and the first collection amounts to a shillin' and a feckin' ha`penny! Not even a piece of paper ta wipe me hole on! I tell yah, Lizzy, not one of the humpy bastards could look me in the eye, except for that hunchback, Sister Gertrude, who'd handed over the collection plate ta me, with a feckin' big grin spread all over that face of hers! And there she was, telling me I should tank the feckin worshippers for their feckin' generous gift! Humiliated, Lizzy! That's what I was! Feckin' humiliated! I didn't know where ta put me face. An' there they all were, holding up their ten bob notes an' wavin' them around like feckin flags, so as everybody could see what they were putting inta the second collection! All except for that tight-arsed auld cow Mrs. Delaney. Always hiding her money in her hand so as no-one can see what she's puttin' in, when everyone knows it's a feckin' ha`penny.'

"Poor Mrs. Delaney," mammy had come to her defence, "She's so old and frail an' she can hardly carry her handbag, let alone lift her feet to walk.

"Aye! Because her feckin' handbag's full with all them ha`pennies!"

-NINETEEN-

Uncle's Oliver and Raphael, two out of daddy's four younger brothers, had turned up at the house in the late afternoon. Just home on army leave from the Kings Own Scottish Borderers, they were still wearing their army uniforms and had looked immaculate in them. Uncle Oliver's first ritual, whenever he came to visit us, was to dish out bags of sweets amongst his "favourite nieces and nephews" and this visit had been no exception. He had thrown his army kit-bag open on the floor and had dished out sweets galore to the youngest of us, giving bottles of perfume to my elder sisters, and a small Swiss penknife each to Paddy and Shamie.

It had also been Uncle Oliver's 26th birthday. And although much younger than daddy, who had looked a lot older than his thirty-three years, he and Uncle Raphael had, what I can only describe as a, boisterous quality about them, which would lift us all up, from what would otherwise have been a dull and dreary atmosphere.

If there was one thing they'd all had in common, then that would have been their toughness. All of them, including daddy's other two brothers, Uncles, Christie and Paddy, were as tough as nails. And just like daddy, they were able to look after themselves. Which had to be an inheritance thing, because we were all tough, to a point. Whenever the five brothers were together they seemed to exude a confidence that was never there when daddy was without them, and it had seemed, he was able to put his miserable existence on hold and become a completely different person, albeit for a short while. But, even for that short while, it was nice when the family got together. And as an added bonus, I'd got to sit on Elizabeth's knee! Though, when Martin had tried his luck with Shamie, our older brother had warned him not to push his luck too far and to, "feck off and find somewhere else to sit yer shitty boney hole on!"

Uncle's Christy and Raphael, were also generous with their offerings. But as for Uncle Paddy. He was, "So tight arsed! He wouldn't even give yah a clinker from his hole!" said mammy.

We'd all known mammy had thought a lot of our uncles. But she seemed to have had a soft-spot for Uncle Oliver and had got on really well with him. Noticeably, to us, in a different sort of way than with her other brothers-in-law. The pair of them were always flirting together behind daddy's back. And once, when daddy was away from the house, and Uncle Oliver was helping mammy to clean her bedroom windows - so she had told us - Martin and I had taken it in turns to have a quick peek in through the keyhole of the bedroom door, to see them having a kiss!

Many times I had wondered to myself, what it would have been like if mammy had not married daddy and had married Uncle Oliver instead. I would often wake up in the mornings, having dreamt the same dream, about him coming to the house, and while we were all sitting down in the back room to listen to what he had to say to us, he suddenly announces, "I am your real father!" and we all rush over to him, throwing our arms around him, crying in our excitement, making me wonder if we had all had that same dream.

A couple of hours and lots of beers later, we were following Uncle's Oliver and Raphael, mammy and daddy, up along Stamford Street, to the Red-Rose pub. And just as Uncle Oliver had walked through into the public bar, we were met by a loud screeching chorus of "Happy Birthday ta yaaaah!" from a large group of our relatives, which included his two other brothers, Paddy and Christie, our Granny and Granddad, that's daddy's, mammy and daddy, and more Aunties and Cousins.

At first, the landlord, Fat Pat; named so, because he was a fat man called Pat, had not been happy about having too many children in his pub. But after a few raised voices, with Uncle Oliver having to step in to keep the peace and telling Fat Pat, "It's a special family gathering, and the children will be no trouble." going on to promise, "If they break anything, I'll personally pay for the damage." Fat Pat, although still not happy, had relented under duress, allowing us to stay as long as we behaved ourselves and kept the noise down.

People said, he weighed in at twenty-two stone, which was two stone heavier than our cousin, Big Martin Rattigan. But while Fat Pat had stood around five feet-seven inches tall and had all his faculties about him. Big Martin in comparison was a giant of a man, standing at six-foot eight-inches tall and was apparently *a sandwich short of a picnic* people had said.

Though Paddy and Shamie had not been old enough to drink alcohol, they were given a pint of Guinness each. Elizabeth was given a Babycham, which she'd pushed across the table to Paddy, on account she never touched the *'Devils drink'* while the rest of us had to contend with a warm glass of lemonade and packets of Walkers crisps. But as me and Martin hadn't liked warm lemonade and we had been content to let Bernie and the others have ours, while we had helped ourselves to the dregs of beer left in the bottom of the empty glasses and the bottles.

As the evening had worn on, the pub had filled with more drinkers, their cigarette smoke creating a misty haze across the whole room, making it difficult to identify the ghostly figures standing off in the far corners. And if the putrid poisons spewing from the chimneys outside hadn't managed to cut short the lives of the people, the shite floating around inside this pub probably did!

The whole family were enjoying themselves and seemed to have had plenty to talk about. Over to our left, the atmosphere was a little more solemn, with the O'Connor clan, celebrating the life of their departed Grandmother, Daisy. Big Martin, was still standing after having already won his sixth bet, drinking down two pints of beer, before his challenger could swig down just the one pint, with the loser having to pay for the beer! Mammy was standing just in front of us, propping up the bar with her two sisters MaryAnn and Brenda. Uncle Oliver, daddy, Uncle Christy, Uncle Paddy and Uncle Raphael, had stood not too far away, talking with a large group of other relatives, including my favorite Granddad, Frankie Gavin.

Short and slim, Frankie was still able to knock out a man twice as big as himself, with only the two punches. "That's all yea'll ever need Tommy! Just the two feckin' punches." He had once told me, when we were out in the back yard play boxing, during his last visit. "Yah keep dead calm and don't let the other fella git inta yer head. That's the secret, Tommy.

Let the bastard shout out his anger while you let all yer anger go down yer arms an' in ta yer fists. And then, when the fecker least expects it! Yah whack the bastard with yer surprise punch, straight in the bollocks! An' when he's doubled over with the pain of it all, yah follow up with a haymaker to the side of his head. And if that doesn't knock the fecker out! Run for yer life!"

Just like the volume on a radio being slowly turned down, the chatter in the pub had suddenly faded into silence, as old Danny Doyle had eased his frail body up off his chair to give his usual rendition of, *"Oh Danny Boy."* At the ripe old age of ninety-five, which must have been nothing else short of a miracle, considering he'd been part of the pubs furniture and had sat in the same pub, in the same feckin chair, singing the same old feckin song, night after night, for almost seventy-years! And when closing time came along, he'd be off home, sitting alone in his own world, waiting for the pub to open up the following day so he could go through the same ritual! But he'd seemed happy with his lot. Daddy had said, "In some way, Danny was living like royalty. Sure, didn't the Queen have ta sit in the same chair all day feckin long and have ta listen to the same old boring song being sung!"

Just as Danny had come to the end of the song, an argument had broken out as to which country the song belonged to, escalating in to an angry debate.

George Campbell's family argued, the song had been written by a Scot, and therefore *Danny Boy* belonged to Scotland! Uncle Paddy had argued, the feckin' bluenoses couldn't write such a lovely song and it had always been an Irish song!

Mammy had suggested, old Sam Butcher, the *know-all* of Hulme, would know the answer and so she had sidled along to the end of the bar, where Sam had been sitting in his usual spot on the barstool, squinting through his gold-rimmed glasses, at the Manchester Evening Newspaper.

"Tell these feckin' heathens, the name of that Irishman who wrote Danny feckin' Boy, will yah, Sam."

Taking his nose out of the newspaper, Sam had taken off his glasses before neatly folding them and placing them down on the newspaper, nervously asking, "If I give you the answer, will you all agree to abide by it?" to which the whole place had agreed in unison.

"Sure we will, Sam!" smiled mammy, "Just feckin' tell them blue-nosed eejits over there, the truth.

"Well." Sam had looked around the quiet room, "The lyrics of Danny Boy were in fact written by Frederick Weatherly, in or around 1913. He wrote these to an Irish piece of music called, Londonderry Air."

"There yah are!" mammy had shoved two fingers up at George Campbell, "Londonderry Air! Only an Irishman could write such lovely words to that tune."

"Actually, Lizzy, he was an English lawyer." said Sam
"Who was?"

"Frederick Weatherly. "He was the writer of Danny Boy."

"Ah well! His mammy and daddy at the least were Irish, so what's the feckin' difference?'

"South Africa."

"Africa? Are yah trying to tell us, a feckin' Zulu wrote Danny Boy, yah gormless looking gerky eejit yah!" mammy

153

had boxed the know-all in the gob, knocking him off his stool.

The pursuing free-for-all had the chairs, beer bottles and people, flying all over the place! Paddy and Shamie had ushered all of us out through the doors, behind those drinkers making good their escape and who'd not wanted to get caught up in the brawl. Once outside, our two brothers had left us standing on the pavement, before hurrying back into the bar. A moment or two later, Martin and I went back in, where we'd immediately set about picking up the loose change falling out of the pockets of the people grappling and rolling about on the ground.

Fat Pat, had been sitting on the floor with his back propped up against the side of the bar, nursing his bloody nose. His wife, Maureen had been kneeling at his side, pressing down hard with one of the cloth bar-runners on the bloody stab wound to his right thigh, while our two brothers, Paddy and Shamie, were up behind the bar robbing the cigarettes! Mammy too had been on her knees. She'd had the little midget, Willie Morgan - known to his friends as *Wee Jock*, and to the Irish, as *wee joke* - in a head lock, and was beating the shite out of the top of his head with one of the large tin ashtrays.

We'd seen our Granddad, Frankie Gavin, kick a man straight in the bollocks. But, as he'd once advised me to do, he didn't run when the man hadn't double over as expected and had just stood there on the spot, glaring at him. Admittedly, the man had looked in a state of shock, perhaps on account of his brain needing a little more time to register what had happened. But the same couldn't have been said about Granddad, when the man's wife had whacked him over the head with the big beer bottle and he'd hit the deck like a sack of spuds.

The only person involved in the fighting who had not thrown a punch-or had been punched himself, was our Cousin Big Martin Rattigan. And by the time he'd thrown the first two Campbell's out through the pub's windows, the rest of their family and friends had already beat the retreat, scrambling out of the doors to safety! It was just after Big Martin had lifted his father high into the air and had thrown him through the window too, had everyone suddenly realised, he'd completely lost the plot, and the whole pub, including my family, had emptied within seconds.

There had been no volunteers from us or anyone else to go back in to the pub and attempt to sweet-talk Big Martin to come out. And so he was left inside to help himself at the bar, until the police had arrived, taking eight coppers almost half-an- hour to eventually beat him into submission, with their truncheons, before bringing him out.

Fat Pat had gone on to ban everyone from his pub that had been involved in the brawl. He'd been incensed by Uncle Oliver's refusal to pay for all the damage, as he'd promised he would do. But our uncle had argued, "Even if it had been Lizzy who had thrown the first feckin' punch. I'd only promised yah, I'd pay for any damage the children caused. And as the children had caused none. Yah won't be getting' a feckin' bean outta me!"

A few weeks later, after the pub had been fixed up and Fat Pat had realised, he'd banned most of his regulars, leaving the pub almost empty every night, he'd had a sudden change of heart and had lifted the ban to everyone, barring the Rattigan's.

-TWENTY-

Just as there had been lots of derelict houses to explore on the way to St Wilfrid's school, there had also been many which had been reduced to mounds of rubble, though it had still been possible to locate the coalholes and climb down into their cellars which, like the Radnor Picture House, had their adjoining walls knocked through, making it possible to walk along the whole street unseen. And it was here, in these coal cellars, on our way to school, that we had cruelly pursued a fat ginger-haired fella, who, without fail, would take the same route every morning. The fella would have been about sixteen or seventeen years-old. He'd been inflicted with a large thick patch of purple skin covering the whole of his left eye, and whenever we saw him coming, we'd scamper, like a pack of rats, down the nearest coalhole and wait until he'd ambled past, before one of us would pop our head up out of the hole and call out to him. "Cookie-Eye!" Incensed, Cookie-Eye would rush towards the coalhole, grunting and throwing lumps of masonry at it, only for one of us to pop a head up from another coalhole further along. "Cookie Eye!" we'd antagonise the poor fellow, until we became bored, safe in the knowledge that he was far too fat to fit down any of the coalholes and come after us.

Our timing was usually quiet good. So, whenever we eventually managed to have made it to the school, it would be around dinner time. And so we would walk straight past it and head off to the annex, which stood away from the main school building, just across Rutland Street and around the corner into

Cooke Street, where the ever smiling, Mrs. Moses, head dinner lady, would be waiting to greet us. I recall one particular occasion, when I had noticed her looking over at me, before she had suddenly leaned into the new dinner lady and had whispered something into her ear, causing a big grin to appear on the new dinner lady's face. It had been cabbage on the menu that day! And if there had been one thing in this whole world that I had hated most of all, then it was that shite! And the new dinner lady was dishing this up!

I had guessed what Moses might have been up to. And if they'd been thinking, what I had thought they'd been thinking, about what was coming up next. Then I had known for a certainty, it wasn't going to happen! Fed up with having disgusting steaming hot, dark green, slug-worm-infested green shite plopped onto my plate! I'd decided I'd had enough and I'd had every intention of changing the routine. If not forever, then at least for one meal.

Walking out of the line, I had made my way up to where Sister Joseph had been standing in the queue. "I'm sorry Sister Joseph, for all the troubles I've caused to you, in your life." I made my most insincere apologies to the grumpy old hen.

"What in heaven's name are yah gibberin' about, yah fool yah!" she'd nearly bitten my head off, "Git back in line - Just there in front of me, so as I can keep me eye on yah!" Which is what I'd hoped she might have said.

"Afternoon, Mrs. Moses!" I'd greeted the auld crab, though I had firmly kept an eye fixed on the large serving spoon, the new dinner lady had raised in the air at the ready, to slop the shite on to my plate in one speedy movement. But I had been too quick for her and I had swiftly moved my plate and myself out of the way, before telling her "No cabbage today, Miss!"

"Yah blitherin' eejit yah!" Sister Joseph had howled, when she'd received the full spoonful of steaming cabbage all down her starched clean habit.

"I don't think Sister wanted any either!" I'd informed the new, red-faced dinner lady, who had stood there with eyes all agog and ready to burst into tears at any minute, as the children had laughed, while Sister Joseph, berated her, cursing the day she'd ever been born! Mrs. Moses was still grinning at me, as I'd moved off down the line to the apple crumble and custard. Yummy! My favourite dessert!

Back in the classroom I had handed Sister Joseph the OXFAM charity envelope, which, earlier, I had slipped the small blank piece of folded paper into, before sealing it up with spit. Sister Joseph, had taken a backward step, on account of the shock, before giving the envelope a little shake and then gawking at me suspiciously.

"Me mammy put a ten shilling note in it.' I'd said, and her good eye had suddenly lit up.

"Thank yer mammy for her kind generosity, won't yah." She'd said, before shooing me back to my desk, almost immediately.

But I had paused just long enough to see her open the middle drawer on her left and place the envelope in on top of all the other charity envelopes. Saving me the time and the effort of having to hunt for them later on!

"Hush children! Hush now!" When Sister Joseph had tapped the wooden ruler down on her desk, the classroom had immediately become silent. "Now I want ta remind yah all about talking with strangers. Yer parents will have already talked ta yah about the dangers of talking to people yea've never met in yer lives. And as well as there being many good people in this world, it's a sorry fact, there are many bad people as well. So. Just a reminder. Strangers! - What must you not do if a stranger speaks to you?" she had asked and thirty hands had suddenly shot in to the air, barring mine and Martins.

"Yes Simon?"

"Not speak to them, Sister?"

"Very Good! - Jennifer?"

"Not to go anywhere with them in their car, Sister."

"Not to speak or go off anywhere with them in their car. No matter if what – Seamus?"

"No matter if they are really kind and nice, Sister."

"And if the man has no car and is on foot - Tommy?"

"I didn't have me hand up Sister."

"Just get on and answer the question! It's children like yea that will benefit from takin' a bit of notice on what's bein' said!"

"Please Sister. What was the question?"

"If the man - the stranger hasn't a car. What wouldn't yah do?"

"Well. Yah wouldn't be able ta go off in the car with him, as he hasn't one, Sister.'

"Dear lord! He's on foot! Yah blitherin' eegit yah!" she'd glared at me, "An' yea'd be walking off with him! Not going off in a car he hasn't got!"

Jasis! She'd completely lost me! I had wanted to ask her, if the man had been offering out any sweets. But the auld crow had seemed antagonised enough as it was, without me having to add to it.

"I thought we weren't supposed ta walk off with him, Sister?" I'd reminded her.

"Lord have mercy!" she'd breathed a heavy sigh while shaking her head, as though she had lost all hope for herself, before ignoring me and continuing going through the do's and don'ts, on how to keep ourselves safe.

In our last lesson of the day, Sister Margaret, had told us a story about a wedding that ran out of wine, and how Jesus, had worked one of his miracles, to turn gallons of water into gallons of red wine! This had got me wondering, if mammy and daddy and all my aunties and uncles made friends with Jesus, they could take him to the pub, with only the need to be ordering pints of water all night long!

"Is there anyone who would like to ask a question, before we finish?" she'd asked. And my hand had shot in the air.

"Yes, Tommy?"

"Is it really true, Sister Margaret, that the Lord Jesus helps those people who help themselves?"

"Indeed it is true, Tommy. And a good question at that!" she'd smiled, before going on to explain to the class, "Those people who try hard at bettering themselves in life, have the Lord Jesus behind them, supporting them in every which way that he can."

I was grateful for the information, which had dispelled any lingering doubts I'd had, about stealing the charity envelopes from Sister Joseph's drawer! The money would certainly benefit us in some way, and along with the blessing of the Lord Jesus! Things were looking up!

I'd waited for Martin and Bernie, in my usual spot outside the schools entrance gates on Lopton Street, which overlooked a large empty expanse of wasteland, where I had been able to see the comings and goings of everyone. I had wondered what their reactions would be when I'd shown them the six full charity envelopes, I'd helped myself to. Knowing the pair of them, they would probably want to go straight off to the nearest shop and buy some sweets, before taking the rest of the money home to mammy and daddy.

Martin and Bernie had seemed to be taking a long time coming out and would usually be amongst the first groups of children rushing across the playground and out through the gates, but they were nowhere to be seen. I'd been sure I hadn't missed them and assumed they'd been held back in the school for one reason or another; which wouldn't have been that unusual, so I had made myself comfortable and had plonked myself down on the ground with my back resting up against the inner wall, where I had waited.

Only last week, Bernie had to wait ages for me and Martin to get out of the school because we'd had to stay behind to see the headmaster, Mr. Coalman. It had only been a lunchtime prank we'd played on Paul Doherty, when we had shoved a chicken's head underneath the pastry of his chicken pie, when he wasn't looking, and then took the tearful lad back to see Mrs. Moses at the serving hatch, complaining on the lads behalf, someone had forgotten to take the head of the chicken when they'd made the pie! In fairness, that wasn't the actual incident that had got us into trouble. The school had just put two-and-two together and had made five out of it, when Sister Joseph had opened her desk drawer to find the huge headless rat with a chicken head staked onto a piece of wood and pushed down through its neck! We had assured the screaming old crab, who'd believed the strange looking creature had been "Sent by the devil himself!" was already dead, but she just wouldn't stop jumping up and down on it, until a posse of teachers had arrived on the scene. We too had jumped up and down for a while, after being given six of the best across the arse with the strap.

I'd overheard a group of parents, waiting outside the gates for their children to come out, talking amongst themselves about the sudden disappearance of the sixteen-year old girl, who had mysteriously vanished from Gorton some while ago, while on her way to a her local dance club, and how she'd still not returned back home. Everywhere we went in Hulme, the City, Longsight, Moss Side, Gorton, we would constantly hear the name, "Pauline Reade" crop up without fail almost every day, which had been a sure sign, she must had been in the thoughts and conversations of so many people, even after so many weeks had passed by since she had gone missing.

Like Mammy, some people had thought and hoped, she would suddenly turn up out of the blue, wondering what all the fuss was about. But, with nothing to indicate any reason why she would just up and go, and with the Manchester Evening News, still continuing to write about her mysterious disappearance. The name, Pauline Reade, was to remain in the public domain.

On a warm July evening, at around 7.30pm, a vivacious and well educated young lady of sixteen, had left her terraced home, on Wiles Street, in Gorton, heading off to her local Friday night dance, at the Railway Workers Social Club. Dressed in her new pink and gold stripped dance outfit, topped off by her black blouse and white boots, the excited teenager had kissed her parents, before leaving for the dance, promising faithfully that she would be home on time, this time, as she had been late back from the last dance, straggling behind with friends. From a close knit, church going family, Pauline had worked as a trainee confectioner in the same sweet factory as her father. Like many other parents, her parents, Amos and Joan, were very protective of their daughter and were coming to terms with the acceptance of *their little girls* disappearing childhood. She had arranged to go to the dance with three of her girlfriends, but at the last minute; so it seemed, her friends had opted to go to the cinema instead, leaving Pauline to walk to the club on her own.

With no apparent worries in the world and probably with the tunes of the week's hit parade playing in her mind, Pauline had set off from her house, on the short journey, which would normally have taken her, no more than five or six minutes to have walked up along Wiles Street, in the direction of the Railway Social Club, in Froxmer Street, 500 yards away.

Heading along Wiles street, Pauline had been seen by two of

her friend; who had opted to go to the cinema, passing their house. Surprised that she'd had the bottle to go off to the dance on her own, the two friends had decided they would follow her, taking a detour along a back entry to surprise their friend, when she would arrive to see them waiting for her outside the club. Hurrying up along the back entry, the two giggling girls had reached the club within minutes, where they had waited outside in expectation of their friend appearing around the corner. But, Pauline Reade never turned up for the dance. She had vanished without a trace, with one of her discarded gloves left lying on the pavement to show that she had been on her way.

Having waited by the schools gates for around half an hour or so, with no sign of Martin and Bernie, I had decided to make my own way home. I'd been positive I'd not missed the pair of them, and if they'd come out through the other entrance on Rutland Street, I was sure they would have come looking for me here. But with no good reason to be hanging round the school any longer than necessary. Especially with the charity envelopes stuffed down the front of my trousers, I'd made my way back up Lopton Street into Rutland Street and up in the direction of home.

On the way, my heart had nearly jumped into my mouth, when the sirens had suddenly blared out and the police car had roared past with its blue lights flashing! And if it had not been for the ambulance following close behind it, I would probably have had thrown my hands up in the air and given myself up.

Further up the street, I could see the police car and ambulance, still with their blue lights flashing, off to my right by a row of half demolished houses. A small group of people had gathered up by the mouth of an entry, where days earlier, we had been drawing matchstick men, on the side wall of the first derelict house. As I'd walked over to have a nose, I could see Cookie-Eye standing with two uniformed policemen. He was crying uncontrollably and talking gibberish, which no-one seemed to understand. The two policemen had then walked him over to their police car, where I had caught a glimpse of his bloodstained hands and coat! Pushing my way even closer to get a better look to where the two ambulance men were kneeling on the rough uneven ground, by the wall, the shock of seeing the sight before me had made my heart miss a beat and my legs turn to jelly. "Martin! Bernie!"

-TWENTY-ONE-

Martin and Bernie, were discharged from the hospital a day later. The pair of them had taken a good beating, for no other reason than to have been in the wrong place at the wrong time. They had told the police, they had never before set eyes on the two older fellas that had attacked them, though they were able to give out rough descriptions of the evil bastards and say that they'd had Scottish accents. A few cuts and bruises and a gash on the side of Martin's head, needing six stitches, and they were otherwise on the mend from their ordeal.

The police had told daddy, if it had not been for Cookie-Eye, chasing Martin and Bernie's two attackers off, before raising the alarm, things could have been a lot worse.

"Well. Ye'd better hurry up and find the bastards! Because, I'm tellin' yah now! The description my kids gave ta yah, won't be the same, if I he get me hands on them first!"

At the time, mammy and daddy, had told the coppers, they had not known anyone, or any reason, why someone would have a grudge against the family. Yet, when the police had left the house, the first person they had accused, was Uncle Mike, because he'd still had the hump over the stolen bag of scrap. But when that was eventually ruled out, they'd blamed, Fat Pat, the landlord from the Red-Rose, before moving on down the long list of other names, who'd had a grudge against the family!

Martin and Bernie were taken, by the police, to see Cookie Eye, so they could personally thank him for helping them. The

167

police had bought a big bunch of flowers and a huge box of chocolates with a red bow tied across the corner of it, for them to give to him, because daddy had told them, "I couldn't even afford ta buy me wife a Milky Bar and bunch of feckin' dandelions, for her birthday! Let alone for a stranger!"

When the pair of them had got back from their visit, they'd told me, Cookie-Eye's name was Gordon, and how he had hid behind his mammy's big arse bawling his eyes out, when he had recognised the pair of them. When I'd heard this, I had felt quiet sad. And for the first time ever, I had suddenly realised, pain came in many different forms and not just from the physical beatings we suffered at the hands of our parents, or strangers, or from the everyday cuts and bruises we sustained throughout our daily lives.

Bernie had laughed when she'd told me, how, when Cookie-Eye's mammy had told her ginger-haired son, to give them both a big hug, for bringing him the chocolates and the flowers, he had completely ignored her, ripping open the box before stuffing handfuls of chocolates into his gob, like there was no tomorrow.

I'd often heard people say, "Time is a good healer." and "They'll soon get over it." as people often do. Some much quicker than others. Last summer, when Aunty MaryAnn, had married Uncle Frank; who wasn't our Uncle Frank, until he married her, I had seen her sitting on her own at a the table, crying. I'd gone over to her and gave her one of my biggest hugs, and I'd told her, "Time's a good healer, Aunt MaryAnn. You'll soon get over it." When she had suddenly burst into fits of laughter, it had made me feel really good about myself, for having cheered her up. Even though she'd seemed sad about marrying Uncle Frank.

Vowing to myself, that I would never ever call Cookie-eye, Cookie-eye, again. I had wished for him to hurry up and find the time, to get over the pain we had caused him, as well as getting an agreement from the others, not to antagonise him ever again.

The following morning, as we had sat waiting for our breakfast, daddy had told Martin to kill three chickens and take them to Ali Baba, over at the mosque in Longsight. "An' make sure yah get the money from the tight fisted cheatin' feckin' Jew first! Before ya hand them chickens ta him!" reminded daddy, as he'd plonked the hot mugs of dark tea down on the table, before making his way back in to the kitchen, to fetch the bread and dripping'.

Mammy had managed to crawl out of her bed and had walked into the backroom, looking bleary-eyed and the worst for wear. She had a lit fag dangling from her mouth, which wasn't that unusual, given the fact she'd smoked about eighty a day! Still in her nightdress, the smell of the perfume, Uncle Oliver had given to her as a present, was overpowering. She'd had a habit of spraying the stuff all over her, especially when she was going out, making daddy exaggerate his normal cough, as well as complaining the stuff was getting into his lungs and killing him. Bernie and Maggie, loved the smell, though the rest of us thought it smelt like the stale dog shite you could smell down the back alleyways during the summertime's, when the hot sun was cooking it.

As she always did. Mammy had gone over to the lit coal fire,

169

where she'd stood with her back to it and hitched up her long nylon nightdress, exposing her bare arse to the flames. She had stood there in silence, staring down at the floor as if she had been put into a hypnotic trance, her subconscious mind probably far off to some distant land, where she didn't have the burden of us to contend with in her dreary miserable existence, as her arse had warmed up.

When Daddy had walked in from the kitchen with the plate of dried bread and the bowl of dripping', mammy had just lit her second fag, when she'd suddenly given out an almighty shriek, like a cat that'd just had its arse singed over the hot flames of a stove!

"Ah Jasis Jim! Me feckin hole is on fire! I'm burning to death!" Mammy's nightdress had suddenly caught alight! She'd hopped around the room like a wild banshee, and we had instinctively thrown our tea at her, in our attempts to douse out the flames. My tea had hit the radio, which had suddenly stopped working, possibly blowing a valve. Martin's tea had hit Churchill full in the face. After doing a backward somersault, the cat had climbed up the wall, stripping off some of the damp wallpaper as he went, before the deranged animal settled to hang from the top of the net curtains. Luckily for mammy, everyone else's tea had hit their intended target and the nightdress had been doused out.

"Ah Jim! Jim!' she'd cried, "Me poor hole!" she was lying on her front with a few little pieces of burnt material stuck to her arse.

"It's out Lizzy! It's out!" said daddy, "God Jasis! Didn't I feckin' warn yah about standin' close to the poxty feckin' fire!"

170

he'd set about easing off the pieces of scorched material from her skin, And then, grabbing the bowl of dripping off the table, before we'd even had a chance to use any of it! He'd rubbed the whole lot of it on to her bare red arse. Which had meant, dry bread for us!

"Oh Jasis! I'm scarred for life! I'm cursed! I'll be walkin' like a duck and never able sit down agin for the rest of me life!"

"Ah give over, will yah!" said daddy, "It could've been a lot worse." he'd given her a gentle pat on the arse, which had only caused mammy to howl out all kinds of obscenities at him and us.

"Could've been feckin' worse!" she had bellowed at the top of her voice. "Jasis! There's me, burning ta feckin' death! And what do them gimpy bastards do! They throw boilin' hot tea all over me and scorch me ta feckin' sunder! An' yah say, it could have been worse! Yah bad man's bastard, yah!"

Daddy had told us to scarper, before mammy swung for the lot of us. Which was a blessing in disguise for us, as we could barely hold back our laughter, while mammy had gone on, cursing everyone living in the surrounding streets, barring the Catholic church, Jesus, the Virgin Mary, and her usual band of favourite saints. His Holiness, Pope Paul VI, and the Shaw family living at No19, who'd always had the time to lend mammy a cup of sugar, or a few coppers, when she hadn't two pennies to rub together, as well as the times, Mrs. Shaw and her daughter, Anne, had given the family sanctuary when daddy, fuelled by drink and after given mammy *"What for"* had wanted to take his temper out on us.

Paddy and Shamie had come out into the yard. Not

surprisingly, they were not on speaking terms with each other, again. Paddy had headed straight out the through the back gate, without so much as a second glance at us, while Shamie had paused briefly to ask, what was wrong with the auld woman.

"She'd caught fire and nearly died of the pain." Maggie had told him. Our big brother had just shrugged his big shoulders before walking out the back way, heading off in the opposite direction to Paddy.

Maggie had volunteered to take Michael, Kathleen and Gosson, to Aunt Brenda's, as she'd wanted to stay out of the way for as long as she'd been able to. She was not wanting to take any responsibility for Nabby, her way of telling us, she'd no intentions of taking him along with her. As young as he had been, she couldn't handle him! Every time she'd tell him to do something, he would refuse to do it, unless it was something, he had wanted to do! She'd said, he was more stubborn than a dead donkey. And I suppose, in some way, she was right. But if she had put some effort into finding out the secret to his stubbornness, she would have realised it was simply to ask him to do something for you and not demand him to do it! At the end of the day, to Martin, Bernie and me, Nabby was just Nabby and wouldn't have been Nabby, if he wasn't Nabby!

Tagging along with us, he'd helped us to corner the three petrified chickens in the yard. Martin went about cutting their throats with mammy's serrated bread knife, while I'd held them down on the wooden cutting block, which daddy had used when he had threatened to chop my fingers off. Normally we would just chop their heads off with the small axe and let them have a run around the yard, until they keeled over with the shock of suddenly realising they'd lost their heads. But Ali Baba's chickens had to have their necks slit, but not cut right off, before being hung up on the hooks, to bleed to death.

'Can I have a turn?' Nabby had asked Martin, as I'd held the last chicken neck down on the chopping block.

'Okay. But yah have to be careful not to cut right through the neck.' Martin handed him the knife.

But our little brother's enthusiasm, to show us he was up to the job without any problems, caused us a big problem, when he'd cut the neck clean through and the head fell off the chicken!

Oh feck!' Now look what yah done!' Martin moaned, 'We'll have ta get another one. Jasis! If daddy finds out we've killed a chicken when there'd been no need, he'll beat the shite outta us!" And he would have done, despite the ordeal Martin and Bernie had recently been through.

"Have yah done with them chickens yet?" daddy had suddenly called out through the open back door, leading through into the kitchen, causing Martin to panic and throw the headless chicken over the wall of our next door neighbours' back yard.

"We're just waiting for them to stop bleeding!" I had called back to him.

"Hurry it up about it!"

The bald head of Mr. Sands, our Welsh neighbour had made a sudden appearance up over his boundary wall. "Would you believe that, boyo's!" he'd told the whole of Hulme! "A flying chicken has just landed in my yard, missing my head by an inch!"

"What's wrong with the two-faced nosey feckin' town-crier, who's nothin' better to do than stand starin' out of the window all day long!" Daddy had shouted from the kitchen, loud enough for Mr. Sands to hear him, "Yer lucky it wasn't a ten-ton feckin' elephant!' he came to the open doorway, "Yah can't stop chickens escapin' over the walls now and agin! It's their natural instinct, just like yer feckin' big gob!"

"Well, perhaps you might like to have a quiet word in their feathery ears and advise them, not to cut their heads off before trying to escape to freedom! They'd probably be better at seeing where they were going!"

Lucky for us, daddy hadn't any time for the Welshman and he'd had already gone back into the house, slamming the door behind him.

"Yah can keep the chicken for a shilling, if yah like?" Martin offered.

"A shillin', is it? Now that's a bargain! I'd love to have it for a shillin'!" grinned Mr. Sands, as he'd leaned further over the wall and offered his empty hand out to Martin. "Come on then boyo! Give us the shillin' then!"

"I hope yah choke on it yah humpy tight-arse sheep shaggin' twat!' Martin had angrily snapped, while Mr. Sands had hysterically laughed at him, before his bald head had disappeared back over his own side of the wall.

We'd set about chasing down another chicken. And with no objections from Nabby, Martin had slit its throat open. But with no time to hang the third chicken up to bleed, I'd volunteered to carry it by its feet, leaving a trail of blood up along the back entry and along the streets for about a mile, until

174

the all blood had drained from it, before I had slipped the bloodless chicken into the spare bag, we'd brought along for it.

Ali-Baba's shop, wasn't a proper shop, in the true sense of the word. Although it had looked like a shop from the outside and was probably once used as a shop. It had nothing inside it to sell. In fact, it was completely bare inside, except for a few small coloured mats spread around on the floor! Stranger still, Mr. Ali wore a long white dress and a small circular white cap on his head, but no shoes! Mammy said, he was a *Himshe*, which meant a cross between a man and a woman! Though to us, he hadn't looked much like a woman, with his long grey straggly beard. Before he would allow us into the shop, he had told us to take off our shoes, which we had done, handing over the three bagged chickens, after he had paid for them first. And then we had watched in amazement as the large group of beardy shoeless men, had ambled into his shop. Some were wearing white dresses like Mr. Ali, and some had carried small coloured carpets, like the ones already on the floor. Mr. Ali had invited the four of us to stay for prayers, but the air inside the shop was becoming pungent with the smell of cheesy feet, and we had made our excuses not to stay.

"We are good Catholics." said Martin.

"Mammy only lets us pray to St Martin, her favourite saint." said Nabby, "An' we're not all *Himshe's* like yea lot! An' yah wouldn't be catching any of us wearin' them dresses!"

"Sister Joseph said, we'd be breaking the first commandment if we'd prayed to false Gods." I had informed him.

I didn't think Mr. Ali's friends were happy about something

175

or other, because they'd started babbling loudly and pointing their fingers in our direction. Perhaps they'd thought, we were the cause of the pong? Mr. Ali, had politely asked us to leave and we had quickly left, screwing up our faces and holding our noses, just to make the point. Outside the shop, a few dozen pairs of assorted shoes had been left on the pavement, and so we'd instinctively picked them up before running off down the street with them. We'd every intention of taking the shoes home to mammy and daddy, but they had stunk to high heaven and we'd thought twice about it before dumping them into some bins along one of the alleyways.

-TWENTY-TWO-

Heading across Alexander Road, our first port of call had been to the convent of 'Our Lady of the Cenacle' which we would often call at in the early parts of the afternoons, begging for food. Banging the large metal door knocker down against the thick oak double doors, we had stood back and waited patiently for a few minutes. When no-one had answered, Martin had continuously hammered the knocker against the door, for what had seemed like an eternity, letting those inside know, we were not going away until they'd answered it! Even so, when it was eventually answered, there would still be a fifty-fifty chance, whether we'd be getting something to eat, or not, depending on who it was who had opened the door to us.

Last time, it had been the old Irish witch herself, Sister Michael, the miserable skinny auld walking Irish skeleton, for a Mother Superior! "No feckin' wonder she's married herself to God!" mammy had said, "There's not a livin' man that'd go near that! Not even the feckin' devil himself!" Without fail, she would shoo us off with a wave of her long boney hand, while dictating her same boring sermon, word for word.

"The starvin' children of the African nations are more deservin' than the likes of yea lot of Irish tinkers, with yer lazy good-for-nothin' fathers who've never worked an honest day in their miserable lives-save for breedin' like rabbits! And yet they still have the means to go off and get drunk every night!" She also had a few choice words about our mammy's, "With their IQ levels below zero, and the decorum to match! And whose idea of a full-time occupation, is forever lyin' on their backs and getting' pregnant year in and year out, with most of them havin' never seen their dirty feet since they were children themselves!" After she'd drawn breath, she'd finish off with her usual slamming of the door in our faces.

This time, the door had been answered by a fresh pink-faced young nun of around twenty years-old. She had smiled, which was a good sign for us, even if it had been an apprehensive smile, as she had looked us up and down without saying a word.

"Is there any food after meals, Holy Sister?" Bernie had asked, with the use of the word *Holy* being deliberately patronising, acknowledging the beneficiary of the said title, we recognised her as being on par with all the saints in heaven. Leaving it to the said individual to prove us wrong, just as the miserable Mother Superior always did! But, unlike the walking skeleton, the new novice had blushed at the very thought of being called holy. "I am Sister Rosemary," she'd introduced herself in a soft, almost timid Irish voice, "If yea'd like to wait just there, I will go and see what I can do for yea." she'd disappeared back behind the door, leaving it slightly ajar -To her own detriment!

To seek out and seize opportunity is a risky business. "But if no-one is prepared to search for opportunities, then the whole world would stop revolving and come to a standstill!" said Father Murphy, who would go on to constantly remind us during every Sunday Mass. He'd tell us, "Seek and yea shall find." But as he had never set out the criteria, as to what it was we were supposed to be seeking and finding, I had assumed, he was saying, grasp at any opportunity that might arise and which might sustain you in life. In other words. Help yourself! Without fail, he would give out the, *Ask and yea shall receive* message. But we'd all known this was a big feckin' lie and only served as a coded message for Sister's Joseph and Gertrude, to start passing around the collection plates, when he said those words!

"It's a feckin' mockery in itself!' was daddy's response, on one of his many rants about the church. "It doesn't matter how much us poor buggers keep askin' of the Church, we receive feck all in return! And yet, the feckin' Church expects us ta give them our last few pennies for the privilege of them feckin' asking us!"

Telling Martin and the others, to wait outside, I had slipped in through the gap in the open door with every intention of seeking out and receiving any opportunities that came my way, being a firm believer in daddy's own saying, *Finders Keepers!*

Hurrying along the hallway's highly polished wooden floor, I had tiptoed past an oak paneled door, which had been slightly left ajar, and I'd headed down toward the end of the corridor in the direction of the larger than life statue of the Virgin Mary, further along, just standing there on a cold marbled plinth and smiling down on the baby Jesus, sitting in her arms. On the way down, I had passed another large oak paneled door which was closed and which had a small sign written in bold black lettering, hanging off the door handle. I'd not been able to read, so I hadn't a clue what the sign had said. Not that I had cared or wanted to know what it had meant. It wasn't meant for me and so wasn't for my benefit.

179

Approaching the statue of Our Lady, I couldn't help but notice the small plain white cardboard moneybox standing at her feet. Making the sign of the cross, I had bowed my head in respect to Our Lady and her baby, before looking up in to her face to see her smiling down at me through her half-closed eyes. And for the briefest of moments, as I had stood looking up at her, I had got to wondering what this saintly woman must have been thinking of me, a poor kid, about to steal from under her very nose. Surely, I'd thought, she wouldn't begrudge me for seeking and finding my *opportunity*. And the baby Jesus, all snug and warm and sitting comfortably in his mother's arms and smiling up at her without a care in the World. Would he miss a few coppers here or there?

That was when I had heard the inner voice uttering the words, *"Take of me as you will. For what is mine, is yours"* Although I had been unsure as to whether the inner voice had been that of Father Murphy, or the Divine Lord himself, I had been certain it had been the voice of a man, ruling out Our Lady! Not that it had really mattered to me who had uttered those divine words. They were, by all accounts the words of the *Lord Jesus* himself, and this had made me feel all the less guilty, when I had snatched up the small money box and had headed back along the hallway in the direction of the main doors.

Halfway up along the corridor I'd suddenly heard the sound of footsteps coming up along a passageway up ahead and off to my right! Stuffing the money box down the front of my trousers, making sure it was safely tucked inside Bernie's pink flowery tight knickers, which were the only clean undies I'd been able to find to wear three days ago, I had pressed myself up against the oak paneled door with the small sign hanging off its door handle, and I'd watched as Sister Rosemary appeared out from the passageway, carrying a large oven dish laden with food. The tantalising odor which had wafted down in my direction, had caused my mouth to water so much, I began dribbling from the corners of my mouth! I'd readied myself to tiptoe out from my hiding place and follow behind her, when the first door, the one which had been left slightly ajar as I had made my way into the convent, had suddenly creaked wide open, leaving me with just the two alternatives, either to get caught, or to take another opportunity and turn the handle of the large oak door behind me and hurry in!

For as long as I have been living on the earth, I had seen many sights in that time! Pleasant, not so pleasant and feskin' horrendous! Not long ago I had seen a man, of about fifty-years of age, jump from a railway bridge in front of an oncoming train. All that was left of him on the track, when Martin and I had climbed on the wall of the bridge to get a better look, was one leg and an arm. The rest of his body had been wedged under the engine of the train and was on its way to Piccadilly station. But nothing could have prepared me for the sight which had stood before my eyes, when I had slipped through into the large bathroom, to see Sister Michael, standing in front of me, dripping wet, and stark bollock naked!

Never having seen a sight like it in all my life, I just couldn't stop my eyes from gawking up and down her wrinkly skeletal body, like an army sergeant inspecting a soldier. There wasn't a hair on her head! Not one strand of hair! She was as bald as a cootie! But what she had lacked on the top, she had made up for it down below, with the huge grey beard around her budgie, rising all the way to her belly button. Which, for some obscure reason, had reminded me of the long grey bearded Ronnie Drew, mammy's favourite Irish singer from the Dubliners. And I could bet if either Paddy or Shamie had been cursed with the opportunity to have been standing where I had been standing, they would not have wanted to write home about her saggy drooping tits, which had looked like lumps of lead in a pair of nylon socks.

"Lord Mercy!" the stunned Sister, had suddenly cupped up her droopy tits in her hands.

I had a feeling, the shock of her seeing me looking her up and down might have filled her with indecisions, because she'd let go of her saggy tits and covered up her hairy budgie with her hands, before cupping up her tits again, before letting them droop and covering up her budgie again, when she could easily have hung her tits over her shoulder.

"Don't yah be tinkin' of gettin' that ting out yah dirty little divil yah!' she'd hollered at me.

I hadn't a clue what the crazy nun was going on about until I'd followed her gaze downwards to the large bulge in the front of my trousers, which had got me to wondering how she could have known I'd had the money box down there in the first place, let alone why I should want to get it out and let her see it, after having gone through all the trouble of getting it for myself. Well, she wasn't having any of it and I'd tapped the bulge with my hand, giving the auld witch a knowing smile, just to let her know it was all mine. And that was when she'd started to holler all kinds of obscenities at me, before picking up a large brown lump of carbolic soap, about the size of half a brick and hurling it straight at me, missing my head by a whisker. I'd managed to hurry out of the bathroom and back into the main hall, as a smaller lump of soap had whizzed past my left ear. And it was here, in the main hall, where I had suddenly found myself confronted by a huge nun!

She'd reminded me of Mick McManus, the Wrestler, and could easily have passed off for his twin! Short, fat, the snarl, the way she'd stood with her shoulders hunched and her legs apart, with huge hands the size of dinner plates dangling at the end of her tree trunk arms just waiting to trap me in a bear hug and crush me half to death, before picking me up and slamming me back down to the ground and bending my legs all the way back over my head in a full Nelson!

Looking past the huge nun, I was able to catch a glimpse of the others through the open front doorway. Bernie and Sister Rosemary were in a tug of war with the tray of food and I could only assume, the young nun must have had a change of heart and had decided to keep the food for herself, while my, now less pious, sister had cursed her with every swear word she could think of! It was only after Nabby had taken the initiative and had stamped on the poor nuns left foot did she let go of the tray, sending Bernie flying backwards, amazingly landing on her arse without spilling any of the food!

Suddenly noticing the shocked expression on the big nuns face as she'd looked past my me, I'd immediately turned to see Sister Michael wrapped in a big white towel, rushing towards me and hollering something about castrating sex maniacs, "No matter how *little* they were!" or words to that affect!

She obviously hadn't seen the small lump of carbolic soap on the floor until she had stepped on it, skating freestyle on the one leg before colliding into me, with the pair of us ending up on the floor in a heap! Dazed. For a few awful moments I'd honestly thought I'd gone blind! But thankfully it had only been Sister Michael's droopy tits resting on my eyelids! When she'd finally dragged herself up off me I'd found myself staring up at the Mick McManus lookalike standing above me, when she'd suddenly bent and grabbed me by one of my legs.

My imaginative thoughts had gone into overdrive and I'd conjured up this terrible thought of her swinging me around her head, like daddy had done to the cat, with every intention of bashing my head off all four walls, before rushing me to the kitchen and holding me over the lit stove scorching my hole, before drop kicking me out the through the front doors of the Convent! But as luck would have it, Martin, my hero, had come to my rescue again. Running into the hallway, he'd upped with his foot and had kicked the unsuspecting nun right up her huge arse, his foot almost disappearing as the toe of his shoe had caught her right up her hole and she'd danced around on tiptoes, just like a ballet dancer, holding her arse while wailing like a huge fat dancing pig!

Scurrying off back up along the Convents cinder path, with Bernie leading the way and firmly holding on to the tray of food, we'd rushed out through the main gates and had headed straight across Alexandra Road towards the Park. I don't recall which sound came first, the car horn or the screeching of the brakes, as the black cab had borne down on our sister, hitting her!

In the seconds it had taken for the moment to have passed me by, I'd thought the black cab was going to stop just in time, or it would steer out of my sister's path to avoid hitting her. I'd seen two wood pigeons fly off the branch of one of the huge trees in Alexandra Park and fly straight over our heads. I'd heard Martin and Nabby scream, louder than I had ever heard them scream before. And then the people around us, shouting and crying. All except for me. I'd wanted to scream. I'd tried to scream out a warning. But it just wouldn't come out! I'd seen the look of terror in Bernie's eyes as she had looked back across the road at me. And I had known in that instance, I was helpless to do anything for her. A dead leaf had floated down from a tree and had landed next to my sisters' prone body lying still in a heap in the middle of the road. All three of us had rushed to her side and by the time we had ran the short distance to her, there were already strangers flocking around her like vultures. A black man was on his knees stroking my sister's hand. Incensed, Martin had shouted at him to leave her alone! The black man was sobbing uncontrollably, and had told Martin and anyone else listening, "She ran straight out in front of me!"

We had stood emotionless just looking down on our sister, not knowing what to say or what to do. There were many tears from the strangers gathered around Bernie, but there were no tears from us. We had wanted to pick her up and take her home, but we knew we couldn't do this, as off in the distance we could hear the sirens. Looking over in the direction of the convent gates, the distraught Sister Rosemary, followed by the

Mick McManus lookalike, had rushed out of the main gates and across in our direction, where they'd fallen to their knees down by the black man, who was still holding Bernie's hand. And Sister Rosemary then blessed herself with the sign of the cross before praying over Bernie's prone body.

Picking the metal oven dish up off the ground, I had automatically begun retrieving the cooked sausages and roast potatoes back up off the ground and placing them back into the dish. An old woman had picked two sausages up and had placed them into it and I'd thanked her. A man had picked some of the roast potatoes up and had placed those into the dish, and then someone else did likewise. I'd thanked each one in turn and I'd thought of how Sister Joseph and Sister Gertrude must have felt saying all those *Thank yea's,* when passing the collection plates up and down the aisles and the people putting their money in them.

Once all the food had been retrieved I'd made my way back over to Martin and Nabby, standing over the two nuns still kneeling at Bernie's side. "As we won't be needin' it now. Yah can give it to the starvin' children of Africa!" I'd thrust the oven dish full of gritty food into Sister Rosemary's hands and she'd suddenly burst into tears.

-TWENTY-THREE-

Daddy and the black man had walked back along the hospital corridor in our direction. Daddy was carrying a huge black doll which the black man had bought for Bernie and which daddy had later sold on to the rag and bone man for three shillings. "Apart from a broken arm and a few scratches, she's goin' to be fine." he'd broken the good news to us. And though at the time, our emotions hadn't betrayed our inner feelings, we had felt overjoyed about the fact our little sister would be back shoplifting and collecting firewood and scrap metal with us very soon.

Daddy had introduced the black man to us. He was the driver of the cab that had hit Bernie. "Samuel says Bernie had just ran out in front of him and he wasn't able to stop in time."

"She'd looked right and left and right agin before crossin'!" lied Martin.

"Bernie never looks anywhere ta see what's comin'," said daddy, "She walks straight out in the road and expects all the feckin' traffic ta suddenly stop dead in their tracks just for her!" Which was true. But that wasn't the point!

The black man had thrown us a big white smile but we had fixed him with accusing eyes, which he had taken as his cue to leave, promising daddy he would come to visit the young girl at the house, which he did a few times, until daddy got into a drunken row with him and had accused him of deliberately trying to murder his little daughter! I think he must have been after another doll to sell.

"Yea lot have ta see the doctor," said daddy, "As yah might all be in a state of shock without knowing it. Though yah don't look any different than yah ever do ta me."

I'd not been able to see how it was possible for someone to be in a state of shock without knowing they were in a state of shock, though I had to admit, if I'd happened to have been in a state of shock I wouldn't have known what it had felt like to have judged whether or not I'd been in one!

Daddy had waited outside the examination room as all three of us had marched in and had stood in front of the long desk, gawking open-mouthed at the sight of the dark chocolate-skinned midget sitting behind it. We'd seen the odd midget now and again, but never a black one! So it had come as a bit of a surprise to us all, though just as surprising to me, was the fact I'd genuinely forgotten about the money box still stuffed down the front of my undies, until a hard edge had stuck in my left bollock!

"Well. You all seem to be very undernourished and anemic." said the little doctor. His observations had not really impressing any of us, considering we had always looked pale, hungry and lifeless. He'd seemed to pay particular attention to me and had asked me, "Is there anything you would like to share with me?" with his eyes fixing me before dropping down to the bulge in my trousers

"No!" I'd abruptly told him. Jasis! They were all at it! "I don't have anythin' I'd like ta be sharin' with yah!"

"Well. If you wouldn't mind going behind the curtain and I'll examine you first?"

"Can't yah examine me Brother Martin first?" I'd suggested,

"He's the eldest, and the eldest always goes first."

Martin had seemed pretty peeved off with my suggestion and had stood scowling at me, while the doctor had been adamant it was me he wanted to examine first! And so reluctantly I'd hurried off behind the curtain, hoping I'd be able to whip the money box out of its hiding place and hide it somewhere out of sight, before the doctor came around the curtains. But I never got the chance, because the little dwarf was right behind me breathing down my neck!

"Right," he had said, "If you would like to undo your trousers and slip them down around your knees." He'd kept his eyes firmly fixed on my bulge.

Reluctantly doing what he'd ordered I'd slipped my trouser down to reveal Bernie's pink pair of flowered knickers. And it was just as he had pulled the front of them away and had peered down them, that I had suddenly noticed the smiling faces of Martin and Nabby peering up at me from underneath the curtain,

"Hmm? That is the most odd looking penis you have there, I must say!" the doctor had slipped his little fat podgy hand down to the cause of my bulge just as the curtain had suddenly flown along its rails to reveal my daddy standing on the opposite side of them, his eyes blazing and him all red-faced with anger.

"Yah big feckin' perverted leprechaun yah!" he'd bellowed before his fist made contact with the doctors gob, the force knocking the little fellow straight across the floor. "What has playin' with me sons flute got to do with shock!" he'd raged, as Martin and Nabby had rushed to the door, ready to run if daddy had completely lost it.

"Git yer kecks up Tommy!" ordered daddy before turning on the doctor, who was on all fours readying himself to get up. "Yer a disgrace to this profession, so yah are!"

"Please let me explain Mr. Rattigan! I'd noticed your son had an unusual bulge in his trousers and -"

"Yah wanted ta have a good feel around with him-did yah? Yah dirty fecking homo ya!" daddy landed a few good kicks up the doctors' hole, as the midget had desperately scurried away across the examination room and managing to take refuge under his desk. "Go on! Git back to Alexander Park where yah feckin' belong with all the other bush perverts!"

"But Mr. Rattigan -!"

"Don't be buttin' me!" bellowed daddy, ignoring the doctors attempts to explain himself, "I'll feckin' see yea'll never work in a circus! Let alone a feckin' hospital agin! Yah feckin little bitch, yah!"

Though the doctor had insisted he'd wanted charges of assault and battery pressed against daddy, after daddy had warned the other doctor fixing the midgets gob, "When the shite hits the fan, some of it will always stick-him being a midget and all!" we'd never heard another word said about the incident, apart from daddy being told he wasn't welcome at the hospital again, barring emergencies to himself.

Martin had once used the same tactic on Father Duggan, from St Anne's church over in Longsight, when the old priest had caught the pair of us in his church, attempting to force open the metal cover of the wall offertory box with a rusty old butter knife. At the time, he'd been in the company of John

Carson, a fat twelve-year-old kid who we knew from Shamie's gang. Carson, with his bloated red face, had seemed a bit awkward when he had first seen us and had hurried past us and out of the church without so much as a *hello* or *goodbye*.

'Tree o'clock next Friday!' Father Duggan had called after Carson, reminding him of the next bible lesson, before turning on us and spewing out his bile on our sinful desecration of his church and how we would be forever damned in hell's fire!

"Once the shite hits the fan some of it sticks!' said Martin, with me following up with a knowing sort of wink, at the red-faced priest.

To our amazement, the flustered Father Duggan had pushed his hand under his cassock and fiddled around with himself for a moment or two before producing a half-crown, which he held out to Martin, angrily telling us to get out of his church and never to show our demon faces in it again!

It couldn't have been long after this when I had tried the same tactic on Sister Joseph. At the time, she was about to give me three whacks of the ruler in front of the whole class, for calling that bastard, Paul Morgan, a bastard! I just couldn't understand why calling him a bastard was wrong in the eyes of God. I'd been called it so often, it became more familiar to me than my first name! Once, when we were walking up along Philips Street, where Morgan lived, his mammy had suddenly come to her front door and had shouted out to him, in her foghorn voice, "Git in here, yah little bastard!" so I couldn't really see what his problem was to be snitching. Anyway. Sister Joseph was having no excuses and so, as I had held my hand out to her I'd looked her straight in her good eye and warned, "Just remember Sister. Once I've shit on the fan it'll stick all over yah," or words to that affect. Besides the class erupting into fits of laughter, the feckin old dragon had given me and extra three whacks for my insolence!

Home from the hospital, we had waited until daddy had headed off to the pub before I finally relieved myself of the bulge in my trousers. Bernie had to stay in the hospital overnight, just so as they could check to see if she'd suffered any damage to her brain, though daddy said, he wouldn't be able to tell the difference anyhow!

Having agreed between the three of us to spend whatever money there was in the box on goodies for Bernie, Martin and Nabby, had eagerly peered over my shoulder to get a better look as I had torn it open and tipped the contents out on the table top. Three halfpennies, two farthings, fourteen black buttons and five Irish shillings! "The tight arsed feckin' auld witches!" cursed Martin.

"What have yeah there?" asked Maggie, walking through into the back room.

"Buttons!" said Nabby.

"I was only feckin' askin' Nabby!"

"That's all we've got is all I'm sayin. Buttons and Irish poxty pennies!"

"Jasis! It's a collection for Sister Bernadette's retirement!" Maggie laughed as she'd read the black writing on the side of the moneybox, "She wouldn't have been gettin' far on that lot!"

"Neither are we!" said Martin "We were going to get something for Bernie! Ah feck it! We'll just have to go and see what we can steal for her."

"I was just on me way inta the city, if yah want ta tag along with me?" Maggie had offered, knowing full well she would have a better chance of getting what she had wanted, if we were there as a distraction for her. She'd attempted to make it clear to us that she was in charge and although Nabby hadn't put out too much, he had made it clear to our big sister, she wasn't in charge of him. Needing us more than we needed her she didn't argue and our journey on foot in to the city, was a reasonably peaceful one.

I'm not sure if it was something about the way we had walked, or talked, or whether it was just my imagination. But there was something definitely odd about the people who worked in the city's large department stores. They never seemed to smile, at least not when we had walked in through their main doors! It had always seemed to me, our very presence had an impact on these people as all eyes would automatically roll upwards, quickly followed by their noses! On the way into the City, we had pinched a couple of tins of spam and a big jar of pickled eggs, which we had shared between us, with Martin polishing off most of the pickled eggs, about eight in all, because the rest of us were not too keen on the vinegar, which sometimes gave us gut ache. And as the rest of us didn't have the farts, we were able to safely put Martin's problem down to the eggs.

We'd been taught an old proverb amongst a lot of other old proverbs, *never judge a book by its cover* which, so it had seemed, didn't apply to the likes of us. But, just because our clothing had been old and grubby and ill-fitting and falling apart. It didn't mean we didn't have two pennies to rub together! And if we'd had two pennies to rub together. Surely, our money would have been just as good as anyone else's? If we'd had the mind to spend it!

It hadn't been too difficult spotting the two store detectives, pretending to be a married couple out shopping, considering the pair of them were pointing straight down at us from the top of the escalators, before rushing down them in our direction. How we had loved the challenge of the chase! To us, this was just another game of cat and mouse. Only the two chasing cats were more like a pair of overweight Bulldogs! We had taken off into the store, dodging around the uniformed Bellboy, who was probably hitting his late nineties and we'd squeezed into his packed lift. The haughty-faced fat woman wearing a brown fur overcoat and matching fur hat, with the dead fox hanging off her shoulder, had given us the once over before tilting her over-made-up face back and letting her wide nostrils search out a pocket of fresher air, before her eyes settled on a spot on the lift ceiling, probably pretending to herself, we were not there. Which must have been a trial in itself, when Martin had suddenly cocked a leg and dropped a silent but venomous fart.

I had pushed my face close into the warmth of the woman's soft fur coat, wiping my snotty nose on it in the process, but she had just ignored me out of hand as if I had been a figment of her imagination. But, even with a good imagination, the stench that had sauntered out and up from Martin's trouser legs had everyone, barring immediate family, standing on tiptoe and gasping for the last remnants of fresher air, until the lift had suddenly come to an abrupt halt.

"Cos-cos-cos -" I think the ancient Bellboy had been trying to tell us, the lift had reached the Cosmetic Department, but was having some difficulty getting his words out. And as the doors had slowly slide open, the fat fur-coated woman had barged the stuttering relic out of her way and staggered from the lift, gasping for breath. She was closely followed by a mad stampede of feet which had trampled the unfortunate Bellboy underfoot. We'd remained inside the lift watching as the old boy had dragged himself to his feet before staggering off through the cosmetic department and past the perfume counter, leaving us to take the lift up to the clothing department.

Martin was kept going on about his stomach ache. He'd said, he needed a shite right there and then and had been about to drop his trousers and do it in the corner of the lift, when Maggie had screamed, she was having none of it.

"Yah can wait 'til we get to the top floor and go to the toilet like proper people do!" she'd told Martin.

"Yah shouldn't have eaten all those pickled eggs Martin." Nabby told him, "Yea'll be lucky ta wake up in the mornin' and find yer not egg-bound."

"Is that dangerous then?" asked Martin.

"Not as much as the stench yer given' out!" said Maggie, "Jasis, can't yah just hold it in til we get out of this lift before yah kill the lot of us!"

When the lift had stopped, Martin had rushed out and headed straight off to the toilets while we the rest of us had waited outside, watching the mad stampede of feet hurrying out only seconds after he'd gone in. A short while later, he reappeared, with a contented smile spread across his face and we followed

Maggie through to the children's clothing section where we had spent a few minutes hurriedly choosing new clothes off the pegs for ourselves, before we'd bundled into the tiny changing rooms, swishing the curtains across and quickly changing into our new outfits, leaving our old rags in one neat pile on the changing room floor before following Maggie back through the clothing department towards the lifts.

The thought had crossed my mind whether or not anyone would recognise us as being the same children who had walked in a short while earlier, but it no-one it seemed had paid us any particular attention as we'd hurried along one of the aisles, with Maggie plucking some blouses off the hangers, before stuffing them inside her new yellow polka dot blouse. She'd followed up with three packs of ladies' knickers, four brassieres and a handful of wooly gloves and had been attempting to squeeze a pair of pink-coloured slacks down her, already full skirt, when Martin shouted the warning.

"Sham! We're corrupt!"

The two store detectives were on to us! As they had hurried along the aisle in our direction, we had immediately separated to confuse them, with Martin and me running off in one direction, while Nabby and Maggie had gone off in another.

Using one of our deliberate diversion tactics, Martin had snatched a red blouse off its hanger and deliberately letting the two dectectives see him, had stuffed it up inside his new green jumper before we had dashed off into the large furniture department, with the two bulldogs in hot persuit, allowing Nabby and Maggie the chance to make good their escape in the knowledge we would be meeting up with them shortly.

"In here." said Martin, and I'd followed after him in to the large wardrobe, closing the doors behind us.

"How can the little sods just vanish into thin air?" we'd heard the female voice ask between heavy breaths.

"The little bastards always manage to give us the fuckin' slip!" said the male voice.

"Ah! They're only kids – At least they keep us on our toes!"

"What's that?"

"On our toes - Exercise?"

"No. I meant. What's that smell?"

"Oh dear yes! It smells like a gas!"

"Sorry." Martin had suddenly whispered in my ear.

I'd been about to tell him, it wasn't his fault we were in this situation and how we'd been in situations like this many times before and always managed to get out of them. But I'd had no time to say anything, as the wardrobe had rapidly filled with the stench and I'd had to hold my breath for as long as I possibly could. But even for me, the stench had become too overbearing. That old saying about, dogs not being able to smell their own shite! That's a load of old feckin' cobblers! Martin had been the first to gasp for air and had pushed the wardrobe doors wide open before we'd gassed ourselves!

Momentarily stunned by the putrid stench, the two detectives were forced to take a backward step, giving us the advantage of surprise and enough time to scarper through the department and down the escalators to the ground floor, where Nabby was standing alongside Maggie, while she was berating a shop assistant, "How old d'ya have to be to be fecking pregnant!"

-TWENTY-FOUR-

Bernie was soon out of the hospital. The doctor had said, "Except for the slight limp, which should go away with time, she seemed as normal as she was ever going to be!" Even daddy had seemed pleased with himself, though I wouldn't have bet it was because Bernie had come home. For her homecoming treat we'd had boiled goose eggs which daddy had stolen and which had looked much bigger than the goose eggs we'd had last Christmas, along with the three chicken legs he'd given to me, Martin and Nabby, as an extra present to play with.

Admittedly. We'd loved them and had great fun playing with them. Pulling the main tendon at the top of the leg made the claws clench tightly together and we would pretend at being the demolition men, using the claws to pick up marbles and other small objects lying about the house, making large mounds with them. And when we tired of that, we'd set about annoying Churchill, grabbing his tail and pinching his boney arse. But like all good things coming to an end, the chicken feet would eventually start to decay and we would have to throw them on the fire and wait for another Christmas to come around again.

I had found myself wondering why there'd only been the three chicken feet instead of four. Daddy had killed two chickens? There'd been no talk amongst the family about a one-legged chicken being born, though Uncle Christy once said, he had a one-legged parrot, called "peg-leg" or "Noisy bastard!" depending on his mood; Uncle Christy's!

When we had broken open the eggs, the stench had been awful! Even worse than some of Martin's farts! My egg had a stillborn baby bird inside it which had instantly made me heave and want to throw up.

"God Jasis, Martin, yah dirty smelly fecker yah!' Mammy gave out to him, as she'd walked in from the kitchen, "Have yah a couple of dead rats stuck up that feckin' hole of yers!" she hadn't bothered waiting for him to reply before rushing out of the room and up the hallway, opening the front door.

"Yer all ungrateful little feckers, the lot of yah!" said daddy, promising never to treat us to *swans* eggs ever again! Which hadn't disappointed any of us in the least. Snatching the rotten eggs up off the table one by one, he'd slung them on the open fire. As he had done so, I could clearly see his eyes were all watery and he was holding his breath, before he'd suddenly gone into coughing fits.

We'd been able to hear mammy from the backroom, talking at the front door with Mrs. Gough, who'd lived on one of the streets up near the bathhouse in Leaf Street. We'd known it was Mrs. Gough, without even having to set eyes on her, because when she had laughed, it sounded just like a demented donkey. She had large stained teeth, which daddy once said, were like the keys on an old piano though he'd not said, if they were the black or the white keys! I thought her teeth were more browny-green, just like the teeth of the donkeys at Belle Vue, which you could ride for thruppence. I remember that little twat, Jonathan McGee, riding the donkeys there. He'd had enough money in his pockets to buy the whole fecking donkey!

Let alone pay for him and all his bum-chums to ride them! I'd never been able to see what enjoyment he could actually get out of riding a piss stinking, shitty arsed, dusty, flea-ridden, hee-hawing feckin donkey! Except to show off to his friends and anyone else minded to gawk at the spoilt little twat! I had also incensed with the little weasel when he'd offered to share a donkey ride with Cathy McCarthy, while her gimpy father, standing there alongside McGee's parents, had gawked across at me with that big feckin' grin spread all over his beardy face! I'd become convinced the miserable old sod was trying to marry off the love of my life to a bigger turd than me, before he'd popped his size-fourteen hobnailed boots. But I wasn't having any of it.

"Oh my sweet dar-link Jon-a-thon! That's very kand of you to pay for dear Cath-ay, to rade with you!' said the snooty-nosed Mrs. McGee, in her best plum-in-the-gob voice, while speaking loud enough for the whole of Belle Vue to have heard her. Well Cath-ay didn't get to rade the feckin' donkey with or without the dear sweet darlink Jon-a-thon! Though the creep did get the ride of a lifetime and one which he'd not bargained for!

I'd always had the habit of carrying a tiny penknife around with me, which had its many uses such as, unscrewing the tiny brass screws of the window catches and brass doorknobs we'd find in the derelict houses. Cutting worms in half so it would rain. And it did work, no matter how long it took for the heavens to open up! Cutting away the chewing gum we had pressed up into the *return* slot of the public telephone boxes to block any of the returned monies to its rightful owners. A good sign to look out for, was when a caller suddenly started beating the shite of the telephone receiver against the phone box! And last but not least! Sticking it in a donkey arse when you want it to bolt off with a big twat sitting on its back, kicking and hee-hawing like Mrs. Gough's laugh! Only the donkey isn't laughing.

With the stench from the swan's eggs still lingering in the backroom, Martin, Nabby, Bernie and me, had made our way out through the front door, where Mrs. Gough was laughing at one of her own jokes.

"Where yah off ta?' Mammy asked us.

"School." said Martin, which, for some unknown reason to us, had Mrs. Gough back in fits of hysterical laughter! We could still hear her hee-hawing as we had turned the corner at the longest end of Stamford Street, heading off in the opposite direction from the School. With Halloween soon coming upon us, we had wanted to get our costumes in as early as possible, so we could go off on our begging sprees in the guise of *trick or treat!* But when we had got to Woolworths, we'd been disappointed to find they were out of stock, though we had been informed by one of the assistants, the Longsight store still had plenty of them in store!

On most occasions we usually walked the route, but because of Bernie's limp we'd decided to catch the bus into Longsight. How we were going to pay for the fare, was something we would only think about when and if, the bus conductor came asking. Planning something in advance wasn't something we were particularly good at doing, finding it much easier to think on our feet and on the spur of the moment rather than confuse ourselves with trying to follow a set plan, though the only plan we ever did have was to pick a landmark on any given journey to meet back at if we'd ever became separated.

Walking was our preference. Mainly because we could see more on foot. And as well as it being more adventurous, it was the not knowing what was just around the corner which made our travels all the more exciting! The streets of Manchester had much on offer for its children like us. And though not quiet feral we had often been called, "Fucking animals!" But we hadn't missed the warmth of a mother's hug or the kind words from a father, or the pampering and kisses outside the school gates, or the *Happy Birthday to you!* Because we had never experienced such things. And the only difference between us and those kids who had experienced all those things was the fact, we could survive without them. People were just a hindrance to our lives and if push had come to shove, we could easily have survived off the streets, alone and without any human contact.

When the black bus conductor had come up the stairs for the fares I had reached inside my trouser pocket and pulled out the foreign coins I'd stolen from the convent a while back.

"Yagga googa pleezy!" I'd handed the coins to the conductor with no clue as to what foreign language I was talking in. And neither, it had seemed, did he.

"Yagga googa? What sort of fuckin language is that man?"

"We. A - fri – ca."

"Africa!" You fucking lot! You're not even black! Well. Apart from the dirt!"

"A – fri – ca." Nabby had got in on the act.

"Ok then. What part of Africa do you come from?"

"The coldest part." Nabby, had quickly answered, not giving us a chance to come up with a better answer. And the three of could only glare at him.

"The coldest part? - That's why you're white! I like it!" laughed the conductor, "So you're able to speak some English then? - At least the little white African fella can?"

We'd said nothing and had sat there staring blankly up at him.

"Ok. If I'm to believe you're all from Africa-and there's no reason to disbelieve you! How much are these Irish coins worth? - So I know what change I have to give you back?"

"Two shillings." I'd said

"Five shillings!" said Martin

"Ten shillings." said Nabby, while Bernie had opted to shake her head at us and say nothing.

"Right! If the inspector gets on the bus, you lot get off it! Ok!" the conductor gave us a smile as he'd slipped the two Irish coins into his jacket pocket.

"Did we have any change to come out of that?" only Nabby had the cheek to ask.

"Yagga googa!" came the swift reply.

Standing outside the Woolworths store in Longsight, we'd agreed between us, it was better to go in one at a time so as not to bring any suspicion upon ourselves. Martin was the first to go in, coming out a few minutes later with a skeleton outfit stuck down his trousers. I'd gone in next and had bagged myself one of the two remaining skeleton outfits which quickly hid up under the armpit of my jumper before hurrying out.

Bernie and Nabby, had gone in together, coming out moments later with Bernie having bagged the last skeleton outfit and Nabby, sulking as usual, having to make do with one of the last two remaining Witch's outfit. He had argued the point, "As Bernie is the girl, she should be the feckin' Witch."

"The last of the two Witch's outfits were too small for me to wear, Nabby, as well yah know! Anyways. My nickname's *Skeleton.*"

"Well yah don't need a feckin' costume, do yah!"

"Yer just jealous!"

"No I'm not!"

"Yes yah are!"

On our way out of Longsight we'd donned our costumes on over our clothing, leaving off the masks, not that Nabby had needed one, before hitching a lift back home. A Volkswagen camper van with its bodywork painted all over in all kinds of psychedelic coloured flowers, had pulled up at the side of the road.

"Hi guys! Which cemetery are you from!"

"We're just heading there," said Martin, walking over to the young long-haired smiling hippy, sitting in the front passenger seat.

"Are yea Jesus?" Bernie had suddenly asked him.

"You've found me!' laughed the hippy introducing the young pregnant driver as his wife, Mary! He'd offered us a lift to anywhere we had wanted to go and without any hesitation, we had hopped into the back of the van.

"So where is this cemetery of yours?' Jesus asked.

"Hulme." said Martin.

"It's not a real cemetery." said Bernie.

"It's worse," I'd added.

"Have you two ha`pennies for a penny?' Nabby had asked, holding out the penny.

"Don't be askin that!" Martin had scolded him, while me and Bernie had given him one of our *Shallup-yer-gob* stares. But Jesus had just laughed it off as he'd rolled himself a cigarette and lit it, before taking a deep drag of it and then putting the fag into Mary's gob, as she drove along the road.

The whiff from the cigarette smoke was nothing like the suffocating smoke from mammy and daddy's cigarettes, which sometimes had us in coughing fits, especially when the whole family were together smoking inside the house and forcing us outside into the back yard. The smell of their smoke was so different-even nice! And I had started to feel relaxed as I had inhaled the air as the lids of my eyes grew heavy.

"Look Martin!' Bernie had suddenly pointed through the van window as we'd headed down the Stretford Road past the Eagle pub, "That's them two bastards that hurt us!" But by the time we'd looked across the road in the direction of the pub, all we had seen as the van drove past, was the back of a fella walking up the big step into the pub entrance.

"Are yah sure it was them, Bernie?"

"I'm as sure as I'm sittin' here Martin! I swear ta God it was them two! Bernie was so adamant we couldn't just ignore her or the tears which welled in her eyes.

Martin promised he would tell daddy the second we'd walked into the house and for the rest of the journey, we had listened in silence as Jesus had told us stories of their travels to distant lands such as Scotland, Wales, Liverpool, London, Margate, and now Manchester. And by the time we had been dropped off by the large croft, just off the Stretford Road, I'd got this notion in my head that one day I too would go on an adventure to these far off places.

"What name do you think we should call our new baby?" Jesus had suddenly asked us as we had climbed out of the van and stood up on the pavement. Bernie suggested Joseph was a nice name and Martin had suggested Moses as being a much better name. I'd suggested, Tommy being the best name of all and Nabby said, "Have yah got two halfpennies for a penny?" while holding the penny out to Jesus.

"Yah shouldn't be begging off people who have just helped us Nabby," Martin scolded him for a second time, "It's not right."

"Don't ever be afraid of asking for anything," advised Jesus, "Or you'll never get anything. And even if you don't get anything. At least you asked." To our surprise, Jesus had reached into his inside coat pocket and had brought out a pound note, which he'd handed to Nabby. "Keep the penny." he'd smiled, before driving off with a wave of his hand.

-TWENTY-FIVE-

The light drizzly mist always added to the atmosphere of the darker evenings, especially during Halloween when all the Witches came out to celebrate and flew around on their broomsticks over the skies of Manchester, with a black cat happily sitting on the back. And although I'd never come across a flying Witch, I had been certain there'd been many who'd answered the doors we had knocked on!

After donning our costumes and Bernie making Nabby's green face up for him eye shadow she'd found in Mary's makeup bag, we'd hung around the house for a little while longer, waiting for daddy or Shamie to come home, with the news, they'd found the two bastards who had beaten Martin and Bernie and they'd given the pair of shitbags what for!

"There'd be more chance of the cat walkin' in off the street with a rat up his hole than seein' them two before the night is out!" said mammy, "An don't dare be showin' me up beggin' along this street! I've enough havin' ta contend with yer feckin' father rolling down the street blind drunk an' calling the neighbours all the names under the sun."

We'd made our way down into Philips Street before we started knocking on the doors. We never had a set list of tricks to play on anyone that refused to give us a treat and were just content as usual to do things on the spur of the moment, depending on the circumstances. Making a shit parcel and setting it alight on the doorstep, before knocking on the door again and then watching the occupier, from a safe distance, stamp out the fire, had been a favourite trick of ours! Coating a door handle with dog turd, throwing a ducker through a window or shoving a banger through the letter box, were other silly little things we did! I'd loved being out in the dark, especially late at night, when there was hardly anyone about, except for the odd drunk or whore, or the odd car whizzing past us. Other than them, Hulme in the dark, belonged to us.

It had always baffled me how people could stand at a window peering out through their net curtains, pretending not to be in! Three skeletons and a Witch standing outside a house, beating on the front door and tapping on their front room windows and people were not curious enough to even come out to see what all the fuss was about! Instead, they'd stand behind their curtains pretending to be invisible, when we could clearly see their tight-arsed shadows moving about inside!

Mrs. Bottomley was a huge woman about the size of an elephant. So when she had come to the front window, after we'd almost kicked her door in, her front room had suddenly gone dark. We could see her huge silhouette standing a foot away from the window swaying to and fro, as all four of us had stood peering back at her for a minutes or so, until Martin decided to get his mickey out and piss up her window! It was amazing how all the banging had got no reaction, yet a splash of piss on her window pane and her big fat face was up under the net curtain pressing right up against the glass!

After about an hour, we'd stopped for a quick tot up of what we had collected in the old metal water bucket we carried with us to put our treats in. This had amounted to three pennies, two stale fairy cakes, a Blackjack sweet, a sweet wrapper wrapped around other sweet wrappers to make it look like a sweet! A silver medallion of the Virgin Mary, nine assorted biscuits, most of them broken as they had been thrown in the bucket, before the front doors were quickly closed back on us.

Turning the dark corner into Daisy Street, we had suddenly bumped into Frankenstein and his strange floozy friend, walking from the opposite direction and almost frightening the lives out of the lot of us, barring Bernie, who oddly enough had recognised straight away, our two older cousins, Paddy and Francis Doherty.

"Why haven't yah dressed up for Halloween, Paddy?" Bernie had asked him, all seriously, which had us all in stitches though not Paddy.

"Who's the laughing floozy with yah?' Martin had jokingly asked,

"I'm a Zombie! Not a feckin' floozy! Francis identified himself. But disguised in his mammy's blonde wig, with his eyes coated in black eye shadow along with his reddened cheeks and lips, he'd looked more like a floozy than himself! He'd seemed really humpy and had told us, the woman living in the house at the bottom of the street had called him a dirty auld whore, before telling him to *feck off* and take his gormless looking pimp with him, threatening to call the coppers on them.

"Jasis!" said Paddy, "We've been on the go for ages and nothin' ta show for it so far! We've had the usual threats ta cut our bollocks off! An' the one large welly which some auld miserable bastard from number thirty-three, slung at us, catchin' Francie on the back of the head an' wakin' him up!

But that's about all."

"Why'd he go and do that for!' Martin asked him.

"We'd stuck a couple of lit bangers through his letterbox for wastin' our time, that's why! An' anyway. We weren't ta know the eegit was standin' behind the poxty door!"

"So, what's the pint of keepin' the one welly, when yah can only put it on one foot?" Nabby had wanted to know.

"It's a left footed wellie," said Bernie, and as he only has the one left foot, he can only wear it on the left foot." she'd pointed out this fact, to Nabby's obvious annoyance.

"But even if he'd had the two left feet, he can only wear the feckin' wellie on the one feckin' foot! That's what I meant' argued Nabby.

"He could cut the toe end off and wear it on any of his feet," I'd smugly added my tuppeny's worth.

"What good's a welly if water can get in?' Francis joined the debate.

"Ah shut yer gob, yah feckin floozy yah!" Nabby angrily retorted.

"I'd only been stickin' up for yah Nabby! Francis whinged, "An' I'm a Zombie come back to life not a feckin' floozy!"

Agitated, Nabby had to rub it more, "Well, yah look the spittin' image of Mary Donnelly who is always hanging around on the corners of Stretford Road all night long. Yah could even be mistaken for her little sister, so yah could."

"And her little sister looks as if she'd died an' come back to life agin!" said Bernie, which had seemed to cheer Francis up no end and he'd stopped whinging!

"Anyway, we're keepin' the welly just in case we get another one thrown at us! laughed Paddy, "And then we'll have the pair."

"Unless yah get another left one!" laughed Nabby.

"Jasis!" Nancy just gave him a look.

Sitting down together on the cold ground underneath the street Gaslamp by the entrance to the coal yard, we had shared out all the biscuits between the six of us. I'd bitten into one of the fairy cakes and had nearly broken a front tooth, so I handed it over to cousin Paddy, who had shoved the whole lot into his gob and devoured it in one go! So I'd given him the other one.

It had seemed quiet strange sitting in the cool night air with the silence around us almost deafening. The mist by now had dropped lower to cover the grey damp rooftops, though it was still possible to see the lines of dark grey smoke spewing upwards from the chimney pots from those fires that had been lit, before vanishing into the mist. I'd no clue as to the time. And even if I'd had, it wouldn't have mattered to me because *time* meant nothing to any of us. We had only known the *time* by the space between different events. Getting up in the mornings, having school dinners, going to church, begging on the streets, searching for scrap or firewood. Spring, summer, autumn, winter. It seemed everyone had wanted time. Everyone needed it. Everyone complained there just wasn't enough of it. And then they'd complain the kids have too much time on our hands! Without it we couldn't survive. And yet with it, it was harder to survive. But for me, time was just an everlasting circle dictating how long we were going to live and when we will drop dead. Without time we would have been nothing. And yet with plenty of it, we were still nothing.

211

The only consolation for me was the night times. It was in those twilight hours and my zone, where I could have done with more time to spend in. I had always felt much safer and more at ease during the nights, more so than at any other given time. Perhaps because there was hardly another soul about, except maybe other children like us. And so not being able to see much of what was going on around me when the nights had set in, made it much easier for me to escape from the harsh realities of life hidden under a thick blanket of darkness.

"Shall we see if the auld bastard will give us the other wellie?" Martin had broken the silence, "He might throw the other one at us if we annoy him long enough! And then Paddy will have a pair!"

We'd all thought Martin's idea was a good one, they usually were! Save for that time the pair of us were seen in the early hours of the morning, rummaging through the milk float parked inside the *Allied Dairies* yard up on Mulberry Road. Like the little early birds so often did, we had been helping ourselves to the creamy tops from the milk bottles to tide us over for the day. But just as we had got to our seventh or eighth bottle, we'd been spotted by a couple of milkmen who had headed over in our direction, only for my clever brother to quickly come up with his idea.

"Sit tight!" he'd shouted, before slamming his foot hard down on the pedal and driving the float out of the main gates of the dairy!

I'd held on for dear life as the float had silently floated off down the road with a posse of milkmen running close behind us, almost catching us, but just not quiet able to get those few extra strides needed, though we were not able to lose them either! I'd screamed across at Martin, "How the feck do yah know how ta drive one of these tings!"

"Easy!" It's just like driving them bumper cars at Belle Vue! One pedal for the accelerator and one pedal for the brake!" Only he'd forgotten to use the brakes at least twenty-three times, which was the amount of cars the arresting police officer had told the desk Sergeant we'd hit, before we'd came to an abrupt halt outside the main gates of the, Mulberry Street Primary School! And only then, on account of the battery running flat because some eejit had forgotten to plug the float on charge overnight!

Daddy had this other saying, amongst others, "There's no use crying over spilt milk." and I'd wished he could have been with us at the time, if only to have told this to the lynch mob who'd had us surrounded. And if it hadn't been for Mrs. Regan, the headmistress of the school, coming to our rescue and waiting with us until the police had arrived, we'd probably have been strung up! So we were grateful to her and the fact she hadn't been aware at the time, her car was the fourth we'd hit on the way down to her school!

At the police station, the bearded police sergeant had scolded daddy, telling him we were completely out of control and he, daddy, should be doing more to keep us under control! Daddy had hit back telling the Sergeant, it wasn't like his little children to be doing such things without the influence of much older kids being involved. And I'd taken this as my cue to make up a pack of lies about our much older cousin, Paddy McGinty; the first name that sprang to mind, and who had jumped from the milk float and had ran off across the primary schools playground before anyone had seen him!

"Do I look like a goat!" the frustrated police Sergeant had glared down over the counter at me.

"Well." I'd studied his face for a moment, "Now yah mention it I can see the likeness."

"If it wasn't for the fact these two are under the age of criminal responsibility! I'd be locking the pair of them up and throwing away the key!' he bawled at daddy, "Now get them out of my sight!"

-TWENTY-SIX-

Martin had led us back along Daisy Street to number thirty-three, where he'd told Paddy and Francis to wait with Bernie and Nabby across the street, warning them to be ready to make a run for it if needs be, while him and me had gone to the front door. I'd only just knocked when the door had suddenly swung open, as if the smiling man standing on the other side of it, had already been expecting us. But instead of getting the verbal abuse we had been expecting to get and hopefully the other wellie with it, he seemed to have been really pleased to see us!

"Just wait there while I get you a nice treat." he'd said, before hurrying off back along the narrow corridor in his bare feet.

Throwing a smile over my shoulder at our bemused cousins, the man had quickly reappeared, hurrying back up along the corridor with the barrel of an air rifle pointing straight at us.

"Here's your treat you little fuckers!"

I'd never seen Martin move so quickly! He'd been standing right next to me one second and gone in the blink of an eye! I'd spotted the lone wellie standing just inside the front door and I'd instinctively made a grab for it, snatching it up just as the man had fired off a shot, which had obviously missed me because I'd felt no pain as I had ran off down the street, following the two skeletons, the witch, the floozy and Frankenstein, who was hollering something about having been killed!

Back outside the coal yard, Paddy was holding his nose. His brother Francis had taken some old newspaper out of a rubbish bin and had walked in to the shadows of the alleyway.

"Here's the other wellie!" I'd thrown it down on the ground next to the other one.

"I've been feckin' shot!' Paddy had moaned, "The poxty gimpy-eyed bastard has killed me!"

"Where'd he get yah?' asked Bernie.

"Me feckin' hotter! Just get a look at it!"

"Take your mask off and let me see it then!"

"I've taken me feckin' mask off!' screamed Paddy, "The pain! I'm dying, I'm dead." he milked it for what it was worth. "Are yah sayin' I'm ugly are yah, Bernie?' he'd suddenly asked her.

"Course I'm not saying that! Who told yah that?"

"Well. Yah recognised me with the mask on."

"That's only because I'd recognised yer voice - And the way yah walked!"

"I was walking like feckin' Frankenstein!"

"Hold still and let me see yer nose."

Unable to hold back our laughter, Martin, me and Nabby had left Bernie to deal with Paddy and we'd walked the few yards to the entrance of the alleyway where we had seen Francis, squatting over the old newspaper with a huge turd hanging down from his hole. Jasis! How something as long as that, could have come out of someone as short as him, was beyond me! It was at least two foot long, if not more and had little white worms crawling all over it! We'd waited until the turd had dropped and then watched as Francis had hitched up his trousers beneath his mammy's nightdress before taking his last four bangers out of his pockets and sticking them into the warm turd like candles in a birthday cake, before wrapping the whole lot up into a tidy shit parcel.

We were still able to hear Paddy moaning and Bernie trying to persuade him, she'd meant, "You'd look better with the mask back on, so as to fit in with the rest of us!" Rather than, he actually looked better with the mask on, full stop! But Paddy hadn't seemed too convinced and had said, he wanted to go home to die.

"Yah can go home ta die or do anythin' else yah feckin want ta do once I've delivered that fecker his feckin' treat!" Francis told his brother. And so we'd waited in the shadows watching him, as he had crossed over to the other side of the street and slowly make his way along to number thirty-three as the fog, growing denser by the second, had quickly descended past the tops of the streetlamps, it having already touched ground level further up the street and was slowly rolling towards us in a huge sprawling wave.

We just about been able to see Francis suddenly drop to his knees and then a moment later, we'd seen the sudden flash of yellow light and him standing up and giving the front door a couple of good heavy kicks before the blanket of thick fog had suddenly engulfed him and he was lost to us and us to him, as the silent wave had suddenly wrapped itself around us.

We'd heard the first two bangs go off followed by a loud shout, "Ahh! My fuckin' foot!" instantly followed by the sound of grotesque laughter and then Francis, like a vison, suddenly appearing out of the gloom. God! Was he was feckin' scary!

"I got the fecker! I think I blew his foot right off his leg!" he was so happy with himself as we'd hurried off, getting to the corner of Upper Willow Street just as we'd heard a third bang and more shouting, only able to make out the last word of, "*Bastaaaaards*!" before we headed off across Henshaw Street and back up onto the Stretford Road, only stopping when we had reached Dixon Street, where our two cousins had lived.

After seeing them to their front door, which we could just about see through the fog, we'd promised Paddy, if he should die of lead poisoning during the night, we'd say a prayer for him at Sunday Mass. He'd told us to feck off, telling Bernie, he didn't like her anymore because she'd said he was ugly. Bernie had teasingly told him, "If yah take yer mask off I'll give yah a peck on the cheek. Which had only infuriated Paddy more, because he'd not been wearing the mask!

Not long after leaving our two cousins, we had become lost to the thick smog which we had never seen as bad before. The fog was bad enough, but the thick murky yellowy smog had been so heavy, we just didn't have a clue as to which way we should turn towards home. Retracing our footsteps wasn't an option! We couldn't even see a hand in front of our faces! Let alone the ground we were walking on! Martin said, to hold hands tightly so we didn't lose sight of each other. And there we were, three skeletons and a Witch walking in a straight line, blind to the world around us.

What a different world it had been to walk were we couldn't see, or be seen. We had listened out in the eerie silence for the odd muffled sounds, attempting to follow in the direction we thought they'd came from. But we had been too disorientated, and found it impossible to concentrate. Now and again, a voice would suddenly call out and we would stop and call back to its owner. But no reply came back. Ghostly figures had crossed our paths and as we had reached out to them for help, they had shrugged us off. A woman's piercing scream had frightened the living daylights out of us before Nabby had caught a sideward glance across the head from her handbag, causing him to put a hex on her, "I hope you git feckin lost in the forever!' he's screamed before cursing her to high heaven, with every abusive word he could muster up.

"Watch out!" - "Oh shit!" - "Where are you?" - "What the fuck were those!" - Walking skeletons and a Witch? My arse!" we'd ignored the voices, straining out ears until we'd suddenly heard the voice of our guardian angel! "Pavement! - Bus on the road! - Pavement!" We had watched as out of the smog, the dimmest of lights from the ghostly red giant had suddenly appeared slowly moving in our direction to save our sorry souls, again! "Bus on the road! - Pavement! - Bus on the road!" the conductors voice had continuously called out his warnings to the unseen pedestrians, as he had walked along the edge of the pavement letting the bus driver know where the wheels of his bus were in proximity to the pavement, so he was able to safely drive along the edge of it. We had been able to follow the voice and safely navigate our way to the bus, hurrying up the stairs to the top deck and settling ourselves in the empty seats right at the back.

I had watched, as Nabby, Martin and Bernie, had quickly fallen off to sleep and with nothing for me to see out of the windows, I had got to wondering, if Purgatory, described by Father Murphy, could have been like this! Just moving around in the thick smog hearing voices but unable to see a thing, with nothing else to do but bump into each other until St Peter decided to open the gates of heaven and let us in, to meet with the rest of our dearly departed. If they'd got in!

I'd had no clue as to how long I had been asleep, only of being stirred awake by the skeleton in my dreams who was trying to pull the skin off my face, almost killing me with the shock, before I had come to my senses and had realised it was Martin trying to pull my cloth skeleton mask off.

"Wake up! Lazy bones! The fogs gone and we're at Piccadilly Gardens!" He'd gone on to tell me, the bus conductor had said it was okay for us to stay on his bus for a free ride back to Hulme, as long as we took the masks off, so as not to draw attention to ourselves. Peering over at Nabby, I see him using Bernie's skeleton mask to rub the green makeup off his face. But it doesn't all come off and had left him with a slight green tone to his skin, making him look seriously ill, drawing attention to himself from the other passengers.

-TWENTY-SEVEN-

A couple of days had passed since daddy, Paddy and Shamie, along with uncle's, Oliver, Christy, Paddy and Raphael, had taken Martin, Bernie; with me tagging along with them, down the Stretford Road to the Eagle pub on the off-chance, they might be able to spot the two fella's who had beaten them up. They'd been back to the pub three times now and had not been able to match the description Martin and Bernie had given to daddy, and so this was their chance.

They'd not been in the pub when we'd got there, but when daddy had spoken to Mick O'Brien, a fella he'd known for a long while, he gave daddy the names of Pat and Jimmy Boyd, as being likely possibilities.

"This is just between me and yea Jim. If their feckin' father, Cliff gets wind it was me that told yah, I'll be dead for sure!"

"Well I'll be sayin nothin' to no-one-so don't worry!" daddy had assured him.

"Some while back now, I'd heard the pair of them talkin' in here with some of their friends. They were bragging on about givin' a hiding to a couple of Paddy's up near St Wilfrid's church. Sweet Jasis! If I'd known it was two defenseless little children, I'd have said something earlier!" O'Brien had been genuinely shocked, "Yah have ta be careful," he'd warned, "Cliff and the rest of that family are over there in the corner." he'd given a slight nod of his bald head in their direction, "The whole lot of them are feckin lunatics! An' believe it or not, that feckin' wife of his is the worst outta the lot of them! She won't

221

have a bad word said about any of her brood!"

"Have a pint on us." offered daddy though he had not stayed at the bar to pay for it, as he and the rest of the family had headed over in the direction of the Boyd family sitting at the tables in the corner, chatting amongst themselves.

"Which one of yea is Cliff Boyd?" asked daddy, stopping a few feet away from the table, while Martin, Bernie and me had stayed a further three feet back near the piano and behind our brother Paddy, while Shamie, always wanting to be in the mix, had stood alongside Uncle's Oliver and Christy, who'd stood at daddy's left shoulder, while Uncle's Paddy and Raphael had stood on his opposite side.

"An' who is it that wants ta know, Paddy?' Helen Boyd had glared at daddy, while her husband Cliff had sat looking us all up and down with a grin spread across his face.

"I tink yea'd better put yer falsies in Jock!" retorted daddy, 'I can't understand a word yer sayin'! An' the name's Jim fuckin' Rattigan ta yea!"

"Well yer all fuckin' Paddy's ta me!"

Aye. An' yea should know! Yea've charged enough of them I wouldn't wonder!"

"Hey! Nobody insults my fucking wife an' gits away with it!"

"Well it seems she gets away with it every time she looks in the mirror. Get a look at it sham!"

"I'm not sittin' here listening ta this!" Helen Boyd was up on her feet, which was the cue for the rest of her family, about eight in all, to stand. Two women and six fellas, and not much difference in size, except for Cliff Boyd, who was probably

222

about the same height as daddy and the rest of my uncles, but much wider across the shoulder, with a huge beer belly almost bursting out of his shirt and looking like someone who could handle himself if the need arose.

"Are yah goin ta tell us what all this is about then? Or do we have ta beat it out of yah!" Cliff Boyd threatened.

"Like yah beat feckin' innocent little children!" said daddy.

"Now just yea fuckin' wait -"

"Pat an' Jimmy? Aye! I'm talkin' about yer two poxty-eyed sons that beat me two little children senseless! I just want yah ta know, I'll be feckin' swinging for the pair of them when I git me hands around their scrawny scotch necks!"

Though it had been Shamie who had landed the first punch which had started the brawl, which had caused the whole pub to erupt into a free-for-all. I had not been witness to much more than seeing him crack a beer bottle over Helen Boyd's head, as she had pushed her way past some of her family to get at daddy, while holding a carving knife as long as a sword, in her hand. The punch, which I hadn't seen coming, had turned my legs to jelly and all I remember seeing as I'd hit the deck, were the thousands of stars dancing in front of my eyes, before the hands came around my neck squeezing the living daylights out of me. Martin had later told me how our older brother, Paddy, had dragged the man off me before half kicking him to death, only stopping when Uncle Christy had grabbed hold of him and had pulled him outside. But as what always happens after a big brawl, some people liked to tell it the way they had wanted to see it and had said, Cliff Boyd had thrown the first punch, knocking daddy clean out. While someone else had said, it was the mother, Helen Boyd that had knocked daddy out with only the one punch! Uncle Christy had told us how Uncle Oliver had called the whole family of Boyd's, a bunch of feckin' blue-nosed child battering bastards, before knocking Cliff Boyd out with just the one left hook, straight up his hotter!! But at the end of the day it hadn't mattered who had said what, or who had thrown the first punch. The end results were still the same. The pub had been wrecked and there had been lots of broken heads and Cliff Boyd had ended up playing the piano with his face! Not surprisingly, there were no arrests! As usual, no-one had seen a thing! And daddy, still incensed by the fact he had still not got hold of Pat and Jimmy Boyd, had warned the family that matters hadn't ended until he'd got his revenge on them!

Our youngest sister, Kathleen, had rushed in off the street to tell mammy, "Father Murphy an' Sister Joseph, are comin' up the street!"

"Did yah all go ta church yesterday?" mammy had thrown the question at none of us in particular. So it wasn't much help to her, when half of us had said, "We had." and the other half had said, "We'd not."

"Oh Jasis! Didn't I tell the lot of yah ta git ta church!' she'd glared at us as we'd stared glumly at the ground, none of us wanting to particularly volunteer an answer.

"Jasis-will yah get a look at them, Jim! I'll be ex-ex-ex, thrown out the feckin' church because of these gormless bastards of yers.'

"Excommunicated." said daddy.

"Exi what?"

"Excommunicated? The word yer looking to say, but haven't the brains ta say it."

"Yah can shove yer big fancy words back up yer hole, the good they do yah!" said mammy, "Sure yah can't even get a job pickin' yer nose for all the big words yah know! An' yea'd better find some big words to say to Father Murphy, or we're all done for in the eyes of the Church and his Holiness the Pope.'

"Father Murphy, and his feckin' church are all hypercritical auld fecker's!" said daddy, "He calls us sinners and heathens, and tells us our children are bastards. An' yet, these righteous fecker's still take the money and the food from out of the mouths of those same sinners and bastards! The Church is a mockery! I tell yah Lizzy. They're like the feckin' Mafia, only instead of shooting yah, they feckin' blackmail yah with God! Where do yah think the feckin' name *God* and *Father* comes from? *Godfather*! That's the feckin' Mafia for yah! Debauched feckin' thieves and liars and whores and queers, the whole lot of them!" he'd raged on, "Only instead of the mobsters dropping by ta shoot yah, they have the priests and their deformed nuns dropping by and threatening, "Yah won't be gettin' ta sit at the *'Right hand side of God'* unless yah pay for yer sins! Who the feck sits on the left hand side of him-that's what feckin' I'd like to know! - Anyway. How'd you know the priest and that auld hen clucking behind him all day long, is coming to this house?"

When the knock had suddenly come at the front door, daddy had told Martin to answer it, "Take yer time so I can tink of somethin' ta say." he'd said. And we had watched with amusement as Martin had slowly walked off in the direction of the hallway placing one foot in front of the other like a tightrope walker crossing the rope.

"Jasis Martin! What the feck is the matter with yah?" daddy looked him up and down, "Have yah the shits again?"

"Yah told me to take me time, daddy."

"A few minutes, not a week! Ah for feck's sake!' he'd shook his head in utter despair, "Bernie! Go and answer the door. And if it's them nosey auld bastards just stand in the way and act all gormless! It shouldn't be hard for yah ta do that! Just try and slow them down ta give me a minute ta tink.'

"What shall I say if it is them?"

"How would I know? That's why I need the minute ta tink! Tell them yah done for the lot of us with the kitchen knife-I don't give a feck! The rest of yah can git down on your knees and pretend yer praying, for once in yer miserable lives!"

We done what he's ordered and had dropped to our knees, as daddy had rushed across to the built-in cupboard at the side of the fireplace and pulled out the big family bible, just as Father Murphy and Sister Joseph came hurrying through into the back room.

"Ah! Hello Father!" mammy had genuflected to the old priest and the scowly faced nun, "We were just in the middle of our usual daily prayers." She'd spoken piously as she had struggled to her knees.

"Is everything all right with yah?' said Father Murphy, looking all red-faced and flustered, "Only yer daughter here told us she'd done for the lot of yah with the kitchen knife!"

"Bernie!" daddy gave out to her, "Why d'ya have ta be sayin'

226

these tings all the time?'

"But you -"

"Come over here and kneel down next ta me." said mammy, through her gritted false teeth.

"It's a shame the family are not saying their prayers in church, Mrs. Rattigan," said the priest, "Sister Joseph here tells me we haven't seen any one of yah at Sunday Mass for a few weeks now, isn't that right, Sister?'

"At least two weeks, Father."

"An' yea've been at the church these last two Sundays ta have not seen us, have yah Sister?' daddy threw the question, before sucking spit in through his teeth.

"Well. I was there last Sunday but not the previous Sunday-though Sister Gertrude was. She always is!"

"Sister Gertrude!" scoffed daddy, 'An' I suppose Sister Gertrude didn't bother ta tell yah, it was my ten shilling note in the collection box? Not this Sunday gone, but the Sunday before, hmm?"

"It isn't unusual to get ten shilling notes in every collection, as well as you know, Mr. Rattigan! At least yer wife certainly would!" snapped the auld dragon, her bad eye twitching out of control, before settling back on her big wart at the side of her hooter.

"There yah are, Father!" Yah heard it straight from the horse's mouth, didn't yah! As the good Sister has just said, *As well yah know*. An' I do know!" smiled daddy, "I know, because Mr. Rattigan-that's me," he jabbed a finger to his own chest, "Was there all along to know! And should know! An' that's how I know, I know!" daddy had put the auld nun in her place.

"What happened last Sunday gone?" Sister Joseph had thrown a knowing smile at daddy.

"You mean, why we weren't in church? Tell them Lizzy. Tell the good people here why we'd not been to church this Sunday gone."

"Ah sham! We'd been robbed!" Mammy had suddenly blurted out before breaking into her crocodile tears, which had started the lot of us off, barring daddy, who'd just stood glaring at her as he'd sucked the air in through his teeth.

Father Murphy had seemed genuinely concerned, though it had been impossible to have gauged what Sister Joseph might have been thinking, as she had cast a suspicious eye over us and then around the room, perhaps attempting to work out what could possibly have been worth stealing from us! The sympathetic priest had told her to take mammy into the kitchen and make her a cup of tea, to calm her nerves.

"And if yah can help her ta write a list of the items she'd had stolen, so as we can put a message up on the church notice board for the parishioners to read. Perhaps they might feel obliged to help replace as many of the missing items as possible." He'd gone on to promise mammy he would present any offerings to her and daddy at the end of this Sunday's Mass!

"What is it you have there?" the priest had suddenly taken a keen interest in the large leather-bound family bible daddy had been holding in his hands.

"The family bible, Father." daddy had proudly handed the bible over to the priest to look at, "An heirloom handed down from one generation of Rattigan's to the next. Better than any book on the shelves!" though in reality he had never read the bible and had not opened its pages since writing the name of the last addition to the family, which had been Michael, three years previously. When Father Murphy began flicking through the book, he'd suddenly stopped and went back a few pages before pulling out a set of photographs stuck between them. "What are these?" He'd studies each one.

'Ah now, they'll be just a few of the family photographs. We like ta keep some in there so as they are close ta God, if yah see what I mean.'

There were eight photographs in the set. All of men and women doing dirty things with each other and a donkey! I'd known this, because I had seen Shamie hiding them in there some weeks back and I'd taken a quick peek for myself.

"These are all members of yer family!"

"Aye they are that Father. All Irish families couldn't be closer and that's what we are. Can I get yah a drink? A glass of sherry will it be, Father?"

"W-w-well-yes, I think I'd better have a large one at that!"

I couldn't help laughing inside and I'd wondered what daddy would say when the flustered priest eventually showed him the porno pictures. But it had seemed, Father Murphy hadn't been in any particular hurry to be discussing the photos with daddy, and was already into his third peek at them while swallowing down a half-pint glass of sherry. "M-m-may I take these pictures for a w-w-while? I mean, it's not really appropriate to be keeping them hidden away in the bible." he'd held his empty glass out for a refill, which daddy had filled.

"Yer welcome to have them, Father. It's not as if I can't take any more of them, is it? I suppose yea'll be wanting to put them up on the church notice board alongside with all them other pictures of the parishioners and their families?"

Father Murphy didn't answer that question and instead had thrown daddy a wry grin, before slipping the photographs into his Cossack pocket and throwing a quick blessing over all of us.

When the auld priest had eventually walked from the house, he had seemed a little worse for wear, though much happier than when he had first arrived. As for Sister Joseph. Well, there wasn't any change in her mood though she must have had a sore hand writing out the long list of stolen items, Mammy had recalled having been stolen. And by the time she and Father Murphy had left the house to go off and save more lost souls, she'd had her work cut out to save him from his usual drunken antics.

The Gossip around the streets a few days later told how Father Murphy had rushed, blind drunk, into Mr. Jordan's house telling both him and his wife, their eight children were all bastards in the eyes of God, because they, Jack and Hilda hadn't taken the sacrament of marriage! Flooring the drunken priest with a punch to his purple hooter, Jack Jordan had reminded him he'd married both him and his wife at St Wilfred's Church, some twenty odd years earlier!

-TWENTY EIGHT-

Me and Martin had been outside the front of the house playing on our own makeshift swing, which we'd made from an old car tyre attached to a piece of rope hanging from the crossbars of the lamppost outside our front door, when Bunny Lewis, one of Manchester's best known drag-queens, had come up from the other end of the street and said hello. He was dressed in his normal clothes, though it would have been nothing out of the ordinary to have seen him walking into the Marsland pub on the Hyde Road' just around the corner from our house, dressed as a lady.

"Go fetch your mammy will yah luvvie." He'd asked Martin, "I just want to have a quick chat with her that's all."

Daddy said, Bunny was a homosexual, and had warned us to keep our backs to the walls and away from the likes of him! Otherwise he'd be giving us his big sausage! But all the kids around here loved Bunny – and sausages too! He would often say hello or kick a football around with us or he'd have a turn at Hopscotch as he had passed by. We all knew he was a singer and an actor and sometimes he would be in character when we'd see him and he'd stop and sing us a song, and play up to his image. But it was all in good fun and he had made us laugh.

"What can I do for yah?' mammy had greeted Bunny like she hadn't really wanted to do anything for him. She'd remained standing in the middle of the open doorway with her arms folded across her chest, which is how she always stood when she wasn't inviting anyone in, though the police would just push her out of the way. A while back, Daddy had told mammy she could invite the whole street into the house if she'd liked, but he'd forbade her to ever invite Bunny Lewis in, as he'd not wanted to be associated with "Bendy boys and shirttail lifters!" He'd often complained about Bunny pretending to be a woman, dressing up like a "Feckin' tart, an' wiggling her fat arse in men's faces!" even saying he was going to have a quiet word with Father Murphy about it, until he'd seen the old priest and another fella in a dress, coming out of Bunny's pub, just around the corner from us, where Bunny lived, laughing and joking and worse for wear! "Debauched Lizzy! The whole feckin lot of them. Whores, Lesheens, an' feckin' puffs!"

Mammy had told daddy, his problem was not being able to get over the night he couldn't keep his eyes off Bunny when he came to perform at the Rob Roy pub, "Offering ta buy her all them drinks an' goosing her big feckin' arse, while pretending ta help her back up on the bar stool! Only yah found out later she was a man! Jasis! Everyone else in the whole place knew it was a feckin' drag queen barring yea, yah humpy bastard yah!" How mammy loved to rub salt in to his wounds, to the point of shaming him. "The truth only hitting yah, after yea'd shoved your hand up the auld floozy's dress for a grope at her budgie, only to get the two biggest surprises of yer life! She had a flute! An' you wakin up in the bed the next morning with a big fat lip and a loose front tooth!

The reason for Bunny's visit was to ask mammy if he could use some of us to star in his Christmas pantomime, Peter Pan, which was coming up in a few months time. He'd pay of course and he'd handed her a large bottle of sherry, her favourite drink, as a goodwill gesture, which mammy had almost snatched his hand off for without a moment's hesitation before disappearing back inside the house.

"No he feckin' can't borrow any of the children for his pufty Christmas pantomime!" it had only taken seconds for daddy's answer to come back, which he'd bawled out at the top of his voice so the whole street could hear, 'Peter Pan me feckin spotty arse! It's bad enough being a homo pretending ta be a woman at the same time! But playin' a feckin' grown up man, who can't grow up, an' wants ta hang around with a gang of little children, is an even bigger pervert!'

By the time Mammy had come back to the front door, minus the bottle of sherry, Bunny had already stepped away from the house and had walked off back down Stamford Street, with daddy still hollering on about homo's being a curse of the devil and how all of them should have been strangled at birth. We had told Bunny we'd liked sausages and asked if we could come home with him for some, but he had ignored us out of hand.

Pushing his way past mammy and out of the front door, Shamie had told Martin and me we were going rafting with him. As we'd no choice in the matter we had obediently gone off with him making our way up to the derelict warehouses close to the Bridgewater Lock canal, where we had set about collecting long pieces of wood, three doors and four discarded car tyres lying about the place, before Martin and me had sat back and watched our older brother set about building his vessel, which had taken him about an hour to complete.

As we were dragging the heavy raft to the edge of the water, we had suddenly heard loud urgent voices calling out Shamie's name, before we'd spotted our two cousins, Paddy and Martin Power, on their own makeshift raft, moving at some speed on the water as they had been chased down by two other rafts which had been slowly catching up with them.

"It's them feckin' Delaney brothers and their scanky crew from Moss Side!" said Shamie, immediately recognising the lads chasing after our cousins. Heaving the heavy craft into the water Shamie had shouted at Martin to jump on, which he did. "Hold on to this Tommy, 'til I'm on.' he'd handed me the thick piece of string to hold the bobbing platform into the edge of the canal bank, while he'd hopped on next to Martin.

For the briefest of moments I'd thought the whole thing was going to sink as the top of the wooden platform had suddenly disappeared beneath the dirty water, before rising back up and settling about an inch above the surface.

"Chuck us over some duckers, hurry! – Big fuckin' ones!"

Keeping a tight hold on the string, I had set about picking up fist sized lumps of broken bricks and concrete lying on the ground around me, which I'd passed to Martin, who in turn placed them in a pile in the middle of the raft.

"That's all we need." said Shamie, "yea can let go of the string."

"What about me?"

"I don't want yah getting' in the way-an' no arguments! An' if them twats try to head over to this side, bomb the fuckers ta death!" he'd ordered. And with that, the raft had floated out across the canal away from me, with Shamie using the piece of floorboard as a paddle, moving the cumbersome vessel in the direction of our two cousins.

The thought of putting up any kind of argument or protest about not being allowed onto the raft with my two brothers, hadn't even entered my Head! If anything, I'd been really chuffed Shamie had made the decision for me to keep my feet firmly on dry land, saving me from having to show myself up! I'd been frightened to death of water since I could remember, and like Martin, I couldn't swim to save my life either though he had seemed comfortable with being on the raft. I don't know why I'd had a fear of water. It wasn't as if I'd had a bad experience involving water, except once, when it was my turn to be bathed after noticing Martin having a good lag in it! Oh. And then there was the time, on my sixth birthday, when daddy was looking for Maggie and I'd told him, she was out in the back yard fast asleep in the buggy.

"Wake the lazy cow up and tell her she's wanted." he'd ordered me.

"Maggie! Maggie! I'd called to my sleeping sister a couple of times, but she wouldn't respond to me. I'd noticed her face had gone bright red from the sun and I'd ran back into the house and told daddy, she wouldn't wake up.

"Flick a little bit of cold water on her face. That'll wake her." said daddy, as a knock came on the front door.

"Shall I get the door first?" I'd asked him.

"Just get Maggie in here. Bernie, get the door. An' tell whoever it is, I'm not here! If yah can manage that!"

Rushing back through into the kitchen I'd half-filled the large saucepan mammy used for almost anything from boiling potatoes and cabbage in to boiling water for the bath, or just boiling her knickers or daddy's undies and socks. Outside in the yard I'd flicked a few little drops on to Maggie's red face, without getting any response from her. "She won't wake up, daddy!" I had shouted in through the back door.

"Give her the lot!" daddy had shouted back, and I'd happily obliged, emptying the full saucepan of cold water all over Maggie's head!

"Yah bastard yah! I'll kill yah til yer dead!"

Jasis! I had never seen anyone looking so dead, come back to life so suddenly! My sister was out of the buggy screaming and hollering and threatening to kill me! Daddy had sworn blind he'd been calling out to Bernie standing at the front door asking, "How many eggs shall I let Aunty Rosie have outta the box?"

And he'd called out, "Give her the lot!"

-TWENTY NINE-

With a pile of my own duckers at the ready, I'd watched as Shamie and Martin had floated off across the canal in the direction of our two cousins. It had only taken them a few minutes to draw alongside their raft out in the middle of the water, just as the other two rafts had got to within a few feet of them, before the gang of five, from Moss Side had started their bombardment, raining their duckers down on my brothers and two cousins who'd immediately returned a bombardment of their own.

It had been a strange, almost surreal image that I had found myself watching, as the battle had intensified. Martin had just managed to duck out of the way of a flying missile about the size of brick, which had missed his head by a whisker, before one of the other rafts had collided with theirs. Shamie and our two cousins seemed to have been in their element whacking out at their enemy with lumps of wood. A fat kid of about fifteen had suddenly let out a cry of pain before dropping to his knees, as cousin Martin had caught him a whack across the back of his podgy legs, causing the fat boy to drop the brick he was about to chuck, before he'd received a whack over the head for good measure!

What I had been witnessing was ordinary teenagers who had played football on the streets. Who'd swung off the lampposts and stood outside the picture houses for Saturday Matinee's. Smashed windows of the derelict houses and played every other game, teenagers often played. And yet here on the canal, this had not been a game. This was a war albeit a kid's war. But it was for real. And the intent to hurt one another had also been for real.

Then, my worst nightmare had suddenly begun to unfold! I had felt the panic rush through my whole body, as I'd watched my brother Martin, suddenly lose his balance and topple into the murky water! I had watched in utter horror when his head had disappeared beneath the surface and hadn't come up again! The sudden realisation that my two cousins and Shamie, had not even been aware, Martin was missing, almost killed me with the fear.

"Shamie! Martin!' I had shouted at the top of my voice just as my big brother had whacked another twat across the head with his makeshift oar. My heart was racing so fast I'd expected it to suddenly give out on me and stop dead! I wasn't able to breath properly as my legs had turned to jelly and I'd felt the nausea rising up into my throat. I'd wanted to jump into the canal to help my brother, but I'd become paralysed at the very thought doing so!

"Shamie!" I had screamed so loud and as long as my lungs had permitted me to do. And then I had stood silent, helplessly transfixed to the scene set out in front of me as, like still photographs trapped in time the images flashed before me. Shamie suddenly dropping to his knees. The Moss Side crew steering their raft back up the canal and holding their blooded heads. Shamie looking back over his shoulder, perhaps at the exact point, when he must have realised Martin wasn't on the raft. Shamie and our two cousins on their knees with water up to their shoulders and hands searching blindly for Martin.

Frame after frame the pictures had flickered through my mind's eye as I had prayed out loud to Jesus, until the last remaining scene came into shot of Shamie - my hero - pulling Martin back up to the surface, coughing and spluttering for his life!

It would usually have taken a lot of physical pain to make me cry and yet I had cried like a baby, making no attempt to hide my tears. The feelings as I had watched Martin sitting up on the raft and puking his ring up, while Shamie had steered it back in my direction, followed by our two cousins, Paddy and Martin, were strangely exhilarating and indescribable.

"Cop hold, Tommy." Shamie had thrown the thick piece of string across to me and I had pulled the raft close into the side of the canal and held it there for Martin, helped by Shamie, to scramble back onto dry land. Then like a true captain of his ship, Shamie had stayed on board his own vessel, while he had seen our two cousins safely on to shore before hauling himself up onto the bank and letting both rafts float off down the canal.

"Jasis!" Paddy had put a consoling arm around our Martin's shoulder. "Yer feckin' guardian angel was with yah today, for sure, Martin!"

"And us," said Cousin Martin.

"Shamie's no angel he's our brother!" I'd snapped sharply.

"Oh feckin' thanks for that, Tommy."

I'd thrown a smile at my big brother, pleased for having said the right thing - For once.

"Yea'll have to get out of them wet clothes," said Paddy, "We saw some workmen's old overalls in one of them bombed warehouses over there, I'll go get them." he'd sauntered off.

"Why were them humpy bastards after yah in the first place?" Shamie had thrown the question to cousin Martin, who at first seemed reluctant to give an answer, until Shamie had told him, he didn't give a shite what they'd done wrong, he'd still stick up for them, as they were family.

"It's not me the fuckers were after," confessed Cousin Martin, "It's me eejit brother Paddy! If he hadn't been madly in love with Mary McGoven all this fuckin' shite wouldn't be happening in the first place."

"So what's up with them twats puttin' out about Paddy being in love? Sure he's only turteen an' he'll have been in love with all the girls in Moss Side by the time he's fifteen. And so will yea! Just wait and see! Yea'll be chasing after the girls with yer tongues an' little mickey's hangin' out!"

"That's the reason why they're after us."

"Yea've been runnin' round with your mickey's hangin' out! Jasis! Yah dirty fellas! See Tommy, yer not the only one running around all the time showing your little worm to all the girls!

"I don't go round all the time with me mickey hanging out an' showin' it to all the girls!" I'd angrily told Shamie.

"Oh. It's just some of the time them!" He'd laughed.

I'd ignored him, as he'd only have another answer. And anyway, I wasn't going to tell him I would probably have let Cathy McCarthy take a quick peek. But only if she'd wanted to. I mean, I wouldn't have just walked up to her with my mickey dangling out of my trousers and say, "Hello there Cathy darlin', how are things with yah today? Here, take a look at me flute!" It probably would have given her the shock of her life, just as it had done to old Mrs. Turner, who had lived in the house directly across the street from us, when we'd caught her, one Saturday afternoon peering out through her upstairs window and across the street into our sister's bedroom. She'd been standing there for a long while just peering across, so me and Martin had taken all our clothes of had pressed ourselves right up against the window pane. By the look on her face she seemed to have been shocked by the sight of us, though she hadn't moved an inch and had just stood there gawking at us.

Daddy had explained later how the ambulance people had told him, they couldn't take Mrs. Turner out of the house, because she had died of a heart attack while gawking out of her bedroom window. The priest had been called, along with the undertakers, the doctor and the police, though not necessarily in this order. The doctor would have to make sure she was dead first, before he can declare her dead, even though the ambulance people were ninety-nine percent certain she was dead, as they had come across lots of dead people before. Then the priest would have to give her the last rites, and the police would have to be satisfied as to what had killed her, before calling in the undertaker. And then the undertaker, once it had been established she was dead, would then have to carry her off and bury her in the ground.

"Promise yah won't say anythin' ta Paddy if I tell yah?" said Cousin Martin.

"Ah feck! Yah know me, Martin! I'm not one for talking." Shamie had reassured him.

"Paddy's been humpin' Mary McGoven," said Cousin Martin with a wide grin spread right across his face. "An' her brother Mick is jealous. That's what it's all about.'

'Yer Paddy is humpin' fourteen-year old Mary McGoven!' Shamie had laughed, "What a feckin show-up for the books!"

We had all watched in silent admiration as Paddy had hurried back to us handing our Martin the grubby workman's overalls, before opening the green canvas lunch bag he'd stolen from one of the demolition workers huts. Getting out of his wet clothes, Martin had donned the overalls turning up the long legs of them just below his knees and the arms above his elbows, before slipping his wet sandals back on his feet, while Shamie had divided the thick doorstop spam sandwiches amongst the five of us, letting our Martin have the two hard boiled eggs and most of the dark stewed tea, which none of us had made a fuss over, considering the ordeal he had been through.

"Heard yer pokin' Mary McGoven then?" Shamie had done what he had promised he wouldn't do, with Paddy going up the wall and wanting to know how Shamie had known.

"Was it yea, Martin?' he'd glared at his brother, "Jasis, you'd tell the whole fuckin' world somethin' happened when nothin' even happened, so you would that!"

"The whole of Hulme, Longsight and Moss Side put together already know about it!" Shamie had lied.

"But yah were humpin' her!" said Cousin Martin, "We were havin' a peek at the pair of yah through the bedroom door only last week, when mammy and daddy were at the pub! We saw you lying on the top of her with your spotty arse going up and down in the air.

"Who the feck's *we!* " Paddy had wanted to know.

242

"Our Bridget was peekin' in too, so she knows the truth.'

"You an' Bridget! Peekin! - Well, it was only the once." Paddy came clean, "But never again! Not after all this feckin carry on!"

"Only the once is all yah need Paddy!' laughed Shamie, "Before yah know it she'll be tellin' yah yea've got her up the duff, and her mammy an' daddy will be marryin' yah off with a shot gun pointing straight up yer hole!"

"A fuck off Shamie. I'd immigrate back to Ireland if they started any of that fuckin' larky!" promised Paddy.

As we had headed back off in the direction of home, our Martin had looked none the worse for swallowing a bit of the Manchester canal, though he was a little worried he might have swallowed rat shite floating about in the filthy water.

"Well I wouldn't worry too much about that, Martin." Shamie had reassured him, "Just keep an eye on the palms of yer hands, an' if yah see any little hairs startin ta grow on them, then yah have to tell someone, otherwise they'll be putting yah in a place like Belle Vue Zoo!"

-THIRTY-

It was the drizzly grey start to Sunday morning. Mammy and daddy were up early despite them being out drinking late into the early hours. There seemed to have been an unusual buzz of urgent excitement about the pair of them, as they'd shouted up at us to get out of our beds and dressed for the morning Mass. I'd been dying to go to the toilet but by the time I'd got down the stairs and out into the back yard, there'd already been a queue waiting at the bog door. Five more shites before it was my turn! I'd had no chance of waiting that long and with no other option, other than to shit myself, I was out the back gate and quickly up astride Mrs. McCormack's metal dustbin standing in the back alleyway, where I'd emptied my full bowls out.

We used to squat down behind any available bin, until daddy, who hadn't known it was us, had a big row with old man Tomlinson, living in Dunham Street with his backyard just a couple of houses up from ours. Daddy had accused the fella of letting his filthy disgusting dog shite near our back gate, "The feckin' flies are treadin all over them turds before flying through the house and walking all over the food, giving the whole lot of us the scutters and other illnesses! An' if it doesn't stop! I'll be rammin' a feckin' cork up yer dogs hole!"

"And how do you know it is my dog making all the mess!"

"Cos no-one else has a fecking dog in these streets, barring yea! That's how I feckin know it's yer dog!'

"But have you seen my dog?"

"I don't need to see a feckin' dog to know it's a feckin' dog! Unless yah have a feckin' cat that yaps like a feckin' dog all night long, keeping us, an' all the neighbours awake!"

"Lassie! Come here boy!"

"Collie yah have then? – Yah can tell!" daddy had fixed his gaze on the two long turds.

"No Jim. He isn't a Collie." the little old Yorkshire terrier had suddenly hobbled into view and had stood alongside his master, innocently peering up at Daddy, "And if this old dog could shit like that!" Mr. Tomlinson had pointed down at the two long turds, which must have been a least three or four inches longer than the dog itself, "Then I'd be contacting the Guinness Book of Records!"

"Ah well, yah would say that." said daddy, sucking air through his teeth before walking away. Up to that point, Mr. Tomlinson had been one of only a handful of people living in the surrounding streets who had been on speaking terms with daddy.

Martin and Nabby had joined me in the alleyway and while Nabby had slashed up the side of the wall, trying to hit Churchill sitting on the top of it and staring down at him, Martin had settled himself on another bin still unable to resist examining the palms of his hands in detail, even though it had been a long while since he'd fallen into the canal!

When the whole family had eventually set off down the street together, for the first time in ages, we had the neighbours out gawking at us as and probably wondering what the special occasion was.

"Whose funeral is it then!" joked Mr. Sands as he'd walked

in the opposite direction past us.

"Yer's if yah don't feck off!" said mammy.

Most of our journey to St Wilfred's Church, was unusually solemn in comparison to what it would normally have been like, if mammy and daddy had not been with us. And though the majority of us were miles apart from one another, in the communication sense of the word, besides Martin, Nabby, me and Bernie, we didn't really see much of the others anyhow. And so communication amongst us was very limited unless the family were at war with outsiders. And only then did we come together as one.

"If that thievin' auld Witch is tinkin' she's having another ten-bob note out of me, she's another feckin' ting coming!' said mammy, as we had reached the path leading up to the door of the Church where Sister Mary was standing outside in her usual spot, with her begging bowl at the ready. "Keep yer hands in yer pockets, Jim.' mammy warned, "Or she'll be dippin' inta yer trousers."

"The only ting the auld hen will find in me trouser pockets will be dust and tin air!' said daddy, 'An' if she digs deeper, she might be lucky and find a pair of hairy bollocks to play with!" he'd drawn on the rollup dangling between his lips, blowing a plume of smoke out of the side of his mouth.

"Jasis! Yah shouldn't be blasphemin' like that outside the chapel! He's feckin' got ears yah know!'

"Who has?"

"The Almighty has!"

"Isn't it just amazin how the Almighty can hear me feckin' blasphemies, but can't hear me prayin' for me horse ta win a

246

poxty race!"

"Whished up and walk in front of me! I don't want ta be talking with that one."

Good morning ta yah, Mr. and Mrs. Rattigan! It's so lovely to see yah all here today - Ah, will yah get a look at all those lovely children of yours!" the lying old hen had gone through the same old ritual, "Thirteen angels this time!' she'd counted us off on her crooked twisted fingers, "Unlucky for some!" she'd cackled at her own joke, "I expect yea've that one a lot of the time?"

"No. I can't say I've ever heard that one said before Sister. I'll have to remember it for sure,' daddy said dryly.

"An' how is Mrs. Rattigan?' asked the insincere patronising nun, holding out the wooden offertory plate to mammy, who had kept her solemn-looking gaze aimed at daddy's back.

"She has the scutters." said daddy.

"Don't yah mean diarrhea, Mr. Rattigan?" Sister Mary had turned her hooter up at him.

"Aye, the shits. All over the show! Oh tanks!" he suddenly stumped the remnants of his rollup into the nuns empty begging bowl, before hurrying into the church, with the rest of us tagging close behind.

"There we are, Lizzy.' daddy had gone straight over to the church notice board, as we'd walked into the inner lobby, "Last on the list we might be, but not least!" he taped a finger on the name **MR & MRS RATTIGAN** written in big bold lettering, before the pair of them had proudly walked in through the inner sanctuary of the church ahead of us. It was the first time I'd ever seen the pair of them arm in arm as they had strolled down the central aisle like a strutting pair of proud chickens. The last time they'd came close to holding hands was a few months back, when they were both arrested for being drunk and disorderly and were handcuffed together before being carted off to the local police station.

It wasn't unusual to see the church full on a Sunday as it was this Sunday. Cathy McCarthy was looking over her shoulder as I had walked down the central aisle. She'd thrown a big wide smile in my direction, before her mother had noticed and nudged her to look back to the front. My biggest dream was to one day see her walk down this aisle with me waiting at the altar for her and her throwing me one of her big bright radiant smiles, while her haughty mammy and daddy looked on like a pair of miserable sods, unable to tell me to bugger off out of it, as they'd often done. Every time I'd seen Cathy, I'd had an urge to fall down on bended knee; like I'd seen the man do in the films, and ask her for her hand in marriage. Just to spite her parents!

Mammy thought Mr. McCarthy wasn't a bad auld codger after all and only acted the way he did, because his stuck-up wife "Tinks she's the Queen of feckin' Sheba and gets on his feckin wick! Always goin' on at him while he works all the hours God sends, for her ta spend the same hours spendin' all the money he's earnt!" Mammy also said, "That woman is a two-faced hypocrite and a member of every feckin' church group including the Salvation Army, the Labour Party! And the Nazi Party, no doubt!"

When me and Martin had sat down in the pew the people sitting there had kindly slid along one by one until and then moved off to another pew letting the whole family have the row to ourselves! Martin had dropped a long smelly fart, which had skidded off the pew and vibrated all over the church, with a sea of accusing eyes automatically staring in our direction. It was the same every time we came to Mass. If someone had sneezed at the wrong time, all eyes would focus on us. If an object was dropped or if someone made a loud noise above what was the acceptable background noises you'd expect to hear in a church, all eyes would automatically focus in our direction. To prove the point, I'd pointed an accusing finger at the boy in the pew behind us, to let the congregation know he was the guilty farter. Martin and Nabby had followed suit. And with three accusing fingers pointing straight at him, the red faced boy had rushed out of the church in tears, as a sea of accusing eyes had focused on us for upsetting the little squirt!

Father Michael, a lightly tanned skinned young priest, had come out of the vestry and had informed the congregation that he was taking the Mass in the absence of Father Murphy who, "Is unable to be with us, as he isn't feeling too well.'

"Pissed more like!" daddy had muttered under his breath, loud enough for the two old women in the pew in front of us to disapprovingly look over their shoulders and glare at him.

"Jasis! Will yah get a look at the faces on them two!' daddy sucked air through his teeth as he'd continued to insult the two old spinsters, Dolly and Ethel Parkhurst, who'd remained gawking at him with their hawkish looking eyes, "Is it a miracle yer after ladies?" he'd thrown them the question, "He might have cured the lepers but he's got he's work cut out with yea two, I tell yah!"

249

"Jasis Jim! Will yah whished up-showin' me off like this!'
said mammy.

"Well they started it!"

"They'd not said a word ta yah."

"They didn't feckin' need ta, with faces like that-sham just
get a look at them!"

"Them two dirty witches from Kent
Pulled an old man into the tent
Them two dirty witches they pulled down his britches
And swung on his nob till it was bent!"

Paddy and Shamie, had recited a Limerick to the old biddies,
who had quickly turned their faces away in utter disgust.

-THIRTY-ONE-

The Mass had seemed to go on for an age and daddy said, "If hell was having ta listen ta this feckin' priest goin' on and on about the same auld tings, then we we're all nearer ta Hell than we'd feckin' imagined!" Not that I had minded listening to the priest drone on about the sinners of the world being doomed to Hell and damnation. It was so easy to spot all the big sinners in the church, as they would lower their eyes and look down at their feet every time Father Michael mentioned the word, *sinners.* His voice seemed to have a calming effect on us, with most of the congregation having either fallen asleep or gone off into an hypnotic state of religious calm, as he had gone on about a time when we would all have to stand before the *Almighty God* and give an account to him, for how we had lived our lives on this earth.

He'd not said whether this was to be through a mass confession, with the whole congregation standing together in a huge field or a football stadium, like Old Trafford, so we could hear what everyone had been up to in their lives! Or whether we were to be on our own, just like in the church confessional boxes. I would prefer it to be the latter, as I'd known Cathy McCarthy would be shocked to have heard what I'd been up to in my life and the dirty thoughts I'd had about her! Worse still. She'd find out it had been me who had loosened both wheels of her mother's bicycle, which had fallen off, the moment Mr. McCarthy had pressed the brakes, as he had got to the first junction half a minute into his downhill journey!

I couldn't say, I'd felt guilty about what had happened to him, though he did look a miserable sight when I'd seen him the following Sunday sitting in the front pew, not his usual place in the church, with plaster casts on his broken left leg and arm. At the end of the day, I'd felt he'd only himself to blame! I wasn't to have known he'd had his own bike stolen the previous night - nothing to do with the Rattigan's! - And he had borrowed Mrs. McCarthy's.

Though I had only been seven-years of age, I was still able to evaluate in my own way what Father Michael was trying to say to those of us, who had stayed awake to listen to his boring sermon. On the one hand, he was telling us, "If we confessed our sins, we would be absolved from all of them." And yet, on the other hand, he is also telling us "We will have to account to the *Almighty* for all our sins." So my take on this was, the Church had been living a feckin lie and had led me into a false sense of security by making me believe that every time I had spilt the beans and confessed my latest sins at confession, I had been absolved of them all up to that date and my sin slate was wiped clean, so I could fill it up again! When this obviously wasn't the case! And if I'd had any choice in the matter, I wouldn't even have bothered going to confession!

Sometimes, when I hadn't even sinned, I would have to make sins up just to prove I was a good Catholic, because mammy said, Father Murphy said, "It's only the good Catholics who go to confession to confess their sins." and so we'd had no choice other than to put on a good show!

Daddy said, "If all the good Catholics were good. Then there shouldn't be a feckin' need for them ta be goin' ta confession! Yea'd not catch me telling the feckin' priest all about me private business, the nosey auld bastard!"

Once, Shamie told me, "If yah can't tink of any sins ta confess, just tell the priest you've been playing with yourself! He loves those sort of sins!"

And so I had given it a go the following week. "Bless me father for I have sinned it's been a week since me last confession. I've been playin with meself!" I'd blurted out.

I hadn't a clue as to why he had asked me all those questions he'd asked! But he had gone on and on throwing question after question at me. Just like the coppers did when they came around the house to see daddy, or one of the others, before taking them down to the police station.

"So. What is it yah tink about when yer playin' with yerself, young man?"

"Nothin' Father."

"Nothin? Ah sure there must be somethin! We all do - I mean those that play with themselves always do. What about girls? Do yah tink of girls – Or is it boys hmm?"

"I think of boys sometimes father. But most of the time I think about Cathy McCarthy, father. I'm in love with her." I'd confessed, "I'm always askin' her to play with me but she is afraid to in case her mammy and daddy get ta find out about it.

"Yah mean yea've actually asked Cathy McCarthy ta play with yah! Dear Lord! What is the world coming ta! An' at such a young age! Just out of interest. Where do yah take her ta play with yah?"

"Well it was only the once with Cathy. The rest of the time

253

it's with boys -"

"Boys! where!"

"Anywhere we get the chance ta Father. Up against the school wall. Up against the back of the church wall. Sometimes with older boys on the crofts. And I can dribble now! Would yah like me to show you how I dribble Father?'

"What!"

Fifty, *Our-Fathers* and as many *Hail-Mary's*, for kicking a feckin' ball up against a couple of poxty walls! Where's the justice in that!

With the Mass nearing its end I had noticed Sister Mary suddenly lean into Sister Gertrude and whisper something into her ear, which had brought a smile to hoppity's face, before she had lurched off to the vestry door and opened it. The low murmur of voices had rippled around the middle pews, as those people sitting in that area, had got a quick glimpse of Father Murphy sitting in a chair and swigging back on a bottle of the church wine, before Sister Gertrude had the time to steady herself before lurching inside and slamming the door shut behind her. A few muffled voices and the sound of breaking glass later, the vestry door had opened a touch and the red-faced Sister Gertrude reappeared, squeezing herself out through the small gap. She was carrying a handful of small brown envelopes and had hobbled back over to Sister Mary where the pair of them had a short exchange of sour looks and ear whisperings between them, before she'd handed the envelopes over to the Mother Superior, who had quickly stuffed them into the side pocket of her black habit.

With the final blessings to end the Mass, Father Michael had asked, "Will those parishioners on Father Murphy's list pinned up on the notice board, would like to wait behind, Sister Mary and Sister Gertrude, will deal with you."

We'd waited, as most of the congregation had herded out of the church, leaving about thirty people still sitting in the pews, although there were only five names written up on the Father Murphy's list.

"Nosey auld bastards." muttered daddy, peering around the church, "look at them. It's not enough for them ta be givin'. They want us ta bow down an' kiss their feckin' arses as too!' Well I won't be tanking any of them for feckin' sure. An' I wouldn't want ta be kissing her big arse!" he'd thrown a nod in the direction of the huge form of Mrs. Chapman sitting directly opposite us across the aisle, taking up at least a quarter of the pew to herself "Kiss that arse and yer head's gone forever! Jesis! She's smiling over at us!" daddy had thrown a smile back at her before sucking through his teeth and quickly looking away.

"Would Mr. and Mrs. Delaney like to come up to the altar,' Sister Mary had suddenly called out to *flasher* Delaney's parents who'd already been out of the pews and halfway down the aisle before the Sister had even finished her sentence!

"Look at them," scoffed daddy, "Like a fat pair of pigs running ta the trough! Look at the arses on them the greedy bastards!"

"Will yah give over Jim!" snapped mammy.

"Can't work!" daddy had ignored her, 'If Pinky and feckin' Perky there tried losing all that feckin' fat, they'd be able to work! It's not as though I can lose me bad feckin' back!"

255

'Will yah shallup before yah loose yer feckin' teeth!" mammy had threatened.

Mrs. Cuthbert, St Wilfrid's church warden, along with a couple of other ancient holy women do-gooders, had helped to carry the three medium sized boxes out of a side room and placed them down on the ground to one side of the altar.

"These are the lovely gifts specially donated for yea from the parishioners of this church." smiled Sister Mary, "Now. As there is too much for yea to carry on yer own we've arranged ta have them delivered to yer house later in the mornin' for yah. Oh! And there's this too." she'd dug deep into the pocket of her habit and had pulled out two small brown envelopes, which she said had contained monetary offering for them. Handing them over to Mrs. Delaney, she'd invited the pair of them to address the congregation, which they had milked for all it was worth. They'd thanked everyone for this, and everyone for that and by the time they had finished their thanking's, it seemed they'd thanked everyone in the whole of Manchester, barring the Rattigan's! Not that we'd given them anything!

While the applause echoed around the church the overweight Delaney's had huffed their way back up the aisle. "Bless yah." said daddy as they'd waddled past our pew, "Yah deserve all yah git." he'd sucked in through his teeth and muttering under his breath, "Yah greedy fat feckers." as they had walked out of earshot.

Another two names had been called out before the one name we, and I had suspected many others, had been waiting with baited breath to be called. "Would Mrs. Cooper like to come to the altar?"

"She'd like to feckin lay on the top of it as well!" snapped mammy, not even bothering to keep her voice low as the stunning dark-haired young woman had made her way out of her pew and past us, with the heels of her high stilettos clippety-clopping out a rhythm like Mr. McCarthy's cart horse, Goliath did, when he was coming down our street.

Wearing the shortest of skirts, Mrs. Cooper had thrown a smile and a delicate finger wave in the direction of daddy, our Paddy and Shamie, as she'd headed down towards the altar. With the exception of my two brothers who'd acknowledged her with their tongues almost hitting the ground, daddy and the rest of the male congregation seemed not to have noticed her as they had searched out imaginary spots on their shoes to stare at, while she had passed by.

The low muttering of women's voices had brought a sudden change to the melancholic atmosphere. Not that it had bothered Mrs. Cooper, who'd seemed to have taken it all in her stride, as she had wiggled her arse all the way up the aisle while the three church wardens and the two auld nuns, had struggled to bring through the six large boxes of goodies gifted to her.

"Donated by all the dirty feckin auld men in Hulme, I wouldn't wonder!" said mammy.

Just as she had done with the Delaney's and the others, Sister Mary, minus her patronising smile, had informed Mrs. Cooper she would have her boxes delivered to her front door sometime during that day, before presenting her with the handful of brown envelopes, one of them slipping from her grasp and falling to the ground as she'd accepted them. Without ceremony, Mrs. Cooper had bent over from the hips upwards and retrieved the envelope in one swift movement to a chorus of loud gasps.

Old Jack Mullins, who'd been sitting only a few feet away on the front pews a split second earlier, ended up on his back, having suddenly keeled over. Mrs. Cooper, standing right over him and giving him a birds-eye view up her jacksie; which was probably what had put the old man on his back in the first place, wanted to know if there was anything she could do to assist, Mrs. Mullins, who'd told her, "Just go away!"

A cold glass of water from Sister Gertrude had revived the old fella, bringing him back to reality, though his smile had been replaced by a look of horror, probably brought on as he'd opened his eyes to find Sister Gertrude kneeling over him with her puckered lips at the ready to give him the kiss of life!

With the help of Mrs. Mullins, Sister Gertrude had helped the shaky Jack Mullins back up onto the pew while Sister Mary had been having a word in Mrs. Cooper's ear. Guessing, she must have told her, it would be better if she hadn't addressed the congregation, because she had walked off and had headed back up the aisle.

"Yah feckin' auld whore yea!" mammy had called out to the young woman as she had walked past us and acknowledged mammy with a wide smile and a flutter of her false eyelashes, before blowing a kiss off her hand in our direction, which had only antagonised mammy even more. "Let me at her Jim! I'll strangle the feckin' lesheen!" she'd tried to get past daddy.

"An' last, but not least! Will Mr. and Mrs. Rattigan like to come to the altar." said Sister Mary, possibly saving the young woman from strangulation.

All week, there had been a sense of expectancy about mammy and daddy, which was understandable seeing no-one had ever given anything to them. And with a long list of items on the stolen property list, even if they'd received a small percentage of the items it would have amounted to a tidy sum. They'd looked relaxed, as they'd calmly walked out from the pew and headed down the aisle, as if they'd been out for a Sunday stroll, with mammy clippity-clopping along in her high heels and easily outdoing Mrs. Cooper's clip-clops, until the heel of her right shoe had suddenly collapsed and fell off, with mammy having to walk the rest of the way doing an impersonation of Sister Gertrude, as the congregation had tittered.

Sister Mary's attention had been drawn to the church warden and her two helpers standing in the doorway of a side room, looking uncertain about something or other. She'd made her way over to them with Sister Gertrude following close behind and we'd watched as the lot of them had disappeared out of view for a short while before the flustered looking Mother Superior reappeared and had gone over to speak with mammy and daddy, waiting with patient anticipation for their gifts.

"Sorry for the delay," she'd said, throwing a nervous smile at them, 'It shouldn't be too long now.'

The sound of squeaky wheels had broken the silence as we'd watched Sister Gertrude, hobbling backwards out of the side room, guiding out the old long metal clothes rack which had been burdened under the weight of an assortment of second-hand clothes. Barring a few men's overcoats, which had evidently looked as if they'd seen better days, most of the clothing had been creased up children's clothes which seemed to have been hurriedly pulled out of bags and slipped onto the coat hangers, which Sister Mary had described as, "Thoughtful gestures." Before asking daddy if he'd wanted to say a few words to the congregation.

"I wouldn't be able ta find the right words ta tell them what I thought." daddy had declined the offer which, by the way his jaw muscles kept tightening up as he'd grinded his teeth together, was in some way a blessing in disguise.

There had been no brown envelopes on offer for them and no offers to have the clothing delivered to our house either, perhaps on account it would have been just as easy to push home the old squeaky clothes rack, which Sister Mary had told daddy he could also keep.

When daddy had called for me and Martin, we had rushed out of the pews and up to the altar like a pair of greyhounds after a hare. "Wheel that lot of rags down ta the back of the church and wait there with them." he'd ordered, before he and mammy had walked away from the altar.

With Martin pulling from the front and me pushing from the back, I'd stood on the bottom cross rail, letting him do all the donkey work as we'd followed mammy and daddy. The clothes rack had suddenly stopped moving and my end had swerved across the aisle, when Martin had fallen over mammy, who'd bent over to retrieve the heel of her shoe, causing the rack to tip over. It had taken only a few moments to right it back on to its four wheels and for the angry Mr. Arnold to remove the old raincoat from off his wife's head. But that was all the time needed for me to have swiped her purse out of her open handbag and slip it into the pocket of the other old overcoat hanging on the rack, before pushing it off up the aisle to the back of the church, where we'd waited.

-THIRTY-TWO-

Pushing the squeaky-wheeled clothes rack along the wet streets in the direction of home, hadn't been as easy as pushing it along the smooth surface of the church floor. Our three eldest sisters, Mary, Rosemary and Elizabeth, had gone off together, while Paddy and Shamie had gone their separate ways. Mammy had taken Maggie and the rest of the family off to her sister Brenda's house, leaving Bernie and Nabby to tag along with Martin and me. Daddy had still been in a bad mood and wouldn't stop going on about being shown up in the church. "A few miserly feckin' shillin's ta tide us over! That's all we needed! An' they roll out a pile of feckin' rags! Good Catholics' of Hulme me feckin' arse! A pile of auld rags none of them greedy bastards would be seen dead wearing, let alone their own children!' he'd walked a few yards ahead of us with his head hunched into his shoulders and his ears sunk into the turned-up collar of his jacket, in a vain attempt to keep himself dry from the cold drizzly rain.

The rain hadn't bothered the rest of us. We were used to being out in all kinds of weather and didn't feel the cold that much, with the exception for the winter just gone, which had lasted right up until March freezing the ponds and the lakes and the bollocks of all the brass monkeys! I'd loved being out in the rain. For me, the heavier the better! The fine drizzles never seemed to have much impact other than to make a damp miserable atmosphere even more damp and miserable! Not only that. We could never find a decent sized puddle to make a big splash in even if it had drizzled all day long! On the other hand, the heavy rains were glorious! They cleansed everything they'd touched. My hair, my clothes, my skin, the dust covered grey slated rooftops and the grime covered buildings. Even the Pigeon shite couldn't last in it! And the puddles galore! We would splash through them to our heart's content, saturating ourselves and any passerby, who could hardly complain, when they had already been soaked to the skin by the downpour.

As we had headed up along Clopton Street, daddy had already stopped and was having a chat to Billy Smart, a rag-and-bone man he'd known for some while.

"Leave the rack there, an' clear off with yah!" daddy told us. And my attempts to tell him I'd wanted to keep the big black coat, had fallen on deaf ears, needing only the one angry glare from him to tell me to scarper or I was in for it!

Hardly able to tell him in front of the rag-n-bone man, I had stolen Mrs. Arnold's purse from the church and had hidden it in the pocket of the black overcoat hanging on the clothes rack, I'd said nothing else and had hurried off after the others. With Bernie and Nabby deciding to go straight home, Martin and me had gone off to play on the crofts, getting home just after midnight, to see daddy at the kitchen sink, stark bollock naked and washing himself down. "Feck off ta bed-the pair of yeah!" he'd drunkenly greeted us.

Early the following morning, as the rest of the family had slept on, Martin and I had decided to leave the house and go off into Longsight and meet up with some of our cousins. On our way out of the back gate we'd bumped into mammy coming along the alleyway. She had looked the worse for wear and hadn't even bothered to acknowledge us as we'd stepped aside for her to pass by us. We'd said nothing to her either, mainly for our own safety! She had obviously had another big row with daddy last night and so everyone would have to be treading on eggshells for a day or two, before they had made up, again.

We'd came across a couple of empty houses just in on the edge of Longsight and although these had already been stripped to the bone, we had been able to crawl down through a small gap leading into one of the cellars where we had found electric cables still attached to the wall and running across the ceiling! I don't know why it would always happen to me, or even why I had cared, but I had always felt a strange sense of sadness, whenever I had searched inside an empty property with me forever mindful of the fact, people had once lived in them. And although my mixed emotions would always differ from one empty house to the next, the atmosphere remained the same. A discarded family photograph, a birthday card or a Christmas card to, Joan, or Donald, or Fred, or someone else from a bygone time, seemed to make those emotions more personal to me as I had walked in through the silence of each room, on someone else's past.

Working quickly together, we had managed to tear down all the electric cable before Martin had crawled back out of the hole and I had passed the thick flex up to him. And by the time I had managed to get myself back out into the open air, Martin had already lit a small fire and a black cloud of smoke had been spiraling high up into the grey sky, to join all the other poisons floating around above our heads, as the rubber had burned away to expose the copper wiring - Daddy's gold! When all the copper had been exposed we had pulled it out of the fire with a stick and had pissed on it to cool it down, before twisting the cooled cooper into lumps and packing it in to the old pushchair and hiding it from view, before going on to search another house.

When we'd arrived back home, in the early hours of the afternoon, there were three policemen inside our house. Two of them were dragging daddy, head first, down the stairs as a third policeman, a sergeant, had looked on. One of the coppers had bashed daddy a sideways glance across the side of the head with his truncheon, causing his head to split open and blood to spill, stopping him from struggling. I had found myself silently applauding the policeman and praying that he would hit daddy again, just for good measure, even though I hadn't a clue as to the reasons why they were arresting him in the first place. But it was a good feeling to look on as he was being bashed by someone while he was unable to fight back!

"Ah Jasis, I'm dying!" daddy had moaned, as his bleeding head had bounced off the last few steps before one of the coppers had lifted him up by his arms, while the other had taken his feet and carried him out of the house like a captured animal ready for the slaughter, before throwing him into the back of the meat-wagon.

Maggie's face was very pale and drawn, much whiter than I'd ever noticed before. Her whole body had trembled, just as Martin's body had trembled when he'd climbed off the raft on to dry land the day Shamie had plucked him out of the canal. Mammy was shouting all sorts of names at the police Sergeant, telling him, someone who had known they were going to be out during the night, must have come in through the unlocked door while everyone was fast asleep, and had hurt our Bernie.

Ignoring mammy, the Sergeant had asked Maggie, "Why are you crying and shaking so much?"

"She's not been well all the week!" mammy had butted, "An' besides, yea fecker's are draggin' her father down from the top ta the bottom of the stairs, half killin' him in front of her and for no good reason!"

"Come on Lizzy! We've every good reason to be arresting your husband on suspicion of assault!" said the Sergeant, "It was the young child herself who'd said, she had thought it was her father who'd attacked her during the night.

"I swear, on the *little flower of Jasis* and all the saints alive, he wouldn't lay one finger on the children!" mammy had protested daddy's innocence, "An' if he ever did smack them it was only ta chastise them for doin' somethin' wrong! Anyways, the child's disturbed in the head! Ask the doctor! She'd say anythin' if she can't remember the truth!" In her desperation to protect daddy, mammy had gone on to argue, "The back door is never locked! Anyone could have come in ta the house while we were out! Me an' Jim got back late last night and had gone off ta bed, together. An' we haven't been out since yea lot called round ta half kill him!"

"Did you hear anything unusual in the night?" the Sergeant had ignored mammy and had asked Maggie, "Your daddy?"

"Don't yah be putting words into her mouth!" mammy had nearly snapped the Sergeant's head off.

"No! I didn't see daddy!" said Maggie, shaking her head,

266

before bursting into tears once more.

"Go back ta bed an' git some more kip!" mammy told her and Maggie had quickly hurried off up the stairs without a second invitation, not bothering to step over the bloodstained steps as she had gone.

I'd wondered why Maggie had not just told the coppers how daddy would sometimes come and take her, or one of our other sisters downstairs to his bedroom to comfort them if they'd been scared in the night when mammy hadn't come home. Perhaps she'd not wanted people to know she'd had a fear of the dark, which was nothing to be ashamed about. Almost everyone had fears. Everyone who had known me, especially the Manchester Fire Brigade! Knew I'd suffered with heights. I was able to climb upwards, that wasn't a problem for me. It was the climbing down again! I would just freeze with fear just at the thought of looking down!

Every time they came to fetch me down from a rooftop, the chief fireman would threaten, 'This is your very last time! We're leaving you up there the next time and we won't be bothering to come out!" But they always came and they always threatened, *Next Time*. Martin too had a phobia. He couldn't sit down on a toilet so he'd stand up on them and crouch down when he'd wanted a shite. Our uncle Sean had a fear of women. Daddy said, "Sean is just a ravin' homo like Bunny!" which had always confused me, because if Uncle Sean had a fear of women, why then did he always dress up like a woman? It just didn't make any sense to me! Even daddy, as tough as people liked to think he was, had a fear of the debt collectors. When they came knocking on the door, he'd be the first out through the back way and up the alleyway, not to be seen again for hours. Failing that, he'd hide under the bed, leaving mammy or one of us to answer the front door and tell the man, "Daddy has run off back ta Ireland! So don't be wastin' yer time calling here again, because he isn't coming back!" But they did keep calling back, just on the off-chance he might have decided to return from his trip!

Before leaving the house the police Sergeant had told mammy that daddy might be home later in the evening, "If no charges are preferred, that is! Otherwise he won't be coming home for a long while!" he had quickly added.

-THIRTY-THREE-

Chain-smoking her way through a pack of ten Woodbines, since getting on the bus mammy, having decided to take Martin and me along with her to see daddy, had also told us, "If anyone asks about yer father yer ta tell them he's gone off and left us." We hadn't dared tell her the whole of Hulme already knew he was in Preston prison waiting to go up before the beak, for hurting our Bernie.

It was Mary who had raised the alarm after coming home in the late morning to discover our sister still lying upstairs in the small bed on her own. She had been burning a fever which is why no-one had bothered her. But when Mary had pulled the bedcovers back to lift her up into her arms, she'd noticed the blood on the mattress. She'd sent Paddy running off down the street to a neighbour who'd owned a telephone and they called for the ambulance. Later in the afternoon, when mammy had got back from the police station after daddy's arrest, she'd told us daddy had admitted to hitting Bernie a couple of times during the night, but only with the back of his hand, because she'd been putting out. But he had sworn blind he'd done nothing else to her, continuing with her argument about the fact the back door had always been left unlocked, which had been true, though none of us had been convinced a stranger had just walked down the back entry and into the house to attack our little sister.

Later that evening, Mary and Rose, had started a blazing row with mammy. She had gone on and on so much about daddy, anyone who hadn't known him would have thought she'd been talking about a heavenly saint! My two sisters had suddenly told mammy they were leaving the house for good. They'd already had their bags packed and waiting in the hallway, but before they'd left, they were going to have their last say, whether mammy liked it or not.

"The problem with yea mammy!" screamed Rosemary, "Is, not only do yah believe the bastards fuckin' lies, yah believe in yer own fuckin' lies as well!"

"I was here with yer father the other night so yeah can't go accusin' him of tings he hadn't done!"

"Yah were not here with him the other night!" snapped Mary, "Yea'd had another fight in the pub with the auld bastard and left him again!"

"An' how would yah know that? The pair of yea are never feckin' here ta know what goes on in this house! Out all the nights with no shame on yah, whorin' yourselves ta yer fancy men! Get a look at yea! How can yah afford all them nice clothes and that fine jewellery ye've drippin' off yah, while we're sittin' here starvin' an' wearin' the same auld' rags!"

Maggie, wrapped in her moth-eaten blue blanket had joined us halfway down the stairs sitting on the step just above us, as we'd listened in on the heated row going on through the open door of the back room as my two sisters had spat their venom out at mammy.

"It's called fuckin' gettin' a job! Which that auld bastard wouldn't know the meaning of!" snapped Mary, "We gave yah money an' yah both pissed it up the four walls of this house, an' any other walls yeah could find to piss it up, instead of spendin' it on the kids, which is what it was intended for! Yea have our Martin, Tommy, Nabby and our little Bernie, out on the streets beggin' all hours of the day and night an' the pair of yah piss that away too! An' if yah want to know how we know yah weren't with the bastard yesterday night! Yer sister, Aunt Brenda, told us yea'd had another blazin' row an' stayed with her all the night an' yah didn't leave til seven in the fuckin' mornin'! That's how we know! And if yah want to know how we know you weren't here all the other fuckin' nights -"

"Jasis! Why are yah sticking up for the fuckin' bastard?" Rosemary had suddenly cut in, "He's done for us! Just like he did in Ireland! Yah know that don't yah? An' the chances are, he's done for the others as well! An' he's beaten the livin' daylights out of yea too! An' yah stick up for him through tick and tin! Yah can't see past yer own fuckin' nose mammy, that's yer problem! Either that or yah know what's been goin' on! But yah don't want to face the truth!"

'And why would yah believe someone just walked into the house an up the stairs to attack little Bernie in the bed-hey!" Mary threw the question, "Only for him to hear her putting out and come up the stairs to chastise her! Where was this fuckin' stranger? Hiding under the fuckin' bed! An' no-one else wakes up?"

"There's no such person! It never happened an' yah know It." said Rosemary, "Yah made it up to save the bastards skin! That's what yea've done! But yea'll be the one that'll live to regret it-I fuckin' tell yah! And yah will regret it mammy! You will regret it!"

"If yah don't stop with all the lies about yer father! I won't be responsible for me actions!" mammy had threatened them. But the threat had fallen on deaf ears, as Mary and Rosemary had laid bare their demons and had continued with their verbal attack.

"The poxty bastard, should have been castrated and jailed a long while ago!" screamed Mary, 'It might have been the fuckin' gypsy way, on the roads in Ireland, with all their interbreedin' and what-have-yah! But we're not in fuckin' Ireland anymore! And we're not putting up with it anymore, so yah can fuckin' tell the fuckin' auld cunt when yah see him at the jail.

"Hopefully! God willing! Someone will have done the evil bastard for good, before yah even get to see him!" screamed Rosemary.

"Yea've no rights talking about yer father like this!" mammy had snapped back. But the venom in her own voice had been lost as she'd searched for the words to throw back at my sisters, unable to find any 'He's clothed yah - He's fed yah! - He's -"

"Used and abused us in every fuckin' way that he could!" spat Mary.

"Get outta my house yah pair of feckin' whores! Get out!"

"Oh, we're going! There's no fear about that!" screamed Mary, "We wouldn't stay another minute under this poxty roof! And if you or the auld bastard come looking for us again, I swear as there's a God in heaven, I'll tell the police an' anyone else that wants to listen to what he's done to us! And he'll fuckin' swing for it!"

The three of us had watched from the stairs as our two sisters had snatched up their bags and hurried off along the hallway and straight out of the house without so much as a backward glance, slamming the door shut behind them.

Getting off the bus on Southall Street mammy had taken us straight across the road to the corner newsagents shop, where she'd asked the larger than life shopkeeper with what had looked like a tatty-haired ginger cat sitting on the top of her head, for a packet of ten woodbines and an ounce of Old Holborn tobacco. The woman had told mammy she had only just run out of the Old Holborn, before suddenly asking her, "Are you new to these parts, or just visiting someone?" while throwing a wink and a sideways nod of her big head in the direction of the door, which had given all three of us cause to look over our shoulders half expecting to see someone standing there. But there hadn't been.

"I'll have an ounce of the Golden Virginia, then."

"Afraid we're out of that as well. I seem to be selling it by the bucket load these days!" she'd quipped.

"Well, I was only after the ounce." said mammy, which got the shopkeeper laughing.

"That's a good-un, missus! I like a woman with a sense of humour!" her laugh had exposed the top row of little white teeth protruding from her big pink rubbery looking gums. "Here." she'd taken a packet of tobacco from off the shelf behind her and had dropped it on to the counter in front of mammy, "Black Shag. A tad cheaper, which most of them over there have a preference for." she'd made me and Martin laugh, while mammy had given us one of her looks, "I mean, *them* if you catch my drift?' she'd winked and thrown another nod, "Unless you'd like the *special* packs?" she'd suddenly lowered her voice, "With the pound note inside-chmm-chmm-' she'd coughed, "If you're inclined that is?"

"Do yea two want anything?" mammy had suddenly turned to us. We were stunned by the question and I'd looked deep into her eyes, unsure as to whether or not she had only been codding us. Looking at Martin for confirmation that my imagination wasn't playing tricks on me, he too seemed to be having some difficulty taking it in and had thrown me a shrug. "Here!" she'd offered out the silver sixpenny piece to me, which I'd been hesitant to take off her. At no time, in my living memory, had mammy ever bought any sweets for us, let alone offered us the money to buy them! The fact we knew, she knew, we didn't need money to buy anything, had only added to our confusion and my thinking was, she'd gone funny in the head. But she'd thrust the sixpence into my hand and had shooed the pair of us off out of earshot, leaving her and the shopkeeper to chat in low whispers about her special packs of tobacco.

We had spent a short while eavesdropping on the conversation as we had wandered around the shop, eventually choosing two penny boxes of *Captain Scarlet* sweet cigarettes before coming back to the counter, handing the four pennies in change back to Mammy which the fat shopkeeper had thought was really sweet of us.

"You can see those two little lovey-dovey's of yours have been brought up proper missus. Not like some of the snotty green-nosed thieving little buggers we get in here at times, trying to steal everything in sight while their mothers, some looking as if they've just managed to drag themselves out of their beds, turn a blind eye to them! It's a shame to say it but half the kids I see in here will probably end up following in their father's footsteps-present company excepted mind!"

Stuffing the special pack of tobacco into her pocket we had followed closely behind mammy as she left the shop and walked across the main road following alongside the towering high wall until we'd reached the main entrance to the prison, where me and Martin shared out all the sweets we'd nicked from the newsagents shop.

Daddy had seemed genuinely pleased to see us! Which, just like mammy back at the shop, had taken us by complete surprise! He had told us so many times in the past he had never wanted to see the backs of us, never missing any of us when we had been out begging from one morning to the early hours of the next. And yet there he was, with his two black eyes and swollen bruised conk, arms outstretched and expecting me and Martin to come running and jump straight into them! Well I wasn't jumping into his feckin' arms, as long as I'd had a hole up my arse! So I had stood back inviting Martin go first. Which he had declined.

"Ah Jasis! Will yah get a look at them beautiful children of mine!" daddy had raised his exaggerated excitable voice so everyone in the visiting room had heard and had looked over in our direction, "It's me two favourite boys!"

I'd had a feeling the policeman's truncheon bouncing off his head, must have done something to his brain, just as I had also sensed something different about him beyond his paleness and the black eyes and the broken nose. To me, it had seemed his confidence, as bold and assured as it had once been, had now diminished and he had not seemed so cock-sure of himself.

"Martin!" he had suddenly taken a long stride forward and grabbed hold of my brother, lifting him up in his arms before whispering something into his right ear, which Martin had responded to with a nod of his head, before daddy had placed him back down. My thoughts were, he'd probably promised to give Martin sixpence to spend on himself or to share with me like mammy had done. And if this was the case, then he wouldn't be getting any change back!

"Ah! Tommy-Tommy! Me little monkey yah! Still climbing up the drainpipes, I hear!"

Well I wasn't climbing up into his arms for sixpence or anything else if that's what he'd been expecting! Not that he'd any intentions of letting me decide on that. In one swift movement my feet were off the ground and he was holding me tightly to his chest! "D'ya see the big black gorilla gawkin' over this way? Do yah Tommy?" The stench of strong tobacco on daddy's breath made me feel like I'd wanted to wretch, bringing a twinge to my arse as I had been reminded of the night of my encounter with the devil in the bombed house! Looking beyond daddy, I could see a big black man staring over in our direction. His huge white teeth smiled at me and I had quickly turned my gaze away to avoid any further eye contact with him.

"He likes to gouge children's eyes out of their sockets and put them up on the kitchen stove so they can watch him as he chops them up into little pieces, before throwing them into his cooking pot to make himself a stew! Then he sucks their eyes like gobstoppers before chewing them! So if yah don't listen to me carefully and do what me and your mother tells yah ta do, I'll be sendin' King Kong to the house for the pair of yea. D'ya hear?'

Just like my brother Martin, I had also nodded my approval, before daddy had gently placed me back down on the ground, scuffing my short hair with his nicotine-stained hand, before telling us to smile and sit at the table and open our big ears.

"When the pair of yea came home the night yah saw me washin' meself in the kitchen sink, where was yer mother?" questioned daddy, "An' before yah say anythin', let me tell yah the answer. Yer mother was sitting at the table in the backroom waiting for the feckin' pair of yah ta come home. That's where she was! An' don't feckin' forget it! So. Where was yer mother, when yea'd both came home late that night, when yah saw me having a wash in the kitchen sink?"

"Mammy was waitin' in the back room for us to come home, because we were late.' Martin confirmed the lie.

"An' yah never saw or heard anyone else, did yea?"

"No, daddy."

"An' you Tommy, with the scowery puss?"

It had been too good to be true for mammy to be giving us money to buy sweets and I should have realised there must have been a catch to it somewhere along the lines. Lying for daddy wasn't anything out of the ordinary for us. It was something we did all the time and came naturally. But having to lie for him against my own sister, especially when it was Bernie, who had meant the whole world to me and Martin! That was difficult. And just as hard to come to terms with was the fact, if he had wanted us to lie for him about the night we'd seen him washing himself in the kitchen sink, then it only showed Bernie must have been telling the truth about him hurting her that night!

"Mammy was sittin' at the table in the back room waitin' for us to come home." I'd heard myself saying, while in my head I was asking Bernie to forgive me for lying. Though I'd been sure she would have preferred me to lie, rather than having to go through the ordeal of having my eyes gouged out and placed by the side of a cooker and having to watch the big black man chopping me to pieces to make me into a stew, before sucking my eyes like gob stoppers and throwing them in the pot after me!

"Good boys!"

"An' yah heard nothin' after yea'd both gone to bed," added mammy, "Stick to the truth and nothin' else, an' everythin' will be all right, d'ya hear?"

-THIRTY-FOUR-

With Bonfire night fast approaching, Martin, Bernie and me, were outside in the back yard making up the Guy Fawkes. It was the middle of the morning and the sun was shining. Mammy hadn't been home for the past few days, not that we had been overwhelmed with grief because of her absence. We knew she was staying at Aunty Brenda's. She'd been staying away from the house more frequently since daddy had been away, coming home whenever and hardly talking to any of us, save to have a good moan about the house looking like a tip! Before she'd set about on her hands and knees scrubbing the floors clean.

I'd wondered if mammy resented having all of us, or had it been the frustration of not being able to cope with looking after all of us on her own which had made her stay away. Or did it go deeper than that? Was it that every time she'd left the house, it was meant to be for good? Only the fear daddy had instilled in her made her come back each time. Perhaps she'd felt incapable of being able to do everything for us on her own, if she'd even cared! It wasn't as if he'd been around to start any rows with her and the house had been more peaceful without his presence. These were questions I had asked myself, if only to understand my mammy. But having a mammy who'd had no bond with her children. What was there for any of us to understand?

We had made the body of the Guy up from old rags stuffed into the workman's blue overalls and the one-sleeved donkey jacket we had found in one of the derelict houses, the previous night, when we were out collecting firewood. Bernie had drawn a face on the yellow balloon for the Guys head but Nabby had come out in to the back and decided to add a few extra touches around the eyes with a pencil, popping it!

"That's the only balloon we had left Nabby!" Bernie had scolded him, "Right! Yer going ta have ta be the Guy, til we get another balloon!"

Yea'll not be feckin' seeing me dressing up as a guy, that's for sure, so yah won't!"

"Well I'm telling mammy it was yea that took the shilling off the mantelpiece a couple of days ago, if yah don't." threatened Bernie.

Nabby had looked the part of the Guy, albeit it reluctantly! We had stuck him in the smaller old pram and Bernie had a go at making his face up with mammy's bright red rouge, black mascara and deep red lipstick. She'd fancied herself as a good drawer and was better than us, if that was anything to go by! She'd added a set of weird looking eyes to his eyelids, so he could shut them when people approached making them look as if they were still open and less obvious he was alive.

When she had stepped back to admire her handiwork, Martin and me had forced ourselves to agree she'd done an amazing job, otherwise Nabby would have kicked off! Though in truth, we'd both found it difficult to keep straight faces! I don't suppose the makeup was that bad considering we'd seen uglier women hanging around the street corners. But those extra pair of eyes, one bigger than the other and grotesquely crocked with one looking towards his nose every time he closed his eyes, made him look like an over made up old tart sitting on a toilet straining to have a shite! He'd not been too happy either, dressed up in the old clothes which he had kept complaining stunk of cats' piss. And he did have a point!

"How d'ya know its cats piss, it could be any kind of piss?" questioned Bernie.

"It doesn't matter if it's cats piss, dogs piss, or pigs piss! They stink of piss and I don't like it! That's what counts!"

"Well yah don't have to like it," retorted Bernie, "We have ta smell yea all day, an' we're not moanin' about it!"

"It's not me that feckin' smells, yah lanky skeleton yah! An' yea's two can stop feckin' laughin' or I'm not doin' it!" Nabby had scowled at us, "An' look at the face yea've drawn all over me!" he'd looked at his reflection in the large broken mirror resting up against the wall, which daddy had broken some while back in a row with mammy, "I look more like a big whore than Guy Fawkes!"

"Since when have yah seen a Guy with the same face?" Martin had asked.

"Martin's right, Nabby," said Bernie, "They've all different faces but can still frighten the life outta yah!"

"Well I want a mask ta wear-or I'm not doin' it! I'm not showin' meself up ta anyone!" Nabby was about to hop out of the pram, but me and Martin had held him back in it otherwise he would have been out the gate and gone.

"I've got an idea!" said Martin, rushing back into the house to reappear a few moments later with mammy's perfume bottle and one of her old stockings. He'd set about spraying plumes of the pungent smelling liquid over Nabby, almost suffocating the lot of us with the fumes before offering the stocking to Nabby "Shove that over yer head."

"Yah can shove it up your hole!" Nabby threw the stocking back at Martin, "Since when have yah seen feckin' Guy Fawkes wearing a women's stocking over his feckin' head? It's bank robbers that do that, an' we're not robbing a poxty bank! Jasis! I smell like a whore's jockstrap!"

"Well there is always a first time." said Bernie.

"Rob a bank!" I'd quipped, as I had stood looking at my sister, struck by her big watery blue eyes appearing much brighter in the light and exaggerated by the paleness of her skin. She'd thrown me a smile making her eyes instantly lit up, as would often happen when she had smiled.

"I meant, a first time for a Guy to wear a stocking over his face, yah eejit Tommy!"

"Well I'm not wearing mammy's auld feckin' stockin' over me head an' that's final!"

"We'll go down ta woollies and steal a mask for yah straight away." Martin had promised. That and bribing him, by letting him look after the small petrol lighter we used for lighting our small fires to burn of the electric flex we'd scavenged, had seemed to satisfy Nabby and he'd reluctantly slouched back in the pram, as Martin had quickly maneuvered it out through the back gate and down the alley in the direction of the Stretford Road, before our little brother could change his mind.

On the way, we had to put up with him complaining about how the streets were too bumpy, his back was hurting and he was starving hungry! Thankfully, by the time we'd got to Woolworths he'd dozed off to sleep, though to the passersby he still appeared wide awake with his crocked eyes glaring down at his nose!

Martin's suggestion, we should leave him sleeping, was a good one. And when we'd reached the Woolworths store we'd left him outside the main entrance as we'd hurried off inside, heading straight to the fancy dress aisle to find him a mask, only to find when we got there, all the Guy Fawkes stuff had already been sold out, or stolen, barring a couple of long rubber Witch's hooters.

"Guy Fawkes had a big conk like them, didn't he?" said Martin, thinking out loud. He'd pulled one of the six inch conks off the hook and was about to shove it into his trouser pocket, when the voice of the assistant manageress had suddenly called down the aisle in her haughty stuck-up accent, all in the one breath.

"One hopes one realises one has to pay for that item and if you have no means or intention of paying for the item then one must replace it back on its hook!" or words to that affect.

"We had immediately recognised the assistant manager's voice even without having to look, as she had been the only person in the whole store, perhaps in the whole of Manchester, who had spoken the way she did. Not that we could understand half of what she had said anyway!

Mammy had said, "The auld lesheen spoke with a plum in her gob!" She'd had a job to understand the woman when she was berating her and Maggie after been caught stealing skirts from the store a short while back. Mammy's excuse at the time was, she'd suffered with her nerves which made her easily forgetful. After assuring the assistant manager she'd had every intention of paying for the skirts, she'd searched around in her bag before screaming blue murder, accusing everyone in the store of stealing her purse!

"Did yah pay for that hooter yer wearing?" I'd asked the haughty assistant manager and to my shocked surprise, she'd ignored me out of hand, when we I'd been waiting for the usual barrage of verbal from her along with our marching orders! Instead, she had suddenly rushed off in the direction of the main entrance doors, as the distant sirens had become even louder and we were able to see the flashing blue lights of the ambulance that had pulled up right outside the entrance to the store!

As the stampede of shoppers and staff had hurried off towards the main exit doors for a nose at what was going on our attention had been drawn to the fact the jewellery counter had been left unmanned! And being children never to miss out on an opportunity, Martin and me had dived behind the counter to seek out any opportunities that might have been waiting for our attention, while Bernie had kept a look out for us – or so we'd thought!

Jasis! It was like walking into an Aladdin's cave! My hands had shook in trepidation and I'd found it difficult to contain my excitement, being amongst all that glittering array of gold and silver diamond rings and necklaces staring back at us from the display cabinets. My first thoughts were, "It's gonna be Belle Vue every single day for some months to come! And catching a bus every time instead of walking! But my dreams were soon shattered when we'd discovered all the display cabinets were securely locked up. But as a consolation we'd found a small unlocked cupboard filled with boxes of watches and cigarette lighters, which we had swiftly removed from their packaging before stuffing as many of them as we could into our trouser pockets.

At one point we'd had to quickly drop down on our hands and knees as two middle-aged men had suddenly walked close by the counter. And although I had suspected at least one of them, the taller of the two, had spotted us and positive that he had made the briefest of eye contact with me, he and his companion had continued past the counter as if nothing out of the ordinary was happening! Which I suppose it wasn't out of the ordinary to us, considering we were always thieving.

Hurrying from behind the counter our little sister had been nowhere to be seen, which was the reason we hadn't received the expected warning call! We'd found her moments later in the next aisle, attempting to stuff a boxed Barbie doll down her knickers, with Martin suggesting, "Take the feckin' doll out of the box first!"

"I found this for Nabby sticking out from under the shelf." She'd shown us the torn green pressed cardboard Guy Fawkes mask.

"Yea were supposed ta be keeping an eye out for us." I'd scolded her, "We could all have been arrested because of yea!"

"Well. As I wasn't behind the counter with yah. They couldn't have arrested me for anything!" she'd smiled.

285

-THIRTY-FIVE-

Outside the Woolworths store we'd got a glimpse of Nabby, still snoozing in the pram. Which I suppose had been a blessing in disguise, considering the long-haired bearded lunatic and the cause for all the commotion, was standing next to him with a lighter in his hand and a large assortment of fireworks strapped to his body with him threatening to blow himself and the whole street to kingdom come if he wasn't taken to the Houses of Parliament straight away, so he could finish the job he had set out to do a few hundred years previously!

Holding the cigarette lighter up for the crowd to see, the man had flicked it into life a number of times to show he had meant business. We had been unable to squeeze through the packed crowd to get to our sleeping brother because we were hemmed in by the doors while some onlookers were egging the madman on, to do what he'd been threatening to do.

"Nabby." I'd called out softly to him, not wanting to shout too loud in case the lunatic took fright and set of the fireworks. But Nabby had not heard me.

"Wake up yah Scalpy bastard yah!" Bernie, had screamed out one of Nabby's hated nicknames, alongside, *Patch, Sitting Bull* or *Red Indian,* which had been bestowed on him by the family on account of the patches daddy would sometimes leave in his head when he'd gone mad with the hair clippers. The secret to a pain-free crew-cut-as we'd kept telling Nabby, was to "Keep feckin' still!" while daddy quickly ran the blunt hair clippers over our heads, otherwise they would snag and he would just carry on clipping, tearing the hair out by the roots, which had often happened to Nabby because he just couldn't hold still, resulting in him being virtually scalped ever time. Hence the nicknames!

Bernie's shout had done the trick and when Nabby's eyelids had slowly opened, they'd immediately fixed upwards on the suicidal maniac standing next to him. I'd half expected my little brother to suddenly leap out of the pram and run for his life! But instead we'd watched as he'd slowly reached into the side pocket of the smelly one-armed donkey jacket and pulled out the cigarette lighter, Martin had earlier bribed him with. Flicking the lighter into life, first time, he'd slowly offered the small flame up to the fuse of one of the large Catherine-wheels, as an eerie silence had descended over the whole street of shocked faces gawking at the Guy, who had suddenly come to life! The silence, as expected, had been short lived when the Catherine-wheel had whooshed into life and the lunatic had screamed like a lunatic, before fleeing off down the middle of the street towards the crowd, just as the police had arrived.

The three of us had rushed to Nabby's side only for him to be slouched back in the pram with his arms folded across his chest and looking pissed off with everything. "Why d'ya have to be callin' me feckin' names for?" he'd moaned, seemingly more put out about that, than the fact he could have been blown sky high.

"Martin an' Tommy, called yah a couple of times and yah wouldn't wake up!" said Bernie, "Yah should be grateful I saved yer life instead of pullin' the long face!" she'd pushed the pram off in the opposite direction of the crowd, with Martin and me quickly following behind her, "Anyways," she'd continued, always having to get her say in, "I didn't call yah *names*. I'd only called yah the one name - Scalp." The short pause going right over my little brother's head, as Bernie had thrown a grin over her shoulder in our direction.

Turning off Stretford Road into Upper Jackson Street, we'd made our way up to the old school building where we hid in the shadows of the tall archway out of view from prying eyes.

"Did yah get anythin'?" asked Bernie, as she'd struggled to get the unboxed Barbie doll out of her knickers.

'We got these!" I'd excitedly shown her the seven watches, slipping them onto my left arm one by one.

"An' these!' Martin pulled six watches and three silver lighters out of his trouser pockets.

"What do yah want all them watches for? Sure, yah can't even tell the time with only the one!' scoffed Bernie, as Martin had slipped them onto his arm.

"Sure I can tell the time! I taught meself." said Martin, looking down his nose at Bernie.

"What's the time then?"

Studying his left arm for a short while, I'd stared intensively at Martin's mouth, watching his lips, in the hope I'd be able to learn his secret of time telling, "Well. The big hand is near the number nine and the small hand is near the number four, so that makes it, nine-ten-eleven-twelve-turteen,' he'd counted on his fingers, 'Turteen o'clock!"

"But all the feckin' watches' hands are pointing at different numbers," said Bernie, studying the faces of Martin's watches. "So which one is telling the right time?"

"I know.' Nabby had suddenly piped up "Our Paddy taught me how to tell the time."

"Go on then, clever-clogs." Martin had shoved his armful of watches up under Nabby's nose, while Bernie and I had gawked over the back of the pram.

For a short while, Nabby had sat studying all the watches on Martin's arm, before suddenly announced, 'They're all the right time!"

It'd seemed all those bangs, our brother Paddy had delivered to our little brother's head with mammy's alarm clock, hadn't taught him a thing about telling the time. And although, when Paddy had first hinted he'd be willing to teach all of us how to tell the time, it had seemed an exciting prospect. After we'd witnessed, at first hand, his teaching method of bonking Nabby; the first volunteer, over the head with the clock every time he'd got the time wrong, we'd decided, *time* after all wasn't that important to us.

"Here." Martin had slid a gold coloured watch off his arm and handed it to Nabby. "Yah can get some more practice while yer sittin' there doing feck all."

It had never bothered me about not being able to tell the time. For me, time was meaningless and had no beginning and no end. Any given morning would follow its usual course into any given afternoon and on into any given evening and a night, before ultimately drifting back into another morning, another afternoon and so on. And as long as it kept doing that, there was nothing for me to worry about. The same for the four seasons. Spring into summer saw all the flowers and the trees in full bloom, with the majority of moody people smiling again and giving away their pennies. Autumn into winter and all the blooms died off, with a penny much harder to come by as the majority of people walked around with their heads hunched into their shoulders, or stuck up their arses moaning the fact, winter had brought the snow, which we had loved! Followed by the Ice, which we had loved! Though it was not much fun when going to the lavvy, only to find a big turd peering out over the top of the toilet because some lazy fecker hadn't bothered breaking away the ice before having a shite!

Christmas too, always came along without fail, with the carol songs and Christmas trees and all the bright twinkling lights that went with them. And Father Christmas coming to see all the good girls and boys, which was the reason why he never came to see us-not that any of us had really cared. While the pot-bellied miserable fat bastard brought the odd toy to all the goody-two-shoes! We were out stealing our own Christmas presents! And lots of them too!

"Okay you lot! You can hand those over right now." the taller man of the two fellas we'd seen walking past the jewellery counter in Woolworths, had stepped into the shadow of the schools entrance. He'd stood in front of us with one hand raised in the air, like a policeman holding up the traffic. Only he wasn't holding up any traffic but a small leather wallet with a Silver Star shaped badge attached to it. His little short fat companion had taken two steps into the shadows and had stood alongside his companion, trapping us underneath the arched entrance and blocking off any escape route.

"Hand what over?" Martin had put his blagging face on, looking so innocently confused, he had *"guilty"* written all

290

over it.

"The items we saw you helping yourselves to from the jewellery department in Woolworths. That's what!"

"You're not having me feckin' Barbie!' yelled Bernie, 'I paid for it, so yah can fuck off!"

"Well, if you paid for the doll, then it isn't a problem, is it?" said the tall policeman, giving Bernie a smile.

"We paid for all the watches too." said Martin.

"And the three lighters Martin has in his pockets," said Nabby. And if looks could have killed, he should have died on the spot as the three of us had angrily glared at him.

"Right! You have two choices," the tall policeman had become agitated with us, "You can either hand over everything you've just stolen from Woolworths and clear off, or we can take you down to the nick!"

"Just give him the poxty tings!" said Bernie, but Martin had other ideas and had suddenly thrown himself to the ground, faking a seizure, which had caused the two policemen to take a cautious step backwards, as they'd watched him writhe on the ground like he was in his death throes.

"He's having a fit!" I'd shouted.

"He's not having a fit!' the tall policeman scoffed.

"He's dying, so he is!" our Bernie pleaded.

"He's always doing that,' said Nabby.

"What-dying?"

"Puttin on-I mean having one of his fits!"

"Hurry an' call the ambulance!' said Bernie, scowling at Nabby

"If he were having a real fit, his feet would be shaking." the tall policeman had stepped forward to take a closer look down on Martin, whose feet, right on cue, had suddenly gone into spasm like a tap dancer tapping out a dance.

"Faking it! Just as I'd thought!" The tall policeman set about sliding the watches off my brother's arm before groping in his pockets for the lighters.

Incensed by this, I had taken a run up and was about to kick the thieving policeman in the gob. But his short fat companion was far too quick for me and had managed to get his small podgy hand around my throat. "Okay son!" he'd snarled, "Let's be having them." He'd roughly searched my trouser pocket, before pushing the sleeves of my jumper and shirt up and forcing me to take off all the watches I'd had on my arm.

"I'm not your feckin' son! I'd angrily snapped at him.

"No you're not! Otherwise you'd had got one of these!" he cuffed me across the side of the head, before letting go of my throat, 'Now clear off or you'll be in serious trouble."

We'd watched as the two laughing policemen, ignoring the names we were calling them, had ambled back down in the direction of the Stretford Road before disappearing from sight

"At least I still have me Barbie," Bernie had been pleased with herself.

"Only because yea'd stuffed it down your pissy knickers," said Martin.

Then you should have stuffed all the watches down yer pants, Martin! They might have let yah keep them!" retorted Bernie, making me laugh.

"I don't know what yer laughin' at." scowled Martin, "If yea had stuffed yer lot down yer shitty undies they wouldn't have took any of them!"

"I'm not wearing any of me shitty undies today, so there."

"Well you should have shoved them up yer shitty hole then!"

"We've still got this,' Nabby had suddenly held up the gold coloured watch Martin had given to him earlier.

-THIRTY-SIX-

There had been a lot of comings and goings at the house. First thing this morning, two detectives had called to speak to Martin and me separately, with Martin going first. They had wanted to know about the night we had come home and saw daddy in the kitchen having a strip wash, while mammy was sitting in the back room waiting for us to come home. They'd said, mammy and daddy said, we could vouch for this.

Like proper robbers, we had asked the two detectives to show their police badges to us just to prove they were real detectives, before we would agree to talk to them. We had seen the baddies do this in the films! Not surprisingly, their badges looked nothing like the star-shaped sheriff badges the other two policemen had shown us! Confirming my suspicions the thieving bastards had been fake policemen all along!

These real policemen had questioned me about what I'd seen when I'd come into the house the night me and Martin had seen daddy washing himself down. Being minded not to let them catch me out telling them something completely different to what Martin might have already told them; I'd been much too clever for that, before answering any of their questions, I'd got them to confirm the answers Martin had given to them, when they'd questioned him first.

"Did Martin say, when we saw daddy washing himself in the kitchen sink, he had some blood on him?" I'd questioned them.

"Something similar." said one of the detectives. And so I had agreed that was the case!

294

Easy-peasy! I'd even stuck up for daddy and had told them, how he would often bring one of our older sisters down into his bedroom to comfort them when they were upset, whenever mammy had stayed away from the house, after another of their drunken rows.

"Was your mam waiting in the house when you came home that night?"

"Did Martin say, we'd passed her coming home early the following Morning?"

"Something similar."

"Then she wasn't in the house that night." I'd said.

The two detectives had thanked me for helping them with their inquiries. And I had only been too pleased with myself for being cleverer than them!

Not long after they had gone, Uncles Paddy, Oliver, Christy and Raphael, had shown up at the house with Father Murphy in tow. We'd had no idea what was going on as the priest had set about blessing the house and everyone in it, before turning to Uncle Oliver and asking him, "Will yer late father be joinin' us at the house? And of course, your dear mother?"

"Aye, they'll be here for sure." Oliver had assured the priest. And knowing our granddad, who was always up for a good family booze up, he'd be here even if he was a little late!

Turning down the bottle of ale from Uncle Oliver, the priest had accepted a glass of sherry from mammy which he blessed before downing it in one gulp and holding the glass out for a refill, which mammy had obliged, before whishing us all out of the house. "Git up ta yer Aunt Maureen's! she'd whished us out of the house, "This isn't the place for children ta be listenin' to grown up talk."

While Martin, Me, Nabby and Bernie had taken the pram and headed off to collect a few more pennies for the Guy, Maggie had taken the younger ones off to Aunty Maureen's, who'd only lived a few streets away in Philips Street. Nabby had said, he wasn't going to be the Guy again and I'd been only too pleased to volunteer. My stomach had been feeling queasy and walking the streets hadn't been such a good idea, especially when having that awful feeling you could shit through the eye of a needle at any moment! Quickly donning the overalls, the one armed donkey jacket, topping it off with the old cloth cap and the broken Guy's mask Bernie had found in Woolworths, we'd made our way back out onto the streets.

The of the morning, right up until the late afternoon, had seen only the odd few pennies pass through our hands which Martin had suggested we might as well spend on Blackjacks. The three of them had left me outside the corner shop, only for me to get stolen by a bunch of thieving little kids, who'd rushed off with me up along Rosmond Street, with Bernie and my two brothers in hot persuit, while I'd desperately fought to keep the cheeks of my arse tightly squeezed together.

"I think we lost them!" said one of the kids as the pram had slowed to a much gentler pace. Having never been stolen before, I'd been unsure what to do next. I didn't know how many kids were involved in my theft and so I'd not been sure if they would make a run for it, if I'd stood up, or bash me up? Worse! Would my bowels drop in the process! Not wanting to tempt fate I'd continued to lay slouched back in the small pram without moving a muscle.

"That's a fine looking Guy Fawkes you have there, John."

"Yes, Mrs. Mullins. Our dad made it for us."

"Yah lyin' fecker! Yah stole me!" I'd been a whisker away from shouting!

"Almost lifelike."

Jesus! Squinting through the mask I'd seen the old biddy open her purse before bending over the pram to have a good look at me sitting there, "Almost lifelike." she'd repeated, while reaching a hand out with the thrupenny piece between her two fingers. Bollocks to this. "Fuck off!" I'd screamed at the top of my voice as I'd snatched the thrupenny piece out of the shocked woman's hand and sprung up out of the pram, running hell for leather and pushing the pram back up the street bumping into Martin, Nabby and Bernie in the next street.

Hurrying over to a group of derelict houses, I'd just managed to scramble over the loose debris and squat inside the entrance to what was once somebody's kitchen, when my bowels had finally dropped its load while the others had gone off to explore the rest of the house - Jasis! The stench! "Can any of yah see any auld rags to wipe me hole with?"

"I've found some electric flex!" said Martin.

"I can't wipe me hole with a lump of flex!"

"I've found tuppence!" Nabby excitedly called.

Spotting the edge of a dirty net curtain poking out from the debris a foot or so away from me, I'd stretched across and gently pulled at it, weedling it out bit by bit until I'd been able to get enough into my hand to pull out a long length of the damp gritty material and give my arse a good wipe. Then, while the others had searched around upstairs, I had stepped just outside, away from the stench, into where the back yard had once stood which was now covered by a mountain of debris.

I had found it easy to be able to drift off into my own world, as I so often did when visiting these empty places, feeling able, so it had seemed to be almost able to touch the silent emptiness which always took hold of me, evoking my imagination and conjuring up images of a forgotten time, of smoking chimneys and children playing along the streets, swinging off the lampposts, racing down the middle of the street on their man-made bogies, chasing after the ice-cream van, playing football, jumping on the back of a moving lorry and generally enjoying their lives, as normal children often did. But here, in these places, the stark reality was always going to be laid bare to me. No smoking chimneys, No lampposts. No back alleyways, or children's laughter. Empty unrecognisable streets and the deafening silence within these empty places which would live on long after everything is else is turned to dust.

"Oh Jasis!' I'd heard Bernie suddenly cry out.

"What's wrong, Bernie?" Martin had called to her.

"It's them! The Boyd's!"

Running back over the debris and into the house, I'd ran up the stairs into the front bedroom, where my panic-stricken sister was pointing across the room to the dirty cracked window panes, where I had been able to just make out, Pat and Terry Boyd, heading straight across the croft in our direction. The pair of them were in the company of a little blonde haired lad, around the same age as myself. And though none of us had ever set eyes upon him before, it was easy to tell he was a

Boyd, even from that distance. The young kid seemed to be having a good time throwing his toy parachute high up into the air and watching it slowly drop back to earth, as Pat Boyd had taken aim with his air-rifle and fired off a shot at it.

"Oh God! They're going to shoot us!" cried Bernie, "What are we goin' ta do?"

"Keep our gobs down for a start!" snapped Martin, placing a finger on Bernie's lips, "Or we'll get corrupt. Anyways. We don't even know they'll come right over this way."

"But the pram's outside!" said Bernie.

"Shit, I left the Guys clothes and the mask in it!"

"I'll get it," Nabby had volunteered.

"Leave it!" said Martin, "They've eyes up their arses them lot. Get the bricks over there and pile them next to the stairs, at the ready. If them feckers start to come up, we'll bounce the lot off their feckin' heads!"

In the circumstances we had found ourselves in, Martin, hadn't seemed too bothered about our approaching doom, or if he'd had been, he'd done a good job keeping it to himself probably putting a brave face on for Bernie's sake, which was the sort of thing he would do. Poor Bernie. She had already pissed herself with the fear and to be honest, I'd been grateful I had already opened my bowels, otherwise I would have probably filled my kecks there and then!

"Yah missed again!" we'd heard the little boy's exited voice.

"Throw it up higher then!" Pat Boyd's voice had sounded very close to the house. Another sharp snap, and we could only sit and watch in silence as the mouse had dangled upside down from its makeshift parachute, which had snagged on the jagged edge of the broken pane of the window. It didn't seem to have been injured though it had desperately wriggled in its feeble attempt to free itself. I hadn't really felt anything for the plight of the mouse, having an acute hate for them. And under normal circumstances I have probably whacked it with a lump of wood or set it alight with the lighter. Not that it was usually *normal* in Hulme to see mice dropping from the sky in parachutes!

Another crack and the mouse was dead with half the right side of its face and brain splattered on the outside of the cracked glass pane.

"Gotcha yea facker!' Pat Boyd had sounded very pleased with himself.

"I want my parachute back!"

"Well yah can go fetch it yerself I'm not gettin' it for yah! 'An' don't expect us to be waitin' for yah either. We've better tings ta be doin."

To our relief, we'd heard footsteps walking away from the house, only for our joy to be short-lived when a moment later we'd heard footsteps outside close to the kitchen area. Putting a finger to his lips for us to keep quiet, Martin had tiptoed out of the bedroom to stand at the top of the stairway where he'd picked up two of the bricks from the small pile and had held them at the ready, to bourn down on the head of the first person to start coming up the stairs.

"Augh! It stinks like a skunk in there!"

We'd listened as the kid had hurried off over the debris before we'd dared stand up and look out through the broken window pane watching as he'd caught up with his brothers disappearing across the large open croft and out of view

-THIRTY-SEVEN-

Shamie was throwing large chunks of old lead down off the old church roof when we'd come across him for the first time in almost three weeks. We'd asked him if he'd wanted us to give him a hand and put some of the lead on the pram and take it home for him.

"Fuck of and don't mention a word to the old woman about seein' me!" he'd climbed down from the small side roof, "I've left for good and won't be coming back to that poxty dump anymore!" which I'd supposed, wouldn't have made any difference to mammy considering she was hardly at home herself to have missed him anyway, if every she would have missed him! It was the same with our eldest brother Paddy, who'd ran off not long after Mary and Rose had left, leaving Elizabeth aged thirteen and Maggie aged ten, to take on the responsibility of looking after all nine of us that were left.

"Is it okay if me an' Martin ta have yer's and Paddy's bedroom? Since yah won't be needing it anymore?" I'd asked.

"Jasis Tommy!" said Shamie, picking up lumps of the lead and taking them along the short path to the small wooden entrance gate of the church "Yea'd jump in me coffin before I got cold!"

"I feckin wouldn't for sure!" I'd argued, "I don't like being cooped up in small spaces!"

A small rusty grey old van had suddenly pulled up opposite the wooden gate and Jaffa; a mate of Shamie's and around the same age as him, had jumped out of the driver's side and began loading the lumps of lead into the back of it. We'd lent a hand, picking up the smaller pieces and throwing them in.

"Yea can have the bedroom. An' I'll also throw in two bob, if yea'll do a favour for me later on tonight.'

"Two shillin' each?" I'd asked.

"A fuckin' shillin' each! Or nothin'! Not even the bedroom! Take it or leave it-I'm in a hurry!"

We'd immediately agreed to the deal even though we hadn't the slightest clue as to what the favour was going to be. Shamie arranged for us to meet him on the corner of Park Street at around seven o'clock, when he'd tell us what we had to do, as well as giving us our dosh.

"Where'd yah get the heap from?" Martin had asked as he'd cast an eye of the rusting old crank.

"Dumped on a croft over in Longsight."

"I didn't know St Philip's was a derelict church?' said Bernie, which Shamie had ignored, though for some reason unknown to us Jaffa had suddenly burst out laughing.

"Hurry up Jaffa and get us outta here!' Shamie ordered, hurrying past us and hoping into the passenger side of the van, which looked as if it was about to collapse any minute under the sheer weight loaded into it.

"You'd better fuck off outta here!" warned Jaffa, suddenly handing me a shilling piece, "And it isn't!"

"What isn't?"

"The church isn't derelict – Shit!"

Following Jaffa's gaze, we'd looked further down the street to see some people, five in all, who'd hurried out of the main entrance gates of St Philip's School and headed up the street towards us. But as we had done nothing wrong, we'd decided, we were going nowhere fast.

"Don't feckin' forget Martin! Seven o'clock on the dot tonight!" Shamie had shouted a reminder out of the broken side window of the passenger door, before the old van had chugged off coughing and farting its way up along Newcastle Street, with three of the posse from the school following close behind it and not quiet able to catch up with the old heap, while the two women, had stopped next to us and had started giving out about stealing the lead from off the church roof and of how, we should be ashamed of ourselves!

"Well yah can search us all yah like" invited Martin, "But yea'll not find any lead on us! An' we don't steal from churches, we're good Catholics!"

"So you don't know those two young men who've just driven away in that van?" one of the old biddies had questioned and all four of us had sworn blind, we didn't.

"Then why were you talking with them as if you had known them?' the smart cow had quickly thrown the question.

"Only to tell them it was wrong ta be stealin' the lead from off the church's roof." I'd said, which they'd obviously hadn't believed, telling us to clear off, before they fetched the police on to us.

Later in the afternoon as the darkness started to slowly creep in on us, we had made our way back home. There had been some discussion between us about whether or not we should be going to Aunty Maureen's or to our own house. Bernie seemed minded to believe, mammy had wanted us to go and stay with her sister indefinitely. Or at least until she had sent word for us to come home. But she had been outvoted by the other three of us who'd decided we should go home first and see what mammy had meant us to do. I had wondered out loud, if Granddad had got to the house on time, but the others were more interested in wondering what the favour Shamie had wanted, to give me an answer.

One of daddy's favourite sayings was, "It's better to be late than never." Not that the black lady sitting behind the counter at the labour exchange had seemed all that impressed with him, when he had turned up two days late to sign on and had tried to use his two "Very ill boys" Martin and me, as his excuse for being late. The woman had laughed in his face, telling him, "Not only would it take you a million years to convince me your two sons are seriously anemic, sir! But it is obvious to everyone looking in this direction, their faces have been powdered white!"

We had smugly shrugged our shoulders at daddy, as if to say, "We'd told you so!" not that we actually did! But it had been as plain to us as the plain flour he had coated our faces with, that his idea had been doomed to failure from the start! Daddy also wasn't impressed by the woman's attitude-and catching him out suggesting to her, "Why don't yah feck off back to the jungle and play with yer coconuts!" which had gotten him arrested and fined forty-shillings from the Magistrate! The fine had originally been twenty-shillings, but having complained the amount was far too much for him to pay and putting it on par with it being enough to feed a whole tribe of Zulus, with him going on to suggest, the Magistrate ask the woman from the Social Security, who'd given evidence against him, as she would be able to back this up! "Given she is one of the tribe!"

Walking in through the back gate we'd found the whole house in total darkness, which wasn't that unusual if there had been no-one at home, which was unusual, given it was only about six o'clock. Martin had tried the back door and found it to be locked so Bernie and Nabby had gone around to the front of the house, coming back within a minute with the news, the front door had also been locked.

As luck would have it, the latch on the sash window to the back room was not completely pushed home. And so with a few bangs against the window frame with the side of his clenched fist, Martin had been able to work the latch across to its open position and pulled the bottom half of the sash window upwards until it had hit the two small blocks of wood, daddy had screwed to each side of the runners to stop the window from opening too far. With Bernie being the skinniest, she had agreed to squeeze in through the small gap of the window so she could unlock the back door for us.

"Get on yer knees Tommy and I'll get up on yer back." She'd ordered and I'd immediately dropped to my knees. I could hardly feel her weight as she'd stepped up on my back, using me as a platform while she'd attempted to squeeze her tiny frame through the gap in the window. "There's loads of beer bottles on the table," she'd called back to us, "And there's a kinda box too."

"How d'ya mean. A box?" asked Martin.

"A box."

"Yeh. But what kind a box?"

"A feckin box-box, Martin!' What other kind of box is

there!"

"A small box! A big box?"

"Let's have a ganders.' Nabby had suddenly stepped up on my back. "I can't really see much but yep, it's definitely some sort of a box all right. A biggish one!"

"Didn't I already tell yah it was a poxty box?" yelled Bernie.

"Can't yah push it out of the way then!" snapped Martin.

"Jasis! Me backs goin' ta break in a minute!" I'd warned the pair of them walking all over me like I was a door mat.

"It won't budge, it's too heavy," said Nabby.

"An' so are yea feckin two! Will yah get off me back!"

"Out the way," said Martin, "I've an idea."

"Don't yea be jumpin' on me back too!"

"There's no need." Martin told the other two to get off me, much to my relief.

Fetching a length of wood from off the pile of firewood he'd had shoved one end through the gap of the window, "Give us a hand then!" he'd invited us and we'd all got behind him and pushed on the wood until the large box had slowly fell away from the table taking most of the empty bottles with it, before falling it fell off the table with an almighty crash.

Up on my back once more, Bernie had managed to squeeze herself through the small gap this time and a few moments later, we we're walking through from the dark kitchen into the dark backroom. Nabby had flicked the light switch up and down, but no light came on, concluding, "The electric's gone, or the bulbs broke."

"That's clever." quipped Bernie.

"Well it's obvious!" snapped Nabby.

"Exactly!"

"I can't see nothing!"

That's cos it's dark Nabby!"

"Well that's feckin' obvious too!"

"Exactly!"

"Will yea two give over, for fecks sake?" I'd told Nabby and Bernie them.

"Light the lighter Nabby an' we'll might be able ta get a better look." suggested Martin

When the lighter had flicked into life and Nabby had held the tiny flame out in front of him, we we're just able to make out some flickering reflections off the empty beer bottles lying about the place, but not much else. In the dim shadowy light my eyes had homed in on the plate standing on the sideboard with a couple of biscuits still on it and I'd concentrated on them.

"It must be someone's birthday." Nabby moved the small flame slowly around the room casting shadows everywhere. "Fuck me sideways!" he'd suddenly shouted, "Feck that's hot!" he'd dropped the lighter leaving us in pitch dark, with me choking on the two biscuits that I'd greedily shoved straight into my gob.

"What the feck's wrong with yah Nabby?" said Martin

"There's someone lying on the floor! I think its Granddad! Where's the poxty lighter!"

"What's Granddad up ta?" asked Bernie.

"Not feckin' much," said Nabby, "Hang on! I found him - Granddad! - Are yah alright? – He's fast asleep in a heap! An' the stench of drink!"

307

"D'ya think he missed the others an' fell asleep waitin' for them to come back?" I'd asked, "That could be the reason why the back door was locked?"

"An' drunk all the party beer ta himself!" laughed Martin.

"What was the big box that fell? Can yah see it?" asked Bernie

"I can't even see me hand! – Hang on! – I can feel something

"What?"

"A wide shiny lump of wood - I think!"

"Where are yah?" asked Martin.

"Here! Where d'ya tink?"

"Hang on."

"Aah he's got hold of me!" screamed Nabby.

"It's me that's got yah! I'm down on the floor!"

"Feckin Jasis, Martin! Yah scared the life out of me!"

"Here's it is!" Martin had got back up on his feet and had flicked the lighter back into life again. A shite! It's nearly out of petrol!" the small glow had given us enough light to barely see each other, "He's obviously drunk himself silly or that box we'd pushed of the table has hit him and knocked him out cold, concluded Martin.

"Oh God! He'll swing for the lot of us when he wakes up! An' if he doesn't, mammy will!" Bernie started crying.

"For God's sake will yah shallup!" Nabby had no sympathy for her.

"We'll have to put him somewhere out of the way." Suggested, the glow from the lighter had by then completely gone.

"In mammy's bed' was Bernie bright idea! Nabby thought

308

we should throw him down the cellar steps, so as it would look like he'd knocked himself out by accident. I'd suggested taking him down the alleyway to the Red Rose pub and leaving him propped up against the wall. "Which wouldn't be unusual, being it was Granddad!

Martin said Bernie's idea was the best of the lot, as he would be much safer in mammy's bed as well as being able to keep warm. Being a small thin man, it hadn't been too difficult to haul him up by his arms and legs and out of the dark backroom through into the hallway and into mammy's bedroom, where counting to three, we'd thrown him on the bed and covered him up with mammy's heavy coats. As well as locking the back door, we'd also made sure the brass window catch was firmly set in its locked position, before leaving by the front door and making our way back along Stamford Street and down in to the town, where we'd bought a portion of chips and mushy peas to share amongst the four of us, before going off to meet Shamie.

-THIRTY-EIGHT-

Heading up along Park Lane, in the direction of Park Street, we'd just turned the corner of Park Place, when we had stopped to watch the four fire engines speed out from the fire station and head off up the street. In the deafening silence which followed, we had noticed the fire station seemed to have been left empty and so we decided, just out of curiosity, we would take a ganders inside.

There had not been much to see downstairs and so we had gone upstairs, where we had found the kitchen, immediately homing in on the long table with the half empty plates of sausages, eggs and beans, buttered slices of bread and half-empty mugs of warm tea, left by the firemen as they'd hurried off to their emergency. It must have been ten minutes since we had polished off the bag of mushy peas and chips between us, yet there had been still plenty of room to fit more into our hungry stomachs. And so, without ceremony, we had snatched up handfuls of the food and greedily stuffed the lot down our throats, swilling it down with mouthfuls of the warm tea.

"Listen!" Martin had suddenly whispered, did yah hear that?"

"Hear what?" I had only just begged the question, when we had heard the flush of a toilet and then a door opening, followed by the sound of squeaky boots heading up along the corridor in our direction!

"We've been corrupt!" said Martin, quickly dashing behind the kitchen door with the rest of us following him, squeezing ourselves tightly in together in an attempt to make ourselves as invisible as possible, as the footsteps had squeaked past us and across the kitchen floor, where they had constantly moved around, backwards and forwards, backwards and forwards! Jasis! It had been so nerve racking I'd found myself wishing the poxty fireman would just walk over and find us! Saving me having to suffer all those heart palpitation thinking "Is he or feckin' isn't he!"

Hearing the whistle of a boiling kettle and then the noise of a spoon stirring in a cup, I had dared a peek around the door to see a giant of a black fireman standing sideways on supping from a mug, which I could barely see in his huge hand!

"Aaaaah! I just couldn't contain the scream of fear as I had been reminded of the big black man at the prison, who'd plucked children's eyes out and sucked them like gobstoppers! With the huge fireman almost jumping out of his skin, spilling his steaming hot drink all down himself, he'd howled in pain as he had rushed over to the sink, where he'd stood throwing mugs of cold water all over himself, giving us our opportunity to rush out of our hiding place and out of the door, before he'd even had the chance to get a look at us!

We had laughed all the way to Park Street, where we had seen Shamie's cranky old van parked up near the corner of Clarendon Street, and we'd sneaked up on our brother to give him a scare.

"Gotcha!" Martin shouted, as we had all banged our fists down on the back of the old heap and watched as the passenger side door was suddenly flung wide open and Shamie had fallen out onto his knees, coughing, spluttering and spitting out bits of tobacco, while Jaffa had got out from the driver's side, roaring with laughter.

"Yah bastard's yah!" coughed Shamie.

"What's wrong with Shamie, Jaffa?' asked Martin, as we'd looked on deeply concerned, because we had never seen him act in that way before.

"We'd thought you were the fuckin' coppers!" laughed Jaffa, "Shamie only tried to swallow the joint he was smoking! Fuckin' hell Shamie! That's the best laugh I've had in ages!"

Piss off, Jaffa! I nearly burnt me fuckin' tonsils ta ashes!" What the fuck did yah go an' do that for, yah gimpy-eyed gormless bastards yah!" he'd raged at us between gobs of spit.

We'd said nothing and had just stood there staring at the ground, like gimpy-eyed gormless bastards, having learnt the hard way, it was better to say nothing as it only antagonised, whoever it was doing all the bawling at us. Daddy had been the worst to answer back to. Usually his reply would be a punch in the gob or the first thing that came to hand, if you were too far away for him to reach you with his fist.

Thankfully, Shamie had not been our daddy and he had seemed to quickly get over the initial shock. He'd reached into the van and had pulled out a full bottle of Tizer, swilling the first mouthful around his mouth before spitting this out. Repeating the process, he'd gargled his throat before spitting that out too. His third and last swig, had emptied the glass bottle of drink down his throat, before he screwed the cap back on and carefully placed it back in the van for his returns money back on his next drink. Then, letting out a loud belch before cocking a leg and letting out a long squeaky fart, Shamie had leaned back into the van and had brought out a small polythene bag half full with dried peas.

"Here." he'd handed the bag to Martin, "Take these with yah ta number sixteen-yea'll have to go down the back way, an' throw a handful at a time up at the top window to the left-hand side of the house when yer looking straight at it. An' when Maureen answers, tell her I'm waitin' up at the top of the street for her, if she's still interested."

"Interested in what?" I'd asked.

"Never mind yah nosey git!"

"What if she doesn't want ta come out?" asked Martin.

"She'll want ta come," said Shamie, all cocksure of himself, "An' if she doesn't, that'll be her loss! There's plenty more tarts in Manchester looking to be humped! An' watch out for her mam! Or the games up! Sly feckin' hen that one. Got a face like a cow chewing' grass an' having' a good auld shite at the same time! An' keep yer voices down, if yah get a chance to talk to Maureen, 'cos her half-dead, bed-bound granny, kips in the bedroom off to your right!"

"And how are we supposed ta know which house is sixteen?" asked Martin.

"Look for the puke-coloured yellow painted back gate. It's the only one along there. It's about eight houses down up on your left. Yea'd have ta be feckin coloured blind to miss it!"

Leaving Bernie and Nabby with Shamie and Jaffa, Martin and I had set off back along the road to the side entry, which led to the back alleyway between the houses. We'd walked in pitch darkness, save for the odd lights from the houses. The air along there had stunk to high heaven of dog shite and if you'd wanted to sneak down here without anyone knowing you were on your way, it would have been miracle, because once the first dog had heard us and had started barking and jumping up against the other side of the back gate, the rest of them had followed suit, growling and barking letting the whole of Park Street and the adjoining Welcome street, know we were on our way!

It had not taken us more than a couple of minutes to come across the puke-yellow painted back gate and I'd gently pushed it open before the pair of us quietly snook into the dark back yard, not that there wasn't enough noise already going on around us with the barking dogs, to have drowned out any noise we might have made! The only light on at the back of the house was downstairs in the backroom. We could see the dim light through the curtains but were unable to see inside. Martin had tipped a handful of the hard peas into his hand and had thrown them up at the bedroom window above our heads on the left hand side looking at the house straight on, as Shamie had instructed. Almost immediately the window had squeaked upwards and a soft female voice had purred down from the dark. "Is that you Shamie?"

"No!" said Martin, keeping his voice to a whisper.

"Who is it then?'

"It's Martin an' Tommy."

"Shamie's brothers." I'd whispered up.

"Shamie sent you, did he?"

"Yeh." I'd kept the conversation flowing as we were both looking skywards trying to get a glimpse of the beautiful tart, our big brother had forever gone on about. But we were having difficulty in making out any of her features, though she did have the soft voice of an angel.

"Why did he send you?"

"Are yea Maureen? Only Shamie says we've to be careful not to let the auld witch catch us!"

"The auld witch?"

"Aye. Yer mammy."

Martin had seemed impressed by the way I'd been handling things and had kept silent for a change, letting me do all the talking, which I'd always thought I'd been good at despite some people thinking I went on just a little too long! Daddy once told me, "You'll talk yer way into prison one day!" though to be honest, I would preferred to be a fireman or a policeman instead. Failing that, I'd liked the idea of working in Woolworths, just so I'd be able to walk behind any of the counters without having to worry about arousing suspicion. Giving me all the time in the world to nick whatever I'd wanted.

"Yes. I'm Maureen. What else did my Shamie say about me mam?"

"Only that she has a face like a cow chewin' grass an' havin' a good shite at the same time!" I'd said, "Anyway. Shamie wants ta know if you're coming' out with him tonight? He said, he'd not be bothered if yah didn't want to, 'cos there's enough tarts in Manchester looking for a good hump!"

"Oh! He did, did he? - Just give me a tick while I get some things together." Maureen went away from the window.

"That was an easy two-bob!" I'd smiled at Martin.

"Do yah think yah should have told her what Shamie said

about her mammy?"

"She's getting her tings-isn't she?"

"Here! Cop this!" Maureen had come back to the window.

Squinting upwards into the dim light, I had just been able to make out what had appeared to be a medium sized handbag, which Maureen had confirmed when I had asked, "What is it?"

"Just a small makeup bag and things."

"Let me catch it!" said Martin, "Since yea did all the talking." which had not been a problem for me since we always did things equally together. And so I had stepped aside, giving Martin ample room to catch the bag.

"I'm ready!" he said, reaching into the air with his hands high at the ready, "Yea can drop it!"

"At the count of three then." Whispered Maureen. "One. Two. Here it comes!"

"Aaah, Jasis!" gargled Martin, as the contents of the pisspot had hit him full in the face. "Yah dirty auld scrubber! Yah feckin' who-er! I curse yah to sunder!" Martin had screamed blue murder!

"Tell that disgusting sex maniac brother of yours!" the angelical whisper had suddenly turned vicious and angry, "If I so much as catch him standing on the corner of this street, I'll cut his fecking bollocks off! Now get away from the house before I get the police on to you!'

The curtain on the ground-floor window had suddenly swung across and we come face to face with a young girl of around fourteen, staring wide-eyed back at us. She'd gently opened the window and had popped her head out. "Tell Shamie me mam is going out in about half hour and I'll come just after then."

"Who are you?" Martin asked her.

"Maureen." she'd answered, quickly closing the window on us.

"We'd better get going or her mammy might get the coppers on to us," I'd warned my pissy brother. And so we'd hurried out the back gate and up the alleyway with Martin cursing everyone who had lived in the house and on the whole street, including all the barking dogs.

-THIRTY-NINE-

"Jasis! What's happened ta yea Martin?" Shamie smirked.

"She threw a pot of piss down on him." I'd said.

"Maureen!"

"Her feckin' mother-we think!"

"Jasis it stinks ta high heaven! It must have been the old Grandmothers piss pot she'd tipped over yah!" said Shamie, he and Jaffa sniggering.

"It's not feckin funny!" snapped Martin.

"Ah! We're only joking with yah Martin! Here, let me pour this over yah." Shamie had pulled the big bottle of Cherryade and a large piece of old cloth out of the van, "It'll at least help get rid of the stench!" he'd slowly poured the whole bottle over Martin's head, as Martin had rubbed it into his hair and face, managing to catch some of it in his cupped hands and drinking it, before drying himself with the dirty rag Jaffa handed to him. "Did ya get to speak ta Maureen?"

"I was me that spoke to her." I'd told him.

"So what did she tell yah?"

"She said -"

"I'll tell Shamie what Maureen said ta tell him!" Martin had quickly cut in on me, but had then refused to give Shamie the message unless he gave him four shillings for his troubles!

Shamie's attempt to barter Martin down to three shillings, fell on deaf ears and Martin had held out for the four shillings, which he had got!

"Here!" Shamie scowled as he'd handed over the money to

Martin. "Well? Is she or isn't she coming out?'

"She said - Are yah sure yah want to hear this, Shamie?"

"Just tell me what her answer was!"

"Well. She said, yah have big fat blubbery lips like lumps of bacon. An' the only humpin' yer up to, is humping tings on yer back. She also said, you have a mickey no bigger than a little maggot!"

"Shullup yah little fecker!" Shamie angrily shouted.

"An' she also said, yah can feck off an' hump as many tarts as yah like, because she never wants to see yer ugly mug again." I'd added for good measure, while Jaffa had lent up against the side of the van holding his sides, as he'd gone in to fits of hysterical laughter. I hadn't been sure what Nabby and Bernie, were doing because they'd had their backs turned to us.

"How did she know about humping other tarts?' our red-faced brother had suddenly thrown the question at me. And as I wasn't willing to give him an answer and risk his anger, I just gave a shrug of my shoulders while he suspiciously eyeballed me for a moment or two.

"She'd said something first about she liked to hump other fellas, before she'd said that." said Martin.

"Yeh! That's what she'd said!" I'd backed up Martin's lie, "Just before she'd said, you'd had a little mickey like a –!"

"Didn't I tell yah ta fuckin' shullup!" snapped Shamie, glaring at me, "That's it Jaffa! She can kiss me arse, that one! Anyway she's so frigid, she'd started to cry when I'd gone to get me mickey out! So she couldn't have seen how little it was! Let's go and find some tarts in the city."

We'd tried cadging a lift home in the van, which Shamie agreed to give us, for four shillings! As we had walked off, we'd suddenly heard the van brake sharply and we'd turned to look back up the road thinking Shamie, out of the goodness of his heart, had changed his mind. But instead, we had watched him get out of the van holding a small lump of lead piping, hurry back the few yards to Maureen's house, before taking aim and throwing the pipe straight through their front window before running back to the van and hopping back in with the van chugging off up the street as we'd ran off in the opposite direction towards home.

Martin's short hair had stood up on end as it had set like the spikes on a hedgehog, caused by the sugar content in the Cherryade having dried solid. We'd laughed and had bestowed him with a new name, *Dennis the Menace,* which I'd been sure he would have preferred to his usual nickname, *Crying Face* which he was lovingly known to us by, on account he cried a lot, even when he was happy!

As we'd turned the corner of Stamford Street, we'd noticed the police car parked further up under the dim light of the lamppost outside our house. Mammy and Uncle Christy were standing outside talking with a policeman, which was all too reminiscent of the times they'd often come along to arrest one of the family, but mainly daddy, even though this time we knew he was already in jail.

We'd taken our time walking up along the street, attempting to hear what the nosey neighbours were whispering about but they had suddenly become dumb as we'd approached, before finding their voices again, once we had passed by. Aunty Mary had come outside to join mammy and Uncle Christy and we could only think there must have been another big row which wouldn't have been out of the ordinary whenever there was a family gathering! Weddings, funerals, christenings, midnight Mass, St Patrick's Day, any day really! None could ever have been in the Irish tradition without a big fight to finish off on a high note!

"Here they are now," said mammy, as all eyes had suddenly fixed on the four of us making our way up to the house.

I had never known why it was, but when a group of people stood staring at me I would come over feeling guilty, even when I had known I'd done nothing wrong! And if anyone should take the blame for this, then it would have to have been our daddy. He'd beaten us and had accused us of doing things we had not done, to the point, we would admit to having done it just to stop the beatings. "I can see by the look in yer feckin' eyes, it was yea that did it!" daddy would stare directly into the eyes of which every one of us he was accusing and he would hold our gaze until our eyes watered and stung so much, we would have to concede defeat.

Often, I had looked in the mirror, trying to work out just what that look in my eyes was which betrayed me, practicing to be able to keep them open whilst I'd stared at myself. But I had found to my cost, the more I had attempted to act innocent even when I was, the more I had looked guilty.

"Have yah been back ta the house since yah left?" asked mammy slipping another fag into her mouth and lighting it with the dimp of the one she had just finished smoking, before throwing the dimp to the ground.

"No, Mammy," said Martin.

"The doors were locked." Bernie dug the hole for us again!

"I thought Martin just said, yah hadn't been back ta the house?" mammy glared suspiciously at Martin.

"I said, we've not been in the house, mammy." said Martin, throwing an angry scowl at Bernie.

"Did yah see anyone while yah were here?"

"How d'ya mean, mammy." said Martin.

"Only Granddad." said Bernie.

"Yea'd hang the feckin' lot of us-so yah would!" Nabby scolded our little sister, under his breath.

"How d'ya mean yah saw yer Granddad! Where?"

"Ah – Well he was -'

"Peering out the window at us." I said, helping out my tongue-tied brother, "An' don't say another feckin' word!" I'd whispered to Bernie.

"What da'ya mean! He was peering out the feckin' window at yah! What window."

"Yer bedroom window, mammy!"

"He waved to us." Nabby got in on the lies.

"Are yah sure it was yer Granddad yah saw Tommy?" questioned Uncle Christy, as mammy and Aunty Mary had scurried back into the house.

'Ah - Well – He'd tapped on the window and said hello ta Martin-not me. Didn't he, Martin?" Feck this! All those questions had made me feel nervous, bringing on that awful *guilty* look. There was something not right, and no one was telling us, was the awful feeling I'd had. And where was Granddad? He obviously hadn't woken up yet – unless – Oh

God forgive us! "It was an accident! We'd banged him on the head with the big box and put him in mammy's bed!" I had been on the point of blurting out, when an almighty scream shocked everyone into silence.

"He's in the bed!"

"It was us!" Nabby had suddenly confessed to Uncle Christy, "We did it!"

"Yea did what, Nabby?"

"We killed Granddad - Well, Martin, Tommy and Bernie, did all the killin'!" the feckin snitcher! "I'd just stood and watched them pushing the big box out of the way! It must have fell on his head! Martin said, granddad was drunk, that's all! An' so we put him in mammy's bed to keep him warm!" he had pretended to cry and after we finished snarling at him, the three of us had followed suit.

"What the feck are they carryin' on about?" mammy angrily snapped as she'd came back outside standing on the front step and lighting another cigarette, "I've enough havin' ta contend with yer dead Grandfather!"

"What's goin' on in the house?" Uncle Christie had asked her.

"The auld man's lying in me bed! An' unless he's one of them feckin' walking dead people. Somebody's been up ta no good! Mary's in there on bended knees at the minute swearing blind it's a miracle! The police have called the doctor, though I can't see what the feck for! He's as dead as he's ever goin' ta be for sure!"

"Here Martin." Uncle Christy had taken us to one side and had placed a half-crown into Martin's hand, telling us to feck off to the sweet shop, "An' don't worry about a ting." he assured us in a low voice, "I'll sort it all out. An' say feck all to yer mammy or anyone else about it." he'd given us a big smile.

"D'ya think he wasn't dead after all?" Uncle Christy had asked mammy in a matter of fact way with the hint of a wry smile on his face.

"He's been laying in his coffin for five feckin days doing nothing Christie! What d'ya tink he was doin'? Havin' a long kip!"

-FORTY-

Standing alongside Martin, Bernie and Nabby, we'd watched the fires flames soar high towards the sky, as they had hungrily wrapped themselves around Guy Fawkes, sitting at the top of the bonfire, while the frenzied cheers and shouts from the crowd had echoed around the croft, "Burn yah bastard! Yah fucking traitor!" mingled with the loud noises and acrid smell of gunpowder and smoke as the fireworks whizzed in all directions across the dark Tuesday skies. The lady with the tray of sticky toffee apples had told us to piss off, as she wasn't "A bleedin charity! If you want a toffee apple then it's thruppence for each one!"

Martin had lit our last Catherine Wheel and had thrown it on the ground close behind the woman, who'd suddenly beat a retreat, hop-skipping and jumping away from the out of control firework dancing around her feet. We'd picked off the bigger bits of dirt sticking to the thick sticky treacle as we had hurried off around to the other side of the bonfire, out of the woman's sight, before she'd had time to get over the initial shock.

Earlier that morning, we'd gone to the church to see our Granddad off to heaven, though Uncle Bernard Ward, along with a few of the others, was minded to believe, "The devil would have been hard pressed to have him!" Mammy and Granny were still none the wiser to how Granddad could have managed to climb out of his and walk through the house and make himself comfortable in mammy's bed, when he hadn't budged an inch all the time he'd laid in the morgue for the previous five days! As for us. We had not known what a 'Wake' was, until we had seen Granddad standing in his coffin, which lent up against the far wall by the window, giving him a good view of the drunken mourners gathered around him. To be honest, he'd not looked much different compared to a few of the others in the room, small, gaunt, skinny and pale, only his eyes were closed and he was dead sober!

At the church, Father Murphy seemed to have had a lot of nice things to say about Granddad, which must have been all feckin' lies, considering what some of the family had been saying about him. The old priest had even said, how lovely it had been to see all his family coming together from as far afield as Ireland and Scotland, to pay their last respects to a *dear family member* only to curse the lot of us when our Granddad Jim, daddy's daddy, had boxed Uncle Bernard in the gob for no other reason than our Uncle having gone into a coughing fit, when it came to Granddad, singing his solo song, *Kevin Barry*.

"He did it on feckin' purpose ta drown out me singing, so he feckin' did!' our drunken Granddad had hit the roof.

Drown out yer singing by feck! Its yea that needs drowning, so we don't have ta put up with the noise anymore! Yah auld bastard yah!" snapped Uncle Bernard, licking his swollen lip.

"Will yah keep the peace!" pleaded Aunty Brenda, as she'd stood in front of her fat husband, "Bernard's had a bad cold all the week! Just look at the state of that nose of his, all red and sore like it is."

"Ah shallup, yah feckin who-ere!' mammy had taken a swing at Aunty Brenda, completely missing her target and falling in a heap on the church floor. As small as she had been, our Aunty could put up a good fight and she had given mammy a good kick up the hole, warning her, she wouldn't be responsible for what will happen next if mammy carried on giving out to her. But there wasn't much she was able to do, when mammy had staggered to her feet and had suddenly grabbed a handful of Aunty Brenda's hair, before dragging the poor woman off up the church aisle and would probably have dragged her all the way back to Stamford Street, if it hadn't been for the big clump of hair which had suddenly separated from her head!

Having already decided between us we'd not wanted to see our Granddad put down into a hole in the ground, Martin and me had managed to sneak off around the corner of the church to the old unused graveyard, where we had hid ourselves from view behind the gravestones, until we were sure everyone had gone, before we had headed across into Longsight where we would often spend hours on end scavenging amongst the empty streets of derelict houses where you could still happen upon something useful, someone else may have missed in their own searches.

We had met up with, Paul Ryan, Kevin Taylor, and a few other kids we knew, allowing us all to drift onto each other's territories without many problems as long as none of us took the piss by refusing to let each other join in searching the same derelict houses. We'd had this unspoken understanding, that nothing belonged to anyone until they had found it, as in *Finders Keepers.* Not long afterwards, we were joined by two of our older cousins, Michael and Sonny O'Connor, who would normally hang out with Shamie and his gang. They lived in Gorton with their mammy and daddy and seven sisters. Their daddy was also in prison for stabbing their Uncle; his brother, for humping their mammy and eldest sister Nancy. Daddy had warned us to keep away from the whole family, "Especially cousin Sonny! That fella's a feckin' screw loose in his head!" When I'd told Cousin Michael, what daddy had said about his older brother, he had burst out laughing and said, "Sonny had a feckin' boxful of loose screws in his bounce, let alone the one!"

Sean Docherty, a tall skinny lad with a long beanpole neck and a tiny head balanced on the top of it, had invited us to play a game of six-a-side football. There were six of them up against four of us, but we'd agreed anyhow because we were Manchester United, the greatest team to have ever lived, up against Manchester City, who had gone four-nil up within the first two minutes of the game! They were of course a much better class of footballer than we were ever going to be, and it had seemed we were on a hiding to nothing! Yet, five minutes later, City had suddenly conceded defeat to United, because of too many injuries! Though I like to think it was more to do with the fact, they had realised they had met their match and we were just too good for them! Especially when Sonny had suddenly cottoned on to the fact, he was supposed to chase down the City players for the ball and not wait in the unlikely event they would pass it to him! Anyhow it hadn't mattered them conceding. We'd been odds-on to win the game, with City still having their four goals while United had gone on to knock in sixteen, Sonny having scored fifteen of them, with the City goalkeeper scoring the last one after kicking the ball, which had belonged to him, through his own post markers before racing off with it across the croft with Sonny in hot persuit, screaming for the ball like a demented lunatic.

The later part of the afternoon had taken the four of us across to Hulme Lock, to explore some of the derelict warehouses there. This is where Shamie had once taken Martin and me, rat hunting. The place to catch them was in the once busy loading bay tunnels of the derelict Merchant Warehouse, where the barges used to float in every day to offload their goods. Lots of kids would come up here with their toy catapults and shoot at the rats with small pieces of brick or mortar or anything else small and hard enough to do some damage.

Shamie would made his own catapults. And they were powerful! But unlike my big brother, who had been a deadeye shot, me and Martin were hopeless. The nearest I had ever come to shooting a rat was on that very first occasion when he had taken us along with him. He'd spotted a cat-sized rat sitting on a windowsill of the Irwell Rubber Company, with its back to us. There it had sat, minding its own business and washing itself clean when Shamie, who was about ten yards ahead and off to my left, had suddenly stopped and had pointed out the monster to me, indicating in sign language so the rat wouldn't hear, that he had wanted me to have the kill! Martin, who had been standing close to me, had stopped still while I had slowly inched my way nearer, until I was no further than about five yards away from it. Closing the one eye, I had taken careful aim at the rat's big brown shiny arse and had let the stone fly. I'd heard a squeal, as the rat had dived off the windowsill back into the water.

"Feckin' hell Tommy!' Shamie had not been too pleased about my useless shot! Holding his hand to the tip of his bleeding nose, he'd bellowed at me, "It was there! A huge feckin' rat, the size of an Alsatian dog! Right there in front of yer gimpy feckin' eyes! I'm standin' a mile away from yah, an' yah still manage to feckin' hit me! God Jasis! Yah must have bandy feckin' eyes as well legs!" And that was the last time and only time he'd taken me rat hunting with him!

By the late afternoon, our two cousins had decided to call it a day and we had made arrangements to come over into Gorton the following day and hang around with them. We'd watched from the top windows of the derelict warehouse as they'd made their way back along the edge of the canal bank, until they had eventually disappeared from our view. And that was when we had suddenly noticed the two fellas, one carrying a smaller kid on his shoulders, heading from the other direction straight towards the warehouses!

It would have been impossible not to have recognised the Boyd brothers, Pat and Jimmy, with their youngest brother, Billy sitting on his brother's shoulders. The fact Jimmy Boyd was pointing a finger straight up in our direction was a good enough indication, they'd seen us. And even if they had not recognised Martin, we still had to be afraid of these!

"Sonny! Michael! Sonny Michael!" We had shouted at the top of our voices, in the hope our two cousins might still have been close enough to have heard us, as the Boyd brothers had reached the derelict warehouse and were gawking upwards.

"Yea's can come down!" Paddy Boyd shouted up to us, "I

only want ta have a word with yea's." though he was pointing the barrel of the air rifle straight up at us. With the light fading quickly, we'd thought, there might have been a slight chance we would be able to get out of the warehouse and slip away unnoticed. Parts of the buildings back walls and roof were already missing, with large areas of flooring ripped out for firewood or other useful purposes, leaving wide areas of empty space where, in the dim light, we were just able to see all the way down to the ground floor.

"Yea'll have to come up here, if yea want ta talk to us!" Martin had called down. But there had been no response from the Boyd brothers, who had moved out of our sight.

Accepting the only possible escape route out of the top room was to make our way across the thick wide wooden beams, spanning about fifteen feet of empty space with a twenty foot drop to the ground floor on both sides and then having to make our way down the demolished parts of the outer wall, we had committed ourselves and made our move. My fear of looking downwards would have been a problem in the daylight, but as there had not been much to see, I had felt relatively safe making my way across the bean with the darkness below me and Martin leading the way staying close to me.

We eventually reached ground level without any mishaps, before quietly sneaking out through a small hole in the wall at the side of the building, relieved not to have come across the Boyd brothers, minded to believe the cowardly bastards had decided not to risk coming all the way up to the top of the building in the ever-decreasing light. But unfortunately for us, we had let our guard down!

331

"Thought we'd gone did yah!" Pat Boyd had appeared from out of the thick undergrowth along the edge of the water. He was pointing the barrel of the air rifle straight at Martin, who'd instinctively threw his arms up into the air, like the cowboys did in the films, when John Wayne pointed a gun at them. His brother's, Jimmy and Billy had stood behind us, blocking off any escape route.

"You. Ugly fucker. In the water. Now!' Pat Boyd snapped at Martin.

"He can't swim," I'd said.

"Boo-fuckin' hoo for him! Then you can jump in! Know-all! Or I'll shoot yah dead!" he'd pointed the barrel of the rifle at me. But unlike my brother Martin and for no particular reason that I could explain, I had not thrown my arms up in the air. Instead, I had defiantly glared up at him just like John Wayne would have done if the boot had been on the other foot and he'd been in my situation.

"He can't swim either," said Martin.

"Well yah can both fuckin' learn! Yah pair of Irish bastards!"

"Can't yah leave them alone!" said Billy Boyd, 'They've done nowt to us."

"Haven't we seen yer ugly mug before?' said Pat Boyd, ignoring his little brother and pointing the rifle back at Martin, who had been shaking so much, I could have sworn I'd been able to hear every bone in his body rattling. Of course, my brother had denied having ever set eyes on the two bastards. And I had not fancied jumping into the filthy water, to be eaten by all those shitty rats, who were bound to recognise Martin and me, as the ones who came up here with Shamie, to shoot at them!

"We're not gettin' in the water." I'd heard myself say, before swallowing the lump of fear down my throat. And though my bones had joined Martin in a duet, it had seemed I'd lost all sense of reality and I had carried on, "An' if yah want us to get in there, then yea'll have ta put us in there yerself! An' if yah try to put us in there yerself, I'll bite yer feckin' nose off yer face, so I will!"

"Oh yah will yah!" raged Pat Boyd, once again aimed the barrel of the air rifle straight at me, "Gobby little fucker aren't yah! Well let's see how gobby yah are!" he'd handed the air rifle to his brother Jimmy, before suddenly grabbing hold of me and throwing me to the ground and undoing the buttons of his trousers. 'Yah can give me a gobble for yer lip. An' shoot that little fucker's eyes out and throw him in the canal if he doesn't!" he told Jimmy Boyd, referring to Martin.

"Leave him alone!" shouted Billy Boyd, rushing away from his brother Jimmy, to stand between me and Pat Boyd, giving me time to get back on my feet.

"Ouch-what the fuck!" Jimmy Boyd had suddenly yelped out, as his hand had automatically shot up to the side of his bleeding head.

"Prepare ta die yah Boydy bastards yah!"

My heart had jumped up into my mouth as Shamie and Jaffa, had appeared from nowhere brandishing their catapults. They had been followed closely by our two cousins Michael and Sonny, charging in from the opposite direction like a pair of demented cavemen wielding lumps of wood high in the air.

The battle, if you could have called it a *battle*, had lasted all of a minute with Jimmy Boyd, after getting a couple of clubs around the head, jumping into the canal and heading off across to the far side, with Pat, the tougher of the two, holding his ground and shoving the barrel of the gun straight up Sonny's left nostril, stopping him in his tracks. "It might be just a lead pellet, but it can still do a lot of fuckin' damage to what's left of your brain!" he'd threatened, although the threat had no impact on Sonny, who had brought the lump of wood down with a heavy blow on Pat Boyd's shoulder, causing him to drop to his knees and dropping the air rifle in the process.

"Ahh! Yah broke me fuckin' shoulder, yah fucker!'

"That's what I meant ta do, twat features!" Sonny whacked him across the side of the head, "An' I'm goin' ta break every other bone in yer body!" he'd raised the lump of wood ready for another swing.

"Hang on Sonny!" said Shamie, as he and Jaffa came over and stood looking down at Billy Boyd. 'Who've yah got there with yah?' he'd asked us, giving Billy the once over.

"Billy," said Billy, "I'm their brother."

"An' our friend," Martin had quickly added, stepping closer to the little kid, "He's nothin' to do with any of this. An' how'd yah know we was here?"

"Yah can recognise Tommy's big gob, anywhere!' said Shamie, 'It's like a foghorn! Lucky for you, me an' Jaffa were further along breaking windows when Sonny and Michael came along and we'd heard yah! Anyway the tree of yea can feck of now, while we have a chat with this fecker.

"Yea won't be hurting him? I mean, not too much, will yah not." Asked Billy, though he'd not seemed too concerned for his brothers.

"Nah. We only want to show him the errors of his ways, especially why he shouldn't be asking little kids to gobble him, that's all.' lied Shamie.

"Just yea wait!' Jimmy Boyd had suddenly shouted across from the other side of the canal, where he'd managed to pull himself up out of the dirty water and on to the towpath. "Yer already fuckin' dead an' buried the lot of yah! He'd threatened while holding the side of his head, "Git over here, Billy! They won't dare hurt yea!"

"I'm not comin' with yea!"

"Just wait till mammy an' daddy hear yer hanging about with them dirty Irish cunts! There'll be murders in the house!"

"There'll be more murders if mammy an' daddy find out yea were showing your mickey to Cathleen when they were off down the pub last week!"

"Don't be feckin' showin' me up with them lies now, Billy!"

"Sure they're not lies! Me and Connor were peeping in at the pair of yah through the keyhole! We saw her kissin' yer mickey! We've seen her doing it before as well!"

"Me mickey got caught in me zip an' she was only helpin', that was all! So don't be fuckin' makin' up these tings as yah go along!"

"Yah weren't wearin' any trousers when we were doing all the peepin' an' she was sucking it like a lollypop! We could see everything goin' on! An' yer big boily arse goin' in an' out!"

"Just wait till I get me fuckin' hands on yah, Jimmy! Yah dirty bastard yah!' Pat Boyd had screamed across at his brother.

He's a liar Pat! He's makin' it all up! I swear!"

"I wouldn't mind this Cathleen helping me with me zip and kissing me mickey better." laughed, Jaffa "whose girlfriend is it anyway?'

"Cathleen's our sister." said Billy.

-FORTY-ONE-

I had been over in Gorton scavenging amongst some derelict houses with Nabby and Martin. These had already been searched through many times and had been stripped to the bone, with hardly any upstairs floorboards left to walk on. But, as we had not searched them previously we did so, on the off chance we might find something of value.

The kids around the surrounding towns lived dangerously throughout their childhood, though I don't suppose as kids, we'd had any thoughts of the dangers we had risked day after day. Until of course something had happened to serve as a reminder. It had seemed we had become blinded by the opportunity of finding something worthwhile to take home, that we had never heeded the warning signs of danger. We had walls and roofs crashing down on the houses we'd been searching through just moments earlier! We'd fallen through floors. Burnt ourselves, burning off the rubber casing from the electrical flex. We'd grazed, bruised and badly cut ourselves. And yet, we still came back again and again for no other reason than, we had to. It was in our blood. It had been our way of life. For the poorest of families of Manchester, this was our means to survival. And if Manchester hadn't been ripped asunder by the demolition gangs, then God only knows how the poor children of Hulme, Moss Side, Gorton, Longsight and the surrounding towns could have survived.

In the early part of the afternoon, we'd been playing in the car park up by the Speedway Stadium near Bellevue Zoo. This

was the place where lots of kids came to race their handmade bogies around the cindered surface, pretending to be one of their heroes from the Aces Speedway team. It was great fun, if you'd had a bogie to ride, which we hadn't this time, because a few days previously some thieving bastards had stolen the one we had stolen some weeks back, when we had left it outside the back gate in the alleyway for no more than a minute or two. So we had to rise the two ladies' bikes we'd stolen from the graveyard of St John's Church, over to the stadium, with Nabby sitting on the handlebars of the bike Martin had been riding

We had great fun racing the bikes across the cinder surface of the ground before hitting the front brakes, causing the back of the bikes to go in a different direction from the front. The idea being to try and get the bike to skid a full circle as well as kicking up as much dust as possible. It seemed easy, if you were just a bystander watching, but it wasn't easy. You had to get the pressure of the braking just right and if you didn't, then there was every chance the back of the bike would rear up in the air, as Martin had found out to his detriment, at his first attempt, which had everyone watching, in stitches.

It had been one of the funniest things I had ever seen in my whole life! There was Martin, madly peddling down the graveled slope before suddenly slamming his front brake on with the front of the bike coming to a sudden stop, as expected, only for the back of it to kept going causing the bike to complete a full somersault with Martin hitting the deck and the bike landing on top of him!

We sold the bikes on to a rag and bone man for two shilling

before heading off back in the direction of Longsight, where we had been chased up along the railway sidings by a one of the rail workers, after he's spotted us searching around in one of the engineering sheds, where we'd found ourselves a small metal sandwich box sticking up from one of the engineer's lunch bags. Martin had taken the box out of the bag and had opened the lid for us to see the four doorstep spam and pickle sandwiches and the three shelled boiled eggs staring up at us.

"Hoy! What are yah doin' in here?' the rail worker had spotted us.

Like greyhounds out of their traps, we'd set off at speed out of the side door of the works shed and up along the track sidings, making our way across the rail lines toward the coal depot on the opposite side. Martin had told Nabby, who was a stride behind us, to hop over the rails and not to touch them as they might be alive. But moments later we'd heard him scream out loud - much louder than any of the screams our older sisters had screamed, when daddy was beating them. We'd hurried back to find him desperately wriggling his skinny right leg trying to pull his foot out from between the two rails that were gripping it. "They just snapped at me foot and grabbed me!" cried Nabby, "Is it 'cos we stole that fella's food? Martin! Get me out! I don't want to be eaten!"

"Yah won't be eaten, so shallup or yea'll have everyone on top of us!" I'd snapped.

"Yah said they were alive!"

"I didn't mean alive feckin' alive, as in them breathing, alive!"

"Anyway, these ones are dead. Otherwise you'd be dead by

now!" I'd tried to pacify him.

"There's a train coming!" Martin had pointed up along the track in the direction of Longsight station, where we could see one of the coal trains slowly moving down the track in our direction, causing Nabby to scream even louder.

"Run to the train and make it stop!' said Martin. And so I'd taken off along the track in the direction of the oncoming coal train waving my arms and screaming at the top of my voice for it to stop! I could see the driver as the train had come alongside me and then just glided past, separating me from my brothers!

"Martin! Nabby!' I'd screamed their names, but my voice had been drowned out by the noise of the train's brakes suddenly grinding against the wheels as they'd squealed and slid along on the shiny metal surface of the rail lines, before the giant metal monster had shuddered to a sudden halt.

I had ran back along the side of the train, fearful for my brothers, until I'd suddenly heard Martin's voice, calmly talking above the other voices, "His foot got stuck!" and then I'd heard my little brother suddenly asking "Has anyone any sweets?"

"Hey! You!" the two rail workers had ran round from the back of the train and had hurried down the track towards me. But they were never going to be quicker than me, as I'd scarpered off like a frightened fox, across the rest of the rail lines and back into Longsight, while they could only stop, out of breath and look on.

The fact Martin and Nabby had not been hurt had filled me with so much joy, I had almost skipped along the street heading up to the recreation ground, known to us as, Sand Park, which we had picked as our meeting place in the event of becoming separated for one reason or another, which had been a common event for us, considering we were always being chased. The Policeman, the Shopkeeper, the Bus Conductor, the Milkman, the Truant Man, the park Pervert, the Priest, the Drunk! The whole world-or so it had seemed, had wanted to chase us down!

Once, Sergeant Turner had shown Martin and me some old documents, while we were sitting in the police station waiting to be charged with *Grand Larceny*. This was our impressive one hundred and eighty fifth charge to date! Mainly for petty thieving, but mostly for stealing bicycles. We'd been caught by the police this time, running up the road on a Sunday afternoon carrying a chewing gun machine, which we had managed to force off the wall of a corner shop. We had told them, we'd found it and were bringing it to the police station! But our protests of innocence had fallen on deaf ears. The fact we had been hurrying off in the opposite direction from the police station, hadn't helped our argument.

"Look at this!" Sergeant Turner, had stabbed his podgy finger down on a tatty page of the old document, "Ten years! That's how old this child had been when he was hung by the neck until he was dead! And what for-hmm? Stealing a silk hanky! That's what for! And another here!" He had gone down the list of children's names, hung for the most minor of crimes, "Hung by the neck for stealing a goat! Children the same age as you pair of little toe-rags! Doesn't it even bother you!" he'd glared angrily at the pair of us, as we'd stared up at the ceiling.

"We don't steal dirty hankies-or goats, for that matter." said

Martin.

"Where you a young lad in them days?" I'd asked a sincere question, but instead of answering me the Sergeant had turned on his heels shaking his head with despair and walked off muttering something about us being, "Born too late!"

I had not known how long I had waited in the Park for Martin and Nabby to show up. Time was always a hard thing to judge, especially when the days grew darker, much earlier than they normally did in the summer. So I had no real idea as to how long I had sat on the swing in the light drizzle, waiting for the pair of them to come along with the rail man's sandwiches. Though, it had seemed an age since the three of us had become separated by the train. For some while, there had been lots of kids playing in the park and I'd joined in a game of football up inside the large open sided shelter. But as the grey light of day had slowly faded towards darkness, they had drifted off to their homes in small groups until eventually I was on my own. Not that being alone in the dark had bothered me too much. But even so, I had taken some comfort from the fact there had been some working street lights dotted about the area.

I had toyed with the idea that perhaps my two brothers had already been taken home by the police and whether I should make my own way home. But torn between that thought the pair of them would suddenly show up any minute, I'd decided to hang about for just a little while longer. It was the flare of a light that had first grabbed my attention before noticing the young couple Myra Hindley and Ian Brady standing together in the gloom.

-FORTY-TWO-

I could see the top half of them standing on the opposite side of the small boundary wall of the park as Brady had lit a cigarette and had then held the flame to Hindley's cigarette before he had taken a long look across in my direction before the pair of them had continued on their way along Ducie Street, seemingly paying no more particular attention to me. I'd began to swing myself high into the air, only noticing as the swing had swung backwards and forwards a couple of times, Hindley and Brady were walking a short distance away, past the swings and heading up in the direction of the shelter.

This time, I did pay particular attention to them as I had continued to swing higher and higher, showing off my fearless prowess I suppose. They had stopped a short distance from the shelter at the top of the park and had seemed to be having a conversation with each other, before they had headed back down the path in my direction with Hindley stopping a short distance away from the swings, which I'd deliberately slowed down with my foot and watched her approach, while Brady had remained where he had stood some fifteen yards or so away, the fag dangling from his mouth and both his hands pushed deep into his dark raincoat, which had the collar of it turned up around his ears. He had seemed uninterested in me or Hindley and had stood looking about his surroundings while she, standing a few yards away from me, had thrown me the sweetest of smiles. I'd anticipated her saying something to me, but when she'd said nothing but just stood looking at me, I had thrown her back a brief smile to let her know, at the very least, I was approachable before returning to my usual facial scowl, bestowed on those people I didn't know, as well as serving its purpose to keep my emotions unreadable.

Standing sideways on to me, Hindley had lent her head slightly to one side and had thrown me a coy look. "Hello." she said, speaking in a soft reassuring voice, "Are you waiting for your friends?"

"No!" I had quickly answered, as if the question had been an accusation, lying as I had always done when not wanting people to know my business. In some way, Hindley had reminded me of my eldest sister Rosemary, though my sister would have been a little younger, around seventeen-years of age, though Hindley had been taller and much heavier in build. But her features, especially her eyes, seemed to soften, just as my sisters always did when she had smiled. Their hair too had matched in style, though my sister's hair was fair in colour, while Hindley's, from what I could make out, had seemed a dull white, which had been covered by a light pink nylon headscarf.

"You're a bit too young to be out in the dark by yourself aren't you?"

"I'm seven and a bit." I'd proudly told her, "An' I'm not scared of the dark".

"You don't have to be." said Hindley, moving a little closer to the swings, while I had used my foot to keep it gently moving backwards and forwards, "I'm not either."

There had been a brief lull in the conversation before she had continued, "Haven't seen you round these parts before. What street are you from?"

"24 Stamford Street, Hulme, Manchester, 15." my address had rolled off my tongue, just as my sister Elizabeth had taught all of us to remember off by heart, until it had been engrained on our brains. Which had served its purpose on the odd occasions we had travelled much further than we ought to have done. Once ending up in Newcastle, when me and Martin had hitched a ride, sneaking into the back of a packed removal truck, while the removal men had taken a break.

"Hulme!" Hindley had seemed quite surprised and had looked back over her shoulder in the direction of Brady, "The lads from Hulme!"

"Hurry up!" Brady had spoken impatiently, throwing a glance down in our direction, before looking back in the direction of the shelter.

"You hungry?" Hindley had asked me, before quickly telling me, "You look hungry."

Bringing the swing to a halt, I had nodded, throwing her the hint of a smile and she walked the few yards to me, where she placed her hand on the chain, "What's the little lads name then?"

In the cool breeze, I had been able to smell a heavy mixture of her perfume and hairspray coming off her and reminding me of the nice lady who had cuddled me, when she had thought the dead old lady who had fallen down the concrete steps, had been my granny.

"Tommy."

"How about a jam buttie? Then we'll get you straight home?" she had enticingly raised her dark eyebrows, while I had swallowed the memory of the last time I had greedily scoffed down lumps of bread covered in thick sweet jam, as I'd nodded my approval to Myra Hindley.

"Come on then Tommy!' She'd playfully shook the swing chain, and I'd slid my arse off, offering my hand out for her to take as I'd did so. But she had ignored the offer and had suddenly thrown her hands deep into her coat pockets, "You mustn't be seen walking with me, or you'll get in to trouble." She'd warned, the brief expression on her face, showing a slight look of concern, "I'll call you when to come." Hindley had walked off around the swings away from both myself and Brady and headed in the direction of Ducie Street.

I had taken her warning to mean, I mustn't get caught talking to her, as we were strangers to one another. We had been told this on so many occasions by Sister Joseph, Mr. Coleman, our Headmaster, Father Murphy and anyone else who had wanted to put out on us, because of the potential dangers of talking to strangers. But we had to make use of every opportunity that came our way, which had played an important part in our survival. And if it hadn't been for the many kind strangers, who had given us their pennies, with some allowing us into their homes, washing and feeding us before sending us on our way, life on the streets would have been much harsher.

I had always considered myself to be more streetwise than the average kid, because I had known the streets better than most having begged off them and almost living off them. And as well as being aware of those places not to venture near, I had a gift of being able to read every given situation that I had found myself in, but even so, I would never have gone off with a man if he had been on his own. But a woman on her own, or a woman with a man was an exception to the rule. For no other reason than having always felt safe being in the company of a woman; unless she'd been a nun, and Hindley had seemed no different to the many other women we had met on our adventures through the streets.

We would often deliberately go to the parks where the perverts would hang around and suddenly peek out of a bush, asking one of us to come over and see something. And as I'd been the fastest runner, I would be the one to go to the bush and ask for a shilling, promising to come into the bushes once they'd handed over the dosh. And when they did, I'd flick the coin to Martin and he'd hurriedly walk away with the money safely tucked away in his pocket before I too made off in a hurry!

I had watched Myra Hindley as she had walked off on her own for a short distance before she had suddenly stopped and called out to me, "Come on then Tommy." Glancing over to where Brady had stood, still rooted to the same spot. He had taken a last deep drag of his cigarette, before throwing the dimp to the ground and digging his hand back into his coat pocket.

"Come on then!" Hindley had called out to me again and I had immediately followed her out onto the street where, we had eventually walked under the railway road bridge further up along one of the roads leading back into Gorton.

There had been no urgency in Hindley's pace as she had walked ahead of me, allowing me to be able to keep the same distance between us. At one stage of my journey I had felt a sudden sense of guilt come over me, as I had thought of Martin and Nabby, wishing the pair of them could have been walking with me, so we could have all shared in the treat. But the guilt had quickly subsided, as I had reminded myself that they had the lunch box and would probably have scoffed the lot down them by now!

The roads along the way had been relatively quiet, with only the odd car passing us by. Above me, the sky had grown darker, the chimneys stacks already at work spewing out their plumes of thick black smoke, which rose up into the darkening grey sky and lending itself to the pollution already hanging not too far above the rooftops of the houses.

Gorton, like Hulme, had its fair share of dilapidating housing hiding away in the shadows of the *better'* streets, with their tarmacked roads and nice Edwardian houses, with front gardens all lit up by their bright electric streetlights. And yet, just a stone's throw away in any one direction, you could walk into a street of back-to-back Victorian slums, some, still with their cobbled stoned streets and lit up by the depressive aura of the Gaslamp's, made the more bleaker by the fine wispy smog hanging in the air.

Taking a glance over my shoulder, I had noticed Ian Brady, was following some way behind us. His hands were still deep inside his coat pockets and his head still bowed low, half hidden inside the collar of his coat, though it had not been a particularly cold or wet evening as such.

Myra Hindley had suddenly turned off the main road into a side street, forcing me to quicken my pace so I wouldn't lose sight of her. And as I had followed her around the corner, I had noticed she had slowed her own pace and was looking over her shoulder in my direction, I assumed to make sure I still had her in my sights, before she'd upped her pace again, crossing over the road and walking in through the gate leading into Gorton Park.

As I'd followed Hindley into the park, I'd suddenly had a flashback of the summer just passed, when Martin, Bernie, Me and Nabby, had walked through the same gates and had joined lots of other people sitting in the warm sun on the freshly cut grass, as a brass band were giving an impromptu performance, as they had practiced. Another of daddy's old saying was, "Where there is lots of people gathered there are lots of opportunities to be had." Finding the odd coin that might have slipped from someone's pocket or the odd shopping bag to dip a hand into! And so we had settled ourselves down on the grass with our vulture-like eyes scouring the area for potential opportunities to be had.

When the band had finished their practicing, we had circled the people who had gathered around to wish the band well for some upcoming tournament. I had my eye on an open shopping bag and the box of Ritz biscuits resting inside, when I had suddenly seen Martin from the corner of my eye, hurrying backwards, away from the crowd, dragging a huge brass tuba with him! We had always had an unspoken understanding about stealing only the smallest of objects. Especially when there were lots of people around! The idea of course, was to make it harder for us to be caught! So it had been beyond my understanding to know what had possessed my brother to grab the biggest feckin' thing he could lay his thieving hands on and drag it across the grass in full view of everyone! The three of us had instinctively dashed off to help Martin, managing between the four of us, to lift the heavy instrument off the ground and run across the park with it.

"What are yah goin' ta do with it?" asked Nabby.

"Play the feckin' ting, what d'ya tink!" said Martin.

"Yea can't play one of them tings! - Can yah?"

"He's only coddin' yah Nabby." I'd said.

"So what are yah goin' ta do with it then Martin? Bernie had thrown the same question.

"We'll hide it in the bushes and come back for it when it gets dark."

How he'd thought no-one noticed four children running across a park with a huge brass tuba was beyond me! The whole of feckin' Manchester must have seen us unless they'd either been fast asleep or feckin' blind! So it had hardly come as a surprise to see what had appeared to be the whole of Manchester hot on our heels, led by the bands conductor. Catching up with us by the second.

Accepting we had no chance of getting away we'd stopped on the footpath and had faced down the conductor, who'd held back the crowd with his baton held high in the air, as if readying himself for the next tune.

"Ten bob or we'll drop it on the path an' dance all over it!" threatened Martin.

We'd settled for three and six, sending Bernie over to get the money from the conductor first. When she'd returned to us, we had gently placed the huge tuba down on the grass before fleeing out of the park and back in the direction of Longsight.

-FORTY-THREE-

Following Myra Hindley across to the other side of Gorton park and along the streets I'd looked over to my right where I had been able to make out the silhouette of the huge red-bricked building of St Francis' Friary standing off in the distance, its tall tower lost somewhere in the mist. I had often stood on the wide open wasteland looking across at the huge red bricked building and wondering, what I would be able to see if I could have climbed right to the top. But as well as suspecting the fire brigade would not have had a long enough ladder to be able to bring me back down again, I had suspected all I would have seen, was a panoramic view of what I could already see from ground level. The derelict houses, the slums, the crofts, the smoking chimneys, the empty mills. And in between all of this, a concrete jungle. The *Crescents,* which had been slowly rising up from the ashes and standing out from what was otherwise a dull and dreary place.

Walking under the bright light shining down over the entrance of a pub which occupied a corner of Taylor Street, Hindley had peered back over her shoulder at me, throwing the briefest of smiles as she had done so on a number of occasions throughout our journey. Nearby, I'd heard the faint sound of a train, and then a group of young teddy boys, five in all, who had suddenly appeared from around the corner of the pub.

Smartly dressed in collars and ties, one of them had playfully stood in Hindley's way and had shimmied from side to side, like a footballer ready to make a tackle, as a few wolf whistles

351

had echoed along the street. But Myra Hindley had completely ignored their antics, walking straight on without deviating from her path, forcing the fella to step to one side, as his friends teased him. As they had disappeared in through the entrance to the pub, just a few strides ahead of me, I had noticed they couldn't have been much older than sixteen or seventeen. A quick glance over my own shoulder had told me, Ian Brady was no longer behind us and I had wondered if he had gone off into the pub for a pint. But other than that fleeting thought, I had thought no more of his sudden disappearance.

Throughout our journey we had walked along streets that were familiar to me, having walked along some of them a number of times before while on my scavenging expeditions. And despite the mix-match of gas and electric streetlights, this part of Gorton had seemed slighter better in some parts than those parts of Hulme where I had roamed, though it still radiated the same dismal dark dank atmosphere which ran through every nook and cranny along its endless dark and relatively silent corridors of streets and alleyways.

Turning off the main street I'd followed Hindley across a small croft between a row of terraced houses, before walking along a short wide entry cutting across two streets which had been lit up by a Gaslamp at the entrance to it. Hindley had paused at the other end of the entry for a brief moment, allowing me to get closer to her, before she walked out into Bannock street. And by the time I had hurried the short distance to reach the point where she had stood, she'd already opened the front door of her house, beckoning to me with her gloved hand, to come quickly. And I'd upped my pace to her.

To my surprise, as I got alongside Myra Hindley, Ian Brady had suddenly appeared from nowhere and was beside me, his hand on my shoulder gently guiding me in through the open doorway following Hindley into the house. I had looked straight up at him, and our eyes had met for the briefest of moments. And in that brief moment, I had noticed his distant unsmiling eyes, which had reminded me of my brother Paddy. Always serious looking, as if he'd forever had something playing on his mind, with his baby-face and deep blue eyes, and a thick mop of swept back hair, which is where the similarities ended. Paddy's hair was jet-black and greasy and swept back with the front of it slightly pulled down with an added twist, teddy-boy style, while Ian Brady's hair more was browner, wavier, and not as greasy as my brother liked to have his. Turning his gaze away from mine, Brady had closed the front door behind us.

Following Hindley through the house in to a back room, with Brady following close behind me, I'd stood watching her as she'd taken off her black leather gloves and dropped them on to the table top, which had only the one leaf up, before undoing her coat and then taking off her pink scarf and a long black silk neck scarf she'd had tucked inside her coat, which she'd hung over the back of one of three old chair, standing around the table which stood beneath the sash window overlooking the back of the house.

Hindley invited me over to sit down, and I'd sat on the frayed seat of the chair opposite the one she had hung her scarves over, with my back facing the fireplace and me facing a small alcove, where an open doorway led off to the left into what I'd assumed to be the kitchen. And despite the house feeling much warmer, dryer and devoid of that distinctive damp smell, which had lingered inside 24 Stamford Street, I had been surprised at how dreary the place had looked and felt, considering both Hindley and Brady, by appearance, were smartly dressed people with a self-assured confidence about them. Especially Myra Hindley, who had oozed, what I could only describe as a 'childlike charm' despite her age.

It was here in the back room that I'd been able to smell a mixture of stale tobacco and alcohol mingled with whiffs of Hindley's hairspray, which had smelt much stronger inside the house. A small saucer had been used as an ashtray and was full with a mixture of tipped and untipped cigarette dimps, sitting alongside some empty glass tumblers. Over to my right stood an old wooden cabinet with a couple of small framed photographs and other odds and sods on the top. Brady had walked straight off into the kitchen without saying a word and I had looked up at Myra Hindley and had smiled at her, as she'd lit a cigarette and blew a plume of fresh smoke across the room, before dropping the Ten Park-Drive cigarette packet down onto the table top, returning my smile. I had liked her. Especially her smile which had made her blue eyes light up.

"Do you have brothers and sisters? - Won't your mam be going up the wall?" Jasis! She was as bad as the coppers!

"Me mammy's gone off and left us on our own and she wouldn't give a shite if she never set eyes on the lot of us again! And me daddy's in prison and I hate him and wouldn't care if I never saw him again!" was the answer I had wanted to give to her questions. But none of us had ever spoken about the goings on within our family, which to us would have been worse than committing an original sin! And so, *Yes* or a *No"* was about the best Hindley was going to get out of me. Not that she had seemed all that interested, as she let her fag dangle from her mouth and slipped off her coat to reveal her knee length boots black skirt and black top. She'd walked away from the table in the direction of the kitchen just as Brady had suddenly came out and hung his coat up on a hook screwed onto a smaller door leading under the stairs, either to a cellar or a cupboard. Hindley hung her coat over his, before the pair of them had walked off into the kitchen together, where I had been able to hear their low muffled voices, along with other sounds, though I had not been able to hear what they were saying. Not that I had been particularly interested in their conversation. As usual and my only reason for being in the house, was on the promise of a bite to eat.

Taking in the rest of my surroundings, behind me stood an open fireplace with a dirty brass coloured mesh fireguard across it. Mammy had always kept our fireplace clean and filled with the cinders from the previous day's fire, which we would wash out in a bucket of cold water, ready to light again. But this fire hadn't been cleaned and was filled with the ashes from a previous fire. I'd homed in on the ticking of the wooden clock sitting on the mantelpiece, only able to see the wooden edge of it because its face had been hidden by some envelopes resting up against it. In the far corner of the room, next to the fireplace, the door of a cupboard stood ajar, wide enough for me to see an assortment of drink bottles on a shelf, easily recognising the large Bells Whisky bottle, because it had been one of daddy's favourite drinks, though he'd been an Irishman!

I'd heard Myra Hindley suddenly speak sharpishly before lowering her voice. And for some unknown reason to me, this had unsettled me. I wasn't able to understand the reason for how I had felt. It wasn't fear. There had been nothing in my thoughts that had made me feel afraid of anything in particular. Indeed, it had been nothing new for me to be sitting in a stranger's house, sometimes much later than this. But the nagging feeling inside my head was telling me, "Something wasn't right!" which I had not been able to put my finger on. The thought had earlier passed through my mind, that Brady and Hindley somehow didn't seem to fit the house, in the sense, everything around me had given me a feeling of much older people. The furniture, the décor, everything about the room had seemed too old for such a smartly dressed young couple and it didn't fit that they would have bought such a mishmash of old bits and pieces of furniture, unlike the old junk which mammy and daddy would get, now and then, from the Social Services.

Hindley had walked back out of the kitchen and had plonked the plate down on the table top. She'd a glass in the other hand with a dark red liquid drink inside, which she had taken a swig of as I'd looked down, wide-eyed, with my mouth watering at the large inviting knocker of bread, thickly coated in red jam.

"Hurry up and get that down you and we'll get you off home." she'd said. And I'd immediately smelt the alcohol from her breath, which had smelt a little like the Sherry mammy always drank. Hindley then left the room, leaving her glass on the sideboard, and I'd heard her footsteps walking up the stairs.

Alone in the backroom, with just the tick-tock-ticking of the mantle clock for company, I had pulled the plate over to me and as I had stared down at the inviting thick slice of bread and jam, I'd noticed straight away, perhaps even disappointed, it had not been buttered. "What is wrong with me?" Usually, I would have been tucking into this kind offering by now, but instead, I had been throwing questions at myself. Had I just imagined Myra Hindley had seemed slightly apprehensive, almost nervous like? And certainly not as talkative or as cock-sure of herself as she had been before. Had I noticed her hand tremble slightly as she'd dropped the plate onto the table instead of placing it there? Had I imagined the warmth in her piercing blue eyes had diminished, leaving them slightly cold looking and distant as she had spoken those words to me? Had I imagined her childlike charm, replaced by a harsher tone in her voice? Why, unlike every other house I had been into, had both Myra Hindley and Ian Brady been the only people to have left me to eat on my own? Oh God! What is it! What are you trying to tell me!

I couldn't help, but feel how the atmosphere had changed since first walking into the house. Perhaps on account of me worrying over nothing. I had started to feel cold, which was unlike me, because, even in the winter I didn't really feel the cold that much. But here in this house, I had begun to feel a different kind of coldness, which had seemed to slowly creep inside my skin, gripping me tight and not wanting to let me go and making me feel uncomfortable!

It is hard to describe the awful feelings I had felt, except that I had become very unsure of my surroundings and I'd began questioning myself as to the reasons why I had been sitting in this house in the first place. And although I had sat in the houses of many kind people unknown to me, I had always made the first approach to them.

"What is it? - What is different? – Why am I even worried?" My senses had bombarded me with the same question over and over again, causing me to feel an overwhelming sense of panic all the way down to the pit of my stomach, which brought me to the point of almost vomiting. These two people, Myra Hindley and Ian Brady, had shown me only kindness and yet I knew I could not accept their kindness! I had a frantic urge to leave the house! And leave quickly!

-FORTY-FOUR-

I had been on the point of calling out, "I want to go home!" when I'd heard footsteps coming back down the stairs and then Hindley walked back into the room. "Are you ok?" she'd asked.

"Can I have a drink of water?"

"Course you can!" she'd picked up her glass off the sideboard and headed straight off into the kitchen, where I was able to hear their muffled conversation again but just as before, not able to hear what they were saying. A moment later and she brought me back a glass of water and placed it in front of me. "Come on. You need to get all that down you so we can get you home!" she'd said, throwing me the briefest of smiles, and I couldn't help but notice the sparkle that had been once there, was no longer there.

Back in the kitchen, I'd heard Hindley raise her voice again, although they were talking in whispers, and then Brady had suddenly snapped at her, "Fucking wait!" I'd distinctively heard his words before the pair of them continued speaking in very low whispery tones. Taking one last look at the huge slice of bread and jam, I'd swallowed my hunger, deciding it was my time to leave. Why had I not just eaten the bread and jam and then told them, "I'm off!" Why had I not just picked the slice of bread and jam up off the plate and walked out with it through the front door? I am unsure of the answers to those questions. But I had let my instincts take over me and I had quietly and quickly got to my feet.

Slipping the brass catch open on the sash window, I had gently lifted the bottom half of the sash upwards, but the window had suddenly jammed as the weights had become stuck, preventing the bottom half of the sash from moving any further than a couple of inches! I'd begun to feel physically sick and thought, at one moment, I was about to faint as the panic had set in when suddenly recalling the fact that our own back window had wooden blocks fixed onto the inside runners to prevent it from opening all the way up. Fortunately for me, this had not been the case for this window and with every ounce of my strength I had in me, I'd pulled up hard causing the weights on each side to suddenly drop, as the bottom half of the sash window shot upwards, making the loudest of noises!

"Little shits out the window!" Myra Hindley had called out and I'd heard someone running through from the kitchen into the room. I'd felt someone grab at my right foot which had become tangle around the curtain but as my momentum had kept me going forwards, the curtain had untangles and I'd dropped the few feet to the ground, just as I heard the distinct sound of the bolt from the back door drawing back and hitting its stopper.

"Basta -' was all I had heard Ian Brady say, before I'd hopped up onto the motorbike resting against the back wall and covered with blue plastic covering and some hessian sacks and I'd dropped down to the other side and ran off in the direction I'd been facing. I'd had no clue as to where I was running to, or which way I should go, or even why I was running! But my instincts took me back along the short alley and across a street, down into another alley, through some broken metal fencing before running on down the side of a large area of wasteland, before squeezing back through the metal fencing further along and then down another narrow street, coming across a smaller croft, exposing the backs of three bombed houses. I'd caught sight of an old dark green toilet door which had been resting up against a large mound of debris in what was once someone's backyard and it was here, beneath the door, that I had hidden myself away from the world for what had seemed like an eternity. Now and again, I would hear voices of passing people. And at one time, I had listened as the footsteps had walked across the croft, coming to a sudden halt right next to the door I was hiding under! I could clearly see a pair of men's black polished shoes, with the toes pointing directly at me, and as I held my breath and the big fart, my mind had raced away with me conjuring up all sorts of scenarios, leading to my demise. The owner of the shoes had dropped the lit cigarette dimp down on the ground, which had come to rest just a few inches away from the edge of the door and my face. I had been in two minds whether to scream and make a run for it, or just lay still and keep quiet, when a line of steaming piss had suddenly extinguished the dimp pushing it further under the upturned door, as the pisser had kept his aim on it, splashing me in the face before eventually the shoes had walked off.

A loud fart later I had ventured out from the safety of the green door and made my way home, managing to beg eight pennies on the way.

It hadn't surprised me to find Mammy wasn't there when I'd arrived back home and walked in through the back gate, where

Maggie was sitting by the fireside, warming her hands on the last remnants of the fires embers. I'd noticed the slight flicker of relief across her drawn face, before she had gone up the wall at me.

"Where the feck have yah been Tommy! It's half-ten! We've been out all the hours searching for yah-well Elizabeth an' Bernie have-an' still are! Yah could have been dead or murdered or something else for all we knew! And we don't have the money ta be burryin' yah!" she'd scolded me.

"I've eight pence." I pulled the handful of coppers out of my trouser pocket and offered them to her, which she had taken out of my hand, placing them on the mantelpiece before continuing to give out at me, "Where have yah been all these hours?"

"Nowhere."

"There's no such place as, nowhere."

"I meant, nowhere ta write home about. It's only half-ten!"

"Yah know yah should never be out on yer own in the pitch dark at these hours, Tommy." Maggie had got up and walked off into the kitchen, "Yah had us all worried ta death."

"I wasn't out on me own all these hours".

"Who were yah with then?" Jasis! She was worse than Gestapo! Always asking questions and asking them in quick succession to try and catch me out. Well, I wasn't going to tell her, I'd been sitting in front of a huge lump of bread with half a jar of jam spread on the top and I'd ran away from it for no reason other than I wasn't sure of the people that had given it to me! She'd have probably killed me, after wanting to know every single detail as to why I hadn't eaten it! Why I hadn't brought it home with me! Why I'd been in a strangers house on my own! She had not mentioned Martin or Nabby and as I wasn't sure whether she was trying to catch me out on a lie, I'd changed tact and the subject.

"Is mammy home?"

"Mammy got arrested in the pub for hittin' Patsy McGuire after she'd asked after daddy. Mammy accused her of having an eye on him, but when Patsy said, she wouldn't have been seen dead with the likes of him! Mammy had boxed her one in the gob, knocking out two of her front teeth!"

"What about Martin and Nabby?"

"What about them?" Maggie came back from the kitchen with two slices of bread and dripping on a plate, which she'd handed to me.

"They must be home - Aren't they?"

"The police brought the pair of them home a few hours back. Poor Nabby! He's lucky to be alive or standing up with both his legs still attached to his skinny little body!"

"He's not been hurt-has he?" I sat on the chair by the table, virtually swallowing the first slice of bread and dripping in one go, as Maggie sat across from me.

"He's okay-the pair of them are. He'd got his foot stuck in the rail tracks up by Longsight station, when him and Martin, were being chased across them by a pack of wild dogs! The train driver only saw the pair of them at the very last second, and slammed his brakes on, managing to stop the train no more than half-an-inch away from their faces!" Jasis! Those two could spin a good feckin' yarn!

My sister never made mention as to the fate of the imaginary pack of wild dogs and as there'd been no mention of me being with the pair of them, I'd blagged my way through a few more of her questions before telling her I'd been out with our two Cousins Paddy and Martin Ward, satisfying her curiosity. Hurriedly finishing off the last slice of bread and dripping, I had gone off to bed and left Maggie to wait for Elizabeth and Bernie to come back from searching for me and give them the good news!

The following Saturday, it had seemed as if the whole of Hulme had suddenly gone into mourning as a somber mood had swept throughout the area, especially amongst the Irish community, when the news had filtered through of the assassination of the American president, John. F. Kennedy. With the streets empty and the pubs full, with the whiskey and the beer flowing along with the crocodile tears and the outpourings of grief, for "One of our own." An American man, none of them had ever met in their lives or had known a thing about him.

-FORTY-FIVE-

Christmas day had been one week away and lots of things had gone on in the weeks leading up to it. Just after the American president had been shot dead, Twelve-year old John Kilbride had vanished from the market in Ashton-Under-Lyne, where he'd been helping stallholders all day long, in exchange for pocket money. But despite extensive enquiries by the police, with people from the surrounding communities helping them, there had been no sign of the kid.

Mammy had come home. The charges against her for assault had been dropped, because Patsy McGuire was too afraid of losing the rest of her teeth, which mammy had promised her, would happen if she gave evidence against her. She'd walked back in the house as if nothing had happened! No explanation as to where she'd been or why she'd left us on our own. Me and Martin had heard her gossiping with the neighbours, talking in low whispers about Aunty Rose's new baby.

"It's not possible that child can be Mike's baby." said Mrs. Kinsella, who'd had no children of her own.

"There's nothing that surprises me anymore," said Mrs. Spencer, "They're all at it! Well, except for Mrs. Kinsella!" she'd whispered behind her back. Mrs. Gough thought it was all so hilarious and just hee-hawed!

"If that's Mike's baby," mammy had said, "Then It'd be the biggest Christmas miracle since the Virgin Mary gave birth to the baby Jesus, the dirty auld whore!" Which had shocked me and Martin hearing her blaspheme the Virgin Mary like she done, considering she was supposed to have been a good catholic and all! But she'd been humpy with Martin and me for a while and had gone on at us, "Because of yea two half-wit eejits, yer father has ta stay in prison for longer! It's a feckin' blessin' the solicitor decided not ta bring the pair of yea ta the courts ta give evidence, as yer father had wanted! What the pair of yea poxty bastards had told them two detectives would have hung him twice over! An' because of it, he had to plead guilty ta child cruelty-even though he was completely innocent! Another eighteen months! Because of yea two!" she's cursed the day the both of us had been born.

I'd no idea how long eighteen months would last, but I had hoped it would be for a long while, so there would be no more beatings and drunken rows with mammy having to run off across the street, with half of us in tow to number nineteen, where Mrs. Shaw and her young daughter Anne, would take us in for hours on end, until daddy had either gone off or had fallen asleep.

Martin, me, Nabby and Bernie, had spent the last week leading up to Christmas day, carol singing. We'd known lots of people were strapped for money, but it had still pissed us off to see them hiding behind their net curtains, pretending they were not at home when; as on All Halloweens Day, we were able to see them skulking behind their curtains! We'd stick our fingers up at them, or drop our kecks and flash our arses, which soon had them out the front doors, hollering all sorts of lewd names after us. It was such good fun and had kept us warm!

Last Christmas wasn't much to write home about either, with a lack of response and even less money, even though we had sang like angels. Well, our granny had told us we did, when we'd called around her house and had given her an impromptu carol concert on her doorstep.

"Ah Jasis, will yah get a listen ta them! Yah sing like a choir of feckin' little angels in heaven-so yah do!" she'd stood on her doorstep blind drunk, before cutting in on, *Away in a Manger,* with her own rendition of, *It's a long way to Tipperary* while attempting a knees-up before staggering backwards into her house.

"Can we have a few coppers-or some biscuits Granny?" Martin had asked.

"Lord Jasis!" she'd slurred, almost toppling over with the shock of the asking, "Don't be beggin' off yer own kind! Git the feck off an' beg from them that can afford it!" she'd slammed the front door in our faces.

Deciding not to pay granny a visit this Christmas, Martin had come up with another one of his ideas, suggesting, "We should sing as lousy as we feckin can, and see what difference it makes."

Well, it had certainly made a difference! We'd had cold water thrown down on us! Told, we were the worst carol singers in the whole world! Told, we sang like cats with strangulated hernias!' We'd even been threatened to be shot, if we didn't fuck-off, by a man pointing a potato gun at us! But at the end of the day, we had made a little more money than the previous Christmas, with a lot of people giving us their spare coppers, on the promise we'd shut up and never returned to their doors ever again!

I suppose it hadn't helped not knowing all the words right

through to the end of every carol, except for *Silent Night;* my favourite song of all time! And so we would hum or attempt to whistle those parts we didn't know. Martin couldn't whistle to save his life and so he would often add his own words to a tune, making me laugh. His rendition of *'Away in a Manger'* had me in stitches as we'd sang and hummed to the two old biddies, standing at their front door, clapping their hands like a pair of sea lions in the circus.

"Away in a manger, I've nits in me head
Don't them auld' witches look feckin' dead
Look at her hooter, isn't it big
And doesn't the other one look like a pig."

The size of the woman's long pointy hooter and flaring wide nostrils, must have been a talking point along the whole street, if only to say, she was the biggest liar of them all! The two of them must have either been tone deaf, completely deaf, drunk, or just taking the piss and going along with it! When they had told us they would love to hear another carol, our fifth! Martin had suddenly dropped his kecks and had flashed his bare arse to them, "Get a listen to this, will yah!" he'd given out a long squeaky fart, sounding very similar to the air coming out of a party balloon when the neck of it has been stretched, before pulling his kecks up and running off down the street with the rest of us following him, in fits of hysterical laughter, just as the two old biddies had been!

Two days to Christmas and mammy had not returned home. She had stayed with us for a whole week without the *devils drink*. And for the short while she had stayed, life had seemed much easier for us, especially as she had taken everything upon herself and had promised us "Tings will be different!" giving Elizabeth and Maggie some breathing space for themselves. But she left and Elizabeth had to take on her duty of looking after us again. Mammy had often complained about us causing her nerves to give out on her and of how she hadn't long left on this earth! Sometimes, when I had watched mammy sitting by the fireside, chain-smoking her way through cigarette after cigarette with her looking so melancholic and distant, I had felt so sad that none of us were able to be part of her world. I was unable to ask her. "What is wrong mammy." for the fear of being told to "Feck off and mind yer business!" I was unable to put an arm around her to comfort her, for the fear of being pushed away, "Get away from me yah ting yah!"

Elizabeth had warned us not say a word to anyone about mammy leaving us, "Otherwise we'll all be separated and will never see each other ever again!"

For the past two nights running, someone had been at the back door attempting to get into the house. There had been no calling out to identify themselves, just the rattling of the door handle and pushing their foot at the bottom corner of the door, testing the bolt. And by the time Elizabeth had found enough courage to peer from behind the curtains of the backroom window, whoever had been there would be gone.

"Do you tink it's Granddad, come back ta haunt us for hurting his head?" Bernie had fearfully asked.

"Well, he wouldn't be after me!" said Nabby, hiding behind me and Martin, "I wasn't even pushing on the coffin!"

"Jasis! How many times have I got ta tell yah! Granddad was already dead in the coffin!" said Elizabeth, "What d'ya tink he was doin' in it in the first place! - Anyway yah can't hurt the dead!" she'd almost reassured us until Martin had to feckin open his gob! "Yah can kill Zombies, so yah can! An' they're dead! Shamie told me!"

"There the livin' dead, Martin! An' it's all made up for the films. Yah shouldn't be takin' any notice of Shamie. He only says them tings ta frighten yah." she'd carried on attempting to reassure us, before suddenly letting out an almighty scream which had frightened the living daylights out of the lot of us, as the back door handle had suddenly rattled a couple of times before going silent again. I'd been so petrified and was the first out of the back room and up the stairs hiding under the pile of coats and bedcovers on the big double bed in the girl's room as the others, barring Maggie and Elizabeth, had followed me up and had joined me. None of us coming out again, until the following morning.

In the very early hours of Christmas day, while everyone else was fast asleep in bed, Martin and me were gawking out of our bedroom window waiting for the tight fisted Santa Clause, to come flying past the house so we could open the window and call him every name under the sun! The other day, we had found Shamie's old blue Gat gun and some lead pellets under his bed and we had planned to take a few pot shots at the fat git and Rudolf's big red conk! Also, with the back door directly below our window, we had decided to bring up the heavy fire companion holding the poker, brush and shovel, as a Christmas surprise for the phantom door rattler if he should call while we were still awake.

It hadn't taken Martin too long to lose interest before falling into the bed and drifting off to sleep, snoring like a big pig. Not long afterwards, as I had been contemplating calling off the watch for fatty and his reindeers, I had noticed the back gate silently creeping open.

"Martin! Martin!' I'd frantically shook my brother awake.

"What! What's wrong?"

I'm still not too sure which noise had come first, the soft *thupp* sound or the scream from Nabby, who'd suddenly leapt out of the bed as if his arse had been set on fire. Dancing around in the dim light he was holding one side of his arse and telling us, "I've been feckin' bitten!"

I'd forgotten Martin still had the loaded air pistol in his hand which, when I'd asked him to let me have it before he'd fallen off to sleep, he had refused on account, "It's too dangerous for little kids to hold!"

Ignoring Nabby, I'd silently opened the window and had taken a peek downwards were I'd been able to make out the dim outline of a shadowy figure peering up in my direction. Whoever it was, seemed to be very unsteady on their feet and was talking in a strange language which I'd been unable to understand.

"I tink he's an Indian," whispered Martin, joining me looking downwards.

"He's no feathers." I'd whispered back.

"I meant a Pakistani Indian! Not a feckin' Red Indian!"

"We've no chickens for sale!" I'd shouted down to the fella, but he had continued to talk gibberish.

"Watch this!" said Martin, suddenly getting his mickey out and pissing out the window!

371

Picking up the fire companion I'd hung it out the window taking careful aim at the face still peering up at us. "Bombs away!" I'd dropped it, knowing I'd scored a direct hit when we heard the loud howl of pain; louder than Nabby's, before the phantom door-rattle had staggered across the yard and out the back gate.

"Jasis! I've been bit by a fuckin' animal or something!" Nabby was still moaning, "Light the lighter an' take a look will yea, I can't see me arse from here!'

Martin lit the lighter and we saw Nabby had his kecks down around his knees with his pale boney white arse pointed towards us.

"It's a bite.' I'd told him, looking at the large welt the lead pellet had made.

"I know it's a poxty bite! I can feel it! I just want to know what kind of bite it is!"

'Well. I don't know! - It looks like a flea bite to me."

"A feckin' flea bite! Jasis! I've been bitten by hundreds of fleas and never felt anythin' like this! It's drawn blood!"

"Can yah get vampire fleas?" I'd jokingly asked Martin.

"Feckin' vampire fleas!' cried Nabby, "Yer havin' a feckin' laugh aren't yah! If there was such a ting! We'd all have bled ta death by now!'

'It must have been Gosson or Michael then." said Martin, closing the window with the one hand while hiding the pellet gun behind his back with the other, "They must have thought yer arse was a drippin' sandwich!"

"Ah bollocks to this!" Nabby had climbed back into the bed, "Anyways, Gosson and Michael haven't got any proper teeth yet, unless one of thems wearin' mammy's falsies! - It was worse than a flea bite! More like a mouse bite! - Or even a snake bite -!"

'Ah, give over and go ta sleep!" Martin had told him.

-FORTY-SIX-

It seemed I had not been asleep all that long when I'd been suddenly woken by Elizabeth shaking me and Martin awake. Maggie was at the other end of the bed, waking the other three.

"We have to hurry out of the house! Now!" Elizabeth had spoken with such urgency in her voice we'd hopped straight out of the bed almost immediately and without question. With no need to get dressed, as we'd always worn our clothes in bed in the colder months, we'd slipped on our shoes and had hurried down the stairs following Elizabeth, who was carrying Michael, while Maggie carried Gosson.

Leading us along the narrow hallway Elizabeth opened the front door and led us onto the damp street. She'd handed Michael to Martin to hold before hurrying back through the house, bringing out the big pram, which she put Michael, Gosson and Kathleen into before heading off down the street with us all grouped tightly together and holding firmly onto the prams framework as we had walked out of Stamford Street, for the very last time, as a family.

Down on the Stretford Road we'd stood outside the Chinese restaurant, gawking through the main window, tasting every mouthful of food the diners inside shoveled it into their gobs. I'd been so hungry, I'd been unable to stop myself from drooling from the corners of my mouth which had become too much for the fat, pig-faced lady, sitting close to the window. If looks could have killed, all of us should have been dead in the instant she'd glared at us, before turning her pig-sized head away in disgust and calling the waiter over to her table, where they'd had a brief conversation with each other.

A Chinese man came out from the restaurant and had handed out bars of chocolate Crunchies to us. He was having a brief conversation with Elizabeth, before a Police car and a big van had suddenly pulled up at the roadside. The two Police women, who had got out of the car, had walked over to speak with Elizabeth and as she had seemed happy enough to talk with them, we'd stayed put, cold, hungry, tired and fearful, and not knowing what was going to become of us.

Coming back to us, Elizabeth had assured us that everything was going to be fine. She told us we had to get into the police van as we were going off to the police station to get a bite to eat. We of course had not needed a second invitation and had been only too happy to hop straight in to the van, without a seconds thought.

"How are they going ta fit the pram in?" Maggie had thrown the question at Elizabeth, not happy just to leave it there on the pavement. Besides the clothes we had stood up in, the pram was the only other useful thing we had possessed which had always served us a purpose.

"Shall I run it back to the house and then come back?' I'd volunteered, worried that someone would steal it.

"There's no need." said Elizabeth." And as the Police van had driven away from the kerb with all nine of us inside, I could only watch on incensed, as the Chinaman had pushed our pram around the corner, leaving it there and walking back into his restaurant.

When we'd arrived at the police station, we were taken

straight to a waiting room away from the main counter and the two drunks giving out to the Sergeant, as they were being booked in. One of the lady coppers said she would fetch us something to eat and drink, before closing the door and leaving us in relative silence.

Looking across at Elizabeth, I had wondered what she might have been thinking. Poor Elizabeth. She'd seemed to have carried the whole world on her shoulders and though the thought must have played on her mind at times, she never did abandon us. As she had looked down on Michael, asleep in her arms, I'd noticed how her frown, which had been a permanent feature for a long while, seemed to have softened. And when she caught my eyes, I could see her tears welling up, as she had thrown me a brief reassuring smile. But she never cried. "What is it Elizabeth? What are you thinking right now? What are your hopes, your dreams, your aspirations beyond this gloomy room and this gloomy life? What is to become of us, as a family? Will you stay with us forever and ever?" I had wanted to ask her all these questions and more. But the fear of the answer not being what I had wanted to hear, had prevented me from doing so.

We'd heard a loud commotion going on outside the waiting room and when Martin, as nosey as he ever was, had opened the door slightly to take a peek out into the main foyer, I could have sworn the gibberish voice we could hear, was the same voice of the phantom door rattler.

"It's our Shamie!" Martin exclaimed.

"Here. Get a hold of Michael!" Elizabeth had handed baby Michael over to Martin and walked out of the room and across the foyer to the counter, where our big brother was giving out to the two coppers standing either side of him. One of them was telling the desk Sergeant, how they had found Shamie, shadow boxing in the middle of Stretford Road up near the Town Hall, where they had arrested him for being drunk and incapable of looking after himself. When Elizabeth had calmed Shamie down, the Sergeant had agreed to let our brother stay in the room with us, provided he kept his big gob shut. Jasis! The state of his half-closed eyes and swollen conk!

"Yah feckin' see this, Tommy?" Shamie had suddenly pointed a finger to his swollen face as he'd walked into the room and glared at me through his swollen eyes. I didn't know why he was picking on me-well I did! Which was my reason for taking a backward step behind Martin. After all, he was the one that had pissed all over Shamie!

"Well. Yah ought ta see the state of the other two bastards! I beat the shite out of all three of them all at once-together-one by one!" he exaggerated, "There they were, all lined up together and I'd given them what for! Ouch! Me fuckin head."

The police had rustled up platefuls of corned beef sandwiches, and a Victorian Jam sponge cake, along with cups of sweet hot tea, which we had gratefully eaten tasting ever last morsel and licking our dirty hands clean, while Shamie, after being given some Disprins for his sore head, had declined any of the grub and had lain himself across three chairs and gone off to sleep.

A while later the policewoman, the first to have spoken with Elizabeth outside the Chinese restaurant, had come into the room and sat with us to explain what was happening. "We've been in contact with the Social Services," she'd said, "But as there isn't anything they can do until tomorrow, we are taking all of you to Nazareth House. It's a nice children's home and you'll be taken care of there until the Social Services decide what's best for you. But rest assured you will all be kept together." She'd reassuringly looked at Elizabeth, who'd been worried this might not happen.

Not long afterwards that, we'd been put back into the big police van and heading out of Hulme. Shamie was still drunk and moaning about his head. While I had already made my mind up that I wasn't going into any children's home and I had whispered my intentions to the others, "Once this van stops and me feet touch the ground, I'm off!" And true to my word, as the van had pulled into the driveway of Nazareth House and we had all bailed out of the van. I was off like a greyhound!

A quick peek over my shoulder told me, the footsteps following close behind were Martin's. All the others, except Shamie, who was leaning against the van and puking his ring up, were just standing in the glare of the van's headlamps, silently looking on. There were no shouts of "Stop!" or "Come back Tommy an' Martin!" And as we had ran out of the main gates, we were unaware at the time, this was the last image we were ever going to see of our family together again.

Making our way back to Stamford Street we'd found the front door was still slightly ajar, just as Elizabeth had left it hours earlier. Making sure both front and back doors were securely locked, we'd hidden under mammy's bed, covering ourselves with the quilt and coats to wait for the morning to hurry along.

We must have fallen into a deep sleep straight away and the

next thing I remember was being suddenly woken by the sound of footsteps coming along the hallway. We'd listened in fear as they had paused for a brief moment outside mammy's bedroom before entering the room. I'd held my breath as the black winkle pickers had walked across the uncarpeted bedroom floor, before the owner of them began to rummage through the cupboards and drawers.

'Yea can come out from under the bed. I know yer there. I can smell yah from here," said our older brother Paddy. The points of his shoes now facing in our direction. "Where is everyone?" he'd asked, as we'd dragged ourselves out from under the bed.

"The coppers took them away to a home." said Martin.

"We escaped! I'd proudly added.

"Yea should have stayed with them." said Paddy.

"Have yah seen mammy?" I'd asked.

"The auld woman's gone off ta Chatham last time I heard. An' she won't be comin' back. An' it's no good whingin' about it 'cos she doesn't give a shite about any of you lot. I'm only back ta pick up anythin' worth takin' and I'm out of it agin. And yea two should do yourselves a big favour and give yerselves up to the coppers. They'll look after yah better than she ever will."

"Can't we come with yea?" asked Martin.

"Yah can't. Even if I wanted ta-which I don't! I can barely look after meself. Anyway, the whole of Stamford Street is comin' down in the next few weeks so there's no point stayin' around this dump any longer. Here." he'd flicked a florin high into the air, "Catch!"

We had both jumped to catch the coin flying over our heads but had missed it and we were quickly down on our knees chasing after it, as it had rolled under the small bedside table.

"Got it!" said Martin.

As we had got to our feet, our big brother was no longer in the bedroom. "Paddy! – Paddy!" I had called up the stairs to him, before running through the house and out into the back yard, "Paddy! Paddy!" I had called his name again and again, kidding myself he was still close by when I had already known he had left us for good. I had so desperately wanted to cry, but I couldn't find any tears to cry them.

We'd spent the next three days in the house, only daring to venture out in the very early hours of the mornings to steal the odd bottle or two of sterilised milk from the milk float. Martin had given me the last morsel of stale bread we had left and I'd greedily shoved it into my gob before going out into the kitchen to swig some water from the tap, where I found my brother eating the old paper lining from the drawer. I'd felt so desperately upset to know he had done this for me, when I would have wanted to have shared the last morsel of food with him, like we had always shared things equally. And as we stood looking at one another, there had been no need to say a word. I had known that he knew, what we both had known. We had to give ourselves up to the police. And in that moment, we had finally accepted no-one would ever be coming back for us.

Taking one last look around the house as we'd made our way out, we had walked into mammy and daddy's bedroom. In the glass tray on the bedside table, I had spotted two of daddy's old lighters. I don't know what had possessed me at the time.

Perhaps it had been a symbolic gesture-I just don't know. There were no thoughts running through my head the moment I had flicked one of the lighters into life and had held it to the bed covers, setting them alight. And as I had momentarily stared down into the flames, I began to hear the voices of my family calling out, crying, laughing, shouting, screaming and singing, as in that moment of time the memories came flooding back, reminding me of what had passed with the four walls of this house. I'd had no feelings of sadness or of happiness or of regret, in what I had been doing. In some way perhaps, it was an instinct to protect my family's past and those secrets locked forever inside, 24 Stamford Street.

Outside, as we had closed the front door for the very last time, the dull grey sky had seemed to lift a little letting a faint glimmer of the sun's rays burst through the clouds. And as we had made our way down the street we were met by Aunty Rosie pushing the big pram up in our direction.

"Where is everyone?" she had asked, "I haven't seen any of you lot for days on end? Are you all okay?"

"Yeh. We're all okay, Aunty Rosie." lied Martin, "Can we get a peek at your baby can we!"

"Of course you can!" Aunt Rosie had thrown a big smile as she'd proudly pulled back the covers to let us take a peek. And there, before our very eyes, Martin and I had witnessed for ourselves, the 'Christmas Miracle' mammy had spoken about with the neighbours, as the wide eyed chocolate-skinned baby's beautiful big brown eyes had stared out at us!

Sitting on the front doorstep of the last house on the corner of Stamford Street, six year-old Georgie Taylor and his younger sister Lucy, were tucking into a sandwich and had hurriedly pushed the last remnants of food into their gobs as we had approached. And as we had passed them by I couldn't help but notice the remnants of jam around their mouths and I'd had a sudden urge to rush over and lick their faces clean! And in that instant, as Martin and I had walked out of Stamford Street forever. I couldn't help wondering. What would I have given for a slice of bread and jam?

EPILOGUE

I know, for some of you who have come along with me on my brief journey through 1963, my story will, I am sure, have probably evoked memories of your own struggles as a kid growing up in the surrounding industrial towns of Manchester and beyond. And though harsh those realities of our lives may seem now, when looking back on that era; all the more if you had been Irish and poor, there had been nothing in our own lives as children to compare ourselves with and therefore, what we had endured had been nothing out of the ordinary against the backdrop of our everyday daily lives. And who of us, in all honesty, wouldn't wish to be able to walk back in on our past, if only to take a quick peek?

I have been touched by the outpourings of emotions and understandably so, from those of you who have been betrayed by one of your own as well as by the mere mention of their names. But unfortunately the names of Hindley and Brady will forever be synonymous with the names of their victims and the people whose lives have been blighted by their cowardly monstrous acts. But it is a price that has to be paid in keeping alive the memory of all the victims, in particular the undying devotion of one particular mother, Winnie Johnson, for her lost boy Keith.

My own story only touches upon my own personal memories of life living in Hulme. There were many things to write and attempting to get the balance right. And then, only as far as I had allowed myself to write, for fear of encroaching upon the memories of my own family who have their own memories to share or keep locked away. But for me. Growing up in an era of constant changes, I can truly say that the three years I had spent as a child living in Hulme, were the happiest days of my childhood! Saturday matinees. Exploring the streets of bombed out building. Being chased by the police! Lighting fires to burn of the electric flex to expose the copper wiring. Breaking windows. Wagging off school. Stealing Bicyles. Belle Vue Zoo! Basically travelling freely around Manchester and going where I had wanted to go and doing what I wanted to do. The challenges, the excitement, all of which can be summed up in just the one word, Freedom!

Whilst writing this book, I have had the privilege of chatting with a number of people who live and had lived in Hulme, Gorton, and other surrounding towns of Manchester. Some have told me about their own experiences with Ian Brady and Myra Hindley, which lends itself to the probability; and one of which I have always believed of there being, which is more unaccounted for victims being the more likelier than not. Unknowingly to me at the time, I too had been picked out as one of their potential victims. I had followed her! I was there with them in the house. I had looked up into his eyes and I had looked up into her eyes, I had witnessed for myself the moment a young woman had walked over to me, so full of confidence and charm, whose beaming smile had enticed me within a matter of minutes to follow her off to her house with the promise of bread and jam. She had oozed excitement and charm, with a somewhat nervous energy about her. And yet, Ian Brady had seemed the complete opposite to her, isolated, unsmiling, somewhat timid in his demeanor with Hindley seemingly the stronger willed out of the two. There are of course, the many righteous people who sincerely believe they knew the true repented Myra Hindley. And there are those who have written their books, based on whatever information she had willing thrown at them or in her personal diary; to be read by gullible people at some stage, in her feeble attempt to show she was in some way, a *victim* of Ian Brady! But it seems those people may have been ultimately blinded by Hindley's calculating murderous charm and lies, as her victims had been. Can we really believe Pauline Reade, all dressed up in in her new pink and gold dance skirt, white boots and white gloves and ready to meet her friends at the dance, had willingly gone off to the moors to help find a purported missing glove? Janet Williams, a police cadet at the time, had the unfortunate task of helping to search on the Moors; praying she wouldn't find anything, will tell you the Moors was open to the elements, wet, windy with soft dampish ground in most places! Can we really accept Hindley's assertions that Pauline willing walked with Brady across this terrain!

Hindley was very much in control of the situation when she had enticed me to follow her to her Grandmother's house. She could easily have told me to run away at any given time during our journey, especially when Brady had walked out of sight for a short time, only appearing again when he'd guided me into the house, which, when looking back, had seemed a well-rehearsed plan. Do I believe there are unaccounted for victims?

Yes I certainly do. Though the only person who could give a definitive answer to this and many other questions, is Ian Brady himself. A pathological liar; as they both are, who in his deluded fantasies actually believes he is on hunger strike, when in fact he gluttons down food in between his forced meals!

In his letter to me, he complains how people had not noticed, Him and Hindley being '*Ordinary people and not dripping in blood.*' As for his deluded ramblings about being some kind of gangster in prison. For the record, Brady was in fact on Rule 43 when he was not in the hospital wing of every prison he had been in, keeping himself segregated from other prisoners for his own safety. Because in the real world those same gangsters he believes he had associated with in the prisons, would have torn him from limb to limb. Still haunted, still afraid, still under the stronger influence of Myra Hindley, Brady is too afraid, too cowardly and too deluded, to give away the locations as to any of his other missing victims, if he in fact actually knows where the remaining ones have been buried.